GRAFFITI
on my
HEART

AN AUTOBIOGRAPHY
1926–1937

AGNESSA LARSEN

PEANUT BUTTER
PUBLISHING

Seattle, Washington

Newspaper articles appearing in this book
are used with the permission of the
Honolulu Star-Bulletin.

ISBN 0-89716-509-8

Printed in the United States of America.
31.5034

Cover design: David Marty

Back cover photo: Motoko Watson

Editor: Martha McDonough

Published by:

Peanut Butter Publishing
226 Second Avenue West
Seattle, WA 98119
(206) 281-5965

To Nancy and Larry

two of my best supporters,

Affectionately,

Agnessa Lisi

May 6, 1994

Dedication

I am indebted to countless persons for adding significance and flavor to my life, and for giving me a good start. I wish I could thank all of them personally, but since that is unlikely, I dedicate this autobiography to five people: My mother, John, Madame Scheyer, François, and my older sister, Astrid. The first four for obvious reasons, and Astrid because she inspired me to become the opposite of what she was. I'm grateful.

Prologue

To some, the Universal Consciousness assigns roots, and anchors them to the ground. It gives wings and liberty of movement to others.

Those in between It endows with free will so they may choose whether to fly or be bound.

All are interdependent, essential to cosmic sequence.

When it was unconventional for women to do so, I preferred wings. More than six decades later, I'd willingly do it again — even face the ill winds, those trials on which our growth depends.

This autobiography, composed from letters and journals written at the time, covers my early adulthood: 1926 through 1937. Set mainly in Honolulu, Paris, Moscow, and Vienna, it chronicles my development as a sculptor as well as my changing political and social views and provides a statement on the institution of marriage.

> *With no effort*
> *We move*
> *To the rut*
> *From the groove.*

Part One

Chapter One

Anna Head School
Berkeley, Calif.
Sept. 20, 1926

Dearest Mom,

Thanks for your sweet birthday letter and all the lovely presents.
Turning sixteen is a big event, but I'd have enjoyed it more if I
were back home with all of you in Honolulu.

I like school more now than at first. The other boarders are friendly.
My roommate is from Montana and a little homesick, too.

I'll feel better when the art class begins next Friday. Mary and
Cynthia, both boarders, have also signed up for it. Mary's a senior
and very clever. I'm interested mostly in portraits. Cynthia says
the teacher is some sort of foreigner. I can't wait.

Take care of yourself, Mama. I hope it's a girl. Then we'll be three
of each.

Till next time — all my love,
Sisi

Friday came at last. As Mary, Cynthia and I crossed the quadrangle headed for the barn-like room where our art class would be
held, Mary said, "I got a rear view of the teacher a while ago. I happened to be passing the office as she was talking to Miss Wilson.
Wait till you see how she's dressed. Well, I don't care as long as she
can teach me perspective. Technique is what I need. Foreigners, especially Germans, are very precise, you know. Our cook at home is
from Hanover — with her, everything must be punctilious."

"We'll soon know," I said. "Here we are."

At the start of the class, our teacher introduced herself. She said
she was Madame Galka Scheyer, that she lived in Los Angeles, and
would be coming up to Berkeley once a week to teach us. Her English reminded me of my mother's. Her clothes were ... well .... No
woman *I* knew would go out wearing a bright Mexican shawl over

an olive-green dress, at least, not to conduct a class at a select girls' school. The combination was exquisite but awfully daring.

Madame went on, "Did I say teach? Not at all. Zat's hardly vat I shall do. I shall guide you to teach yourselves. You vill be creative artists — not copying nature, or following rules, but using your own imaginations. Za camera can copy far better zan you. You vill do only vat *you* like to do. Zat may sound reckless but to free yourselves, you must be daring."

My six classmates and I exchanged glances that expressed doubt of Madame's competence. Free us from what? Her job was to show us how to paint a landscape or a bowl of fruit. Weren't there techniques she was supposed to demonstrate? Was Madame a fraud?

From the opposite side of the broad table, Mary winked at me as though to say, "Watch — I'm going to call her bluff."

We could always count on Mary to do something outlandish. Without a word, she dipped a wide brush into her green poster paint, brought it up dripping and held it poised over the jar as she surveyed the large sheet of white paper on the table before her, considering her next move. All eyes were on her. No one moved or even dared breathe as she swept the brush with determined zig-zag strokes diagonally across the paper, from top to bottom. Then, clasping another brush full of red paint, she directed it in the same pattern, below the one green band and across it in places, ending with a delicate swirl in the lower right-hand corner of the paper.

Taking a step backward, she announced with a conspicuous dash of irony, "*Voilà, Madame!*"

Madame Scheyer coolly contemplated the painting while the rest of us waited speechlessly for ... we didn't know what. Mary's posture was still defiant when Madame turned to her with a warm smile.

"Zere are not many who understand me so qvickly. You haf, yes, painted abstract before?"

Sensing she was no longer in charge, Mary could do no more than shake her head.

"Vell, no matter. Look — " she spoke to all of us, "at zose spontaneous strokes of contrasting colors and how, ver zey cross, zey make a neutral brown. Ze composition is gratifying to ze eye. *Brava,* my dear Mary. You are an artist."

That's how it began. Mary's audacity infected us. We, too, could shed our restraints, could show originality. Throughout the week, every week, we looked forward to those two hours on Fridays when we could remove with impunity our masks of accepted convention. For they *were* masks. The world never saw the undisguised selves hidden within us, too timid to risk exposure to ridicule. Madame Scheyer helped us put on paper or canvas, with paint or pencil, brush, or even fingers, whatever we felt ought to be expressed.

"Ze only bad art," Madame said over and over, "is ze insincere. Some of ze *most* insincere is zat vich is technically excellent."

We believed her, and knew firsthand what it felt like to say something in graphic form that would seem bizarre to most people, yet be understood, not only by Madame, but by our fellow artists. The seven of us cherished a secret life where we learned to communicate in a new language known only to the initiated.

But Madame Scheyer remained an enigma even after she told us more about herself. Born of a Jewish family in Germany, she was educated there, in Paris, and in London, among people to whom the arts were as indispensable as food and sleep. Her intimate friends included most of the great names of modern art. Eventually she came to the United States as the representative of a group called The Blue Four, namely: Klee, Kandinsky, Jawlensky and Feininger. She said they, and especially the Russian Kandinsky, had pioneered abstract painting. Who'd have guessed, then, that not many years later I'd have tea with him and his wife at their home near Paris?

By deliberate plan Madame secured employment at Anna Head School. She convinced its administrators that her experimental method of "teaching" was worth a try.

At the end of the scholastic year, we exhibited our achievements on the walls of the arcade around the quadrangle. Madame Scheyer and seven proud pupils hung the paintings and drawings. Some of the art was abstract, and some figurative, but not one piece copied anything in nature.

The drab walls came alive with novel lines, forms and bright colors. We, the artists, circulated among our invited friends and relatives, faculty and student body, quite prepared for the inevitable reactions. No praise was expected or heard.

At one point Cynthia whispered to me, "Some of the ridicule is ridiculous."

I listened to a well-dressed man say, "Gawd-a-mighty! Where'd all this crap come from? I thought we were sending Phoebe to a school where she'd learn something useful."

The woman at his side put her hand lightly on his arm. "Watch your language, Dear. I've heard that this sort of ... hmm ... art is becoming fashionable."

Farther along, someone else said, "I don't know much about art, but I sure know what I like. And I don't — like — this!"

And someone else, "Haw, haw! Look at that one! You can't tell whether it's right side up or not."

While they laughed at the paintings, we, the anointed, as Mary called us, laughed at the observations. Philistines, with closed minds, who would never know the exhilaration of being free from conformity, made such remarks and criticisms.

In Berkeley, we girls gave one another support and courage, but back in Honolulu, I had no one. Apparently none of our species had yet crossed the wide Pacific to challenge the established manner of painting. At Punahou School, I signed up for the art course in my junior year. The teacher, Mrs. Walker, a graduate of the Boston School of Fine Arts, was one of those technically qualified instructors.

Our first project was to reproduce a vase of flowers in water colors. I strung along. What harm could it do? None ... until I signed my name using no capital letters.

"My deah," Mrs. Walker said, "people will think you don't know any bettah. Please write your name properly."

For Pete's sake! Even in my signature I couldn't express individuality! I did as she requested, and we became enemies.

Then, there was the painting I did at home — not a portrait of anyone — just a woman's head with unusual coloring. It could not have been mistaken for anything but a head. Or so I thought.

"What on Earth is that supposed to be?" Charlotte asked.

Charlotte and I had been friends, best friends, since the fourth grade. Why couldn't she at least try to see it through my eyes? She had never let me down before. Most of my family thought it hilarious.

"Whoever saw purple and green hair on anyone but a clown?"

"Nobody, not even jokers, have eyes like that."

"What's the matter with you, Sis? Can't you see straight anymore? You used to draw such pretty pictures."

Mama was noncommittal. She told me to always do what I thought right. Fine! But I needed allies who could actively support me and lend me strength.

5

It was just as well I had not brought back any of the pictures I did in Berkeley. Madame Scheyer wanted to take them on her annual lecture tour in the States and Europe to demonstrate the success of her method. They would do more good in her hands than among provincials.*

Chapter Two

Honolulu hadn't changed. To be happy there, did I have to climb back into the old groove — even if it turned out to be a rut? I felt I had neither the zeal nor the qualifications to be a crusader, or to lead a movement, no matter how much I believed in it.

So what should I do? I was seventeen — not too soon to start thinking of my future. My classmates, Charlotte and Francie, were going steady with officers in the military. Finding a husband, we had been told, was important, and it didn't present a problem — there were so many men to choose from. Should he be a local fellow I'd grown up with — Sito, maybe? Or one of those handsome bachelors in white linen suits, who arrived every year from Ivy League universities looking for a job and adventure? Should he be in the armed forces, or perhaps the son of an officer — someone like Mickey?

Honolulu had earned the nickname of Mother-In-Law of the Military. Half the girls in town were either going steady with, or engaged to someone in uniform. As the wives of military men, they would always have lots of parties and plenty of travel. Wow! Traveling all over the States and even across the world ... with all expenses paid.

Mercenary? Yes. But didn't everyone agree that money made the world go around? Being calculating may be sordid, but I didn't invent the system, I merely followed, albeit willingly.

Yet, somewhere inside of me, I hurt. It had to do with that secret part of me Madame Scheyer had unlocked with her magic key. But the door had slammed shut, and none of the other parts of the mansion contained anything to compare with the treasures she revealed. She warned us there would be a price to pay for being different. Perhaps by joining the opposition, I might discover a gem I could nurture? If not, at least the hurt might go away, and I could live to fight another day.

* See the forthcoming book *The Blue Four: A Dialogue With America* by Professor Peg Weiss; University of California Press.

Meanwhile, I intended to be happy. My goal would be as other girls', namely, to be beautiful, to find a rich husband, give sensational parties, have my picture in the society section of the weekend papers, travel, and be envied by other women. To express it otherwise, I wanted to be a social butterfly.

There was no hurry to get engaged, but I couldn't wait too long. If a girl didn't marry in her early twenties, it meant no one wanted her. Automatically, she'd be put on the shelf with the other "old maids," and become an intellectual and an awful bore.

My friend Jenny pointed out, quite rightly, that most teachers didn't marry. Girls who knew too much, we agreed, were never popular because they made men feel inferior. If a man was handsome and rich, was it fair to expect him to have brains as well? Francie maintained that intellect could mess up a guy's social and business life. And if he didn't surf with the wave, she insisted, he'd get nowhere.

Charlotte's mother taught her that people should converse only about things that didn't offend anyone. The two main untouchables were, of course, religion and politics. There was nothing to discuss about them, anyway. "Republicans want to conserve our way of life, and so do we," Charlotte said.

About religion — everyone who was, or wanted to be someone, was a Protestant and attended St. Andrew's or Central Union Church.

"That doesn't mean," Charlotte emphasized, "that you have to be pious, or even go to church. Only, if someone asks, you say you're a Protestant — the same as when you say you're a Capitalist. It only means you believe in Capitalism and hope to be one some day."

"In an article recently," I said, "some man claimed that wanting to be like everyone else was a mindless may of living. He said we cling to the herd because we're afraid to think on our own for fear of revealing secret ideas that might get us into trouble."

"What a pile of nonsense!" Jenny said, raising her voice.

"It sure is," Francie echoed. "We're *not* like everyone else. This is a free country. Maybe *some* people are sheep, but I'm not, that's for sure."

What could I say? To dispute the issue would have led me nowhere — like that poor guy on the surfboard: Without the wave, he was literally at sea. Who did I think I was? Some great artist who had all the answers? Or a deluded girl who wanted to chase a will-o'-the-wisp?

7

Wiser and safer to be a butterfly ... with a slender body and gorgeous wings — wings that would carry me from one luscious bauble to another — nourished by the exotic nectar I'd find, and with a permanent smile painted on my face.

In the meantime, however, I was still a chrysalis in my cocoon, preparing for my grand entrance into maturity. But — what if, after my metamorphosis, I ended up a moth, or a tadpole, instead of a butterfly?

Chapter Three

There were antidotes for the malaise I suffered. Leaping into the whirlpool of parties and dates was one. A few uncomplicated flirtations helped restore my self-confidence, and before long, I could have used a dozen weekends every month to fit in all the invitations I received. There were some delicate moments of diplomatic maneuvering — it wasn't easy to decline without offending or discouraging someone. High school helped pass the time. My courses were a snap, and the new boys ... well ... promising.

I liked Mickey best. With him, I didn't have to pretend to be sophisticated, as I did with some older fellows. Besides, he danced better than anyone else, and had the manners of a gentleman. His father was a captain in the Navy and an M.D., and his family lived at Pearl Harbor in a large house filled with people — especially on weekends. I was invited there often, and so was Mickey's best friend, Doug, the son of an Army colonel. Both Mickey and Doug were in my biology class at Punahou and made everyone laugh.

We often went to dances on the military post. Doug seldom brought a date. Whenever the band started, he whirled somebody else's girl around the floor. On Sundays, we usually swam or played tennis.

Our new house at Kahana, on the other side of the island, was another diversion. Even before the foundation had been laid, we knew it would be what we wanted: scope for our big family and our friends. We had the beach right out front, then a lawn which sloped up to the house. Behind the house, lava cliffs rose almost straight up to a rock formation that resembled a crouching lion. There, I would treasure hours alone with my private thoughts, painting, writing poetry, and just relaxing.

The best room, the one above the kitchen, with windows on three sides, was mine. At dawn the sun would rise out of the sea to shine in and waken me. Early morning, the time I liked best, I could have stolen down to the beach and swum in my birthday suit. But if caught, I'd have been criticized, so I never tried it.

To keep in touch with the progress of our new home during construction, we had to drive less than an hour from town, so one or another of us was often at Kahana. The great fireplace and the thick exterior walls, built of lava stones dug from the property, went up quickly. Then the hand-hewn beams went in to support the roof of the vast living room. Although electricity had not yet been brought to that part of the island, the wiring was installed to be used at some future time. Meanwhile, we had to make do with candles and Coleman lamps. To fuel the stove and refrigerator, we used gas that was delivered in five-foot tanks. The water was our very own from the well we dug — pumped to the house with a gasoline motor.

Like the candles, our telephone suggested more primitive days. It was one of those wooden boxes attached to the wall, with a receiver hooked to its left side when not in use, a mouthpiece, and, on the right, a crank to rouse the operator when turned even slightly.

By the end of the year, the garden was landscaped but the house couldn't yet handle our holiday crowd, so we celebrated Christmas in town. As usual, it was a Norwegian gathering of our family and those friends who had no family, on the evening of December 24th.

Food and gifts, wrinkled wrapping paper, wine and hubbub, carols and laughter, all superimposed themselves on my perception as they had done for years, leaving an imprint that told me the old ideal was still as it should be and that all was well.

My new sister, Joan, only a year old, had no idea what all the confusion was for; but Dick and Stan were ten and twelve and able to share in the make-believe.

New Year's Eve was different. Mickey and I celebrated it in the American tradition — dancing till nearly dawn at the Royal Hawaiian Hotel. I didn't have to paint on my smile often in those days. Sometimes it was easier to grin of my own accord. The hurt inside me ebbed, sidetracked by dreams and hopes of one day turning into that butterfly.

9

To see out the old year, I wore a new evening dress with a waistline around my hips and a skirt ending at my knees. I liked the new fashions. Doing the Charleston under those long skirts would make any skillful leg-work meaningless and, besides, Mickey paid me such nice compliments.

When he arrived to get me, he put a lei around my neck, stepped back and said, with no trace of guile, "Gee! You sure look swell. That white dress sets off your tan and your blonde hair."

Half of Honolulu was at the Royal, it seemed. Doug came with my friend, Ellen, and we saw lots of others from school and the Army and Navy. To accommodate the crowd, tables were placed close together on the lawn, far from the dance floor. Everyone wasn't able to dance at the same time, and most didn't try. Many were obviously more interested in the booze they had brought to spike their drinks.

Long before midnight, some were so drunk they lost all inhibitions. One man took off his shoes and climbed a coconut palm. Another fellow argued with the drummer of the orchestra. He looked as though he wanted to take over for the musician.

"Come on," said Mickey, "Let's sit out a couple of dances. I'm tired and thirsty. Look. Doug wants us to join him and Ellen."

As we sat down, Mickey told a waiter to bring four glasses of ginger ale, while Doug, with exaggerated gestures, made like he was despondent.

"All my flasks are dry," he wailed.

Mickey laughed. "I hope you know how lucky you are I'm your friend. I just happen to have a spare one that's full."

It was a variation of an old routine. I could see Ellen had heard it before. We settled down to consume our diluted gin and revive our vim. Ellen raised her glass. "Here's to 1928! And more prosperity!"

The noises around us multiplied and Mickey shouted, "Only ten minutes to go!" He grasped my arm. "Come on, Sugar, bring your glass and let's take a breather till the pandemonium subsides a bit."

We followed the sea wall to the far end of the terrace where the warm air blew soft and sweet. Drinking and acting the fool was not the only way to welcome in the new year. Out there in the waves, showing clearly in the half-moon light, swimmers and surfers sported. And on the sand below the wall, a group of beach boys, strumming ukuleles and guitars, sang softly to a small crowd of admirers. I wished the evening would never end.

Was it only the gin that made me glow? I didn't think so. Drinks were nothing new, but this — this new buoyancy was different. I wanted to tell Mickey, but hesitated. Put into words, it might sound corny. I didn't want him to laugh, so I just stared at him. He looked at me and for a long time. Neither of us spoke.

Then he clinked my glass. "Here's to you, Sisi. May you always be as happy as you are now."

"Does it show?"

"It sure does, and it's becoming." He took my hand. "I'm glad I'm the one with you tonight."

"You know, Mickey, 1927 was a wonderful year. So many fabulous things happened to me, and this is my first grown-up New Year's Eve party."

"Yeah, I guess we *are* growing up. We're in high gear, all right, and life is going to be even better — you'll see." He drained his glass and went on, "My old man's being transferred to the East Coast."

"Gosh. Then you won't graduate with us next year, will you?"

"I guess not. But that isn't the end. Doug and I have decided to go to Annapolis and become pilots." He waited for me to say something, and when I didn't, he continued, "How would you like to be the wife of a Navy flier?"

"Hmm .... Never thought of it." Then I had to laugh. "Oh, I'm supposed to marry one of you and live happily ever after, never knowing when I'll get a telegram saying you've crashed?"

"Aw, come on. I'm going to be the best of the best. There's no sign of a war, so we won't be in any danger. I thought you'd like the idea. You want to see the world, don't you? And we'd get transferred all over the place."

I was a little surprised to hear myself say, "Yes, but only where the *Navy* wants you to go. No, thanks. When I travel, I'd rather choose my own itinerary."

"You'll see," he said. "I'll be so dashing when I come zooming back here out of the wild blue yonder in my officer's uniform and wings, you won't be able to resist me. You just wait and see."

"Maybe I'll wait, and maybe I won't," I said.

Chapter Four

How many good things would 1928 bring?

Wait and see. Wait! Wait! That's what women have always done. First they wait *for*, then they wait *on*.

To begin with, a girl waits for the crumbs in her family, for what the boys don't need. Then she waits for some man to choose her for his wife. He gives her children whether she wants them or not, and for the rest of her life, she waits on her family. No one bothers to ask her what she would have liked to do.

Was I doomed to be one of those — always just waiting? If I did become a butterfly, how could I flit about as I wished? I'd need money. Whose? If it had to come from some man it meant — oh, gosh — it meant I'd have to do his bidding.

Some women liked it that way and were good at it. What about those who were not, or who were better at doing something else? Must they stay trapped, willy-nilly?

Madame Scheyer wasn't trapped. She didn't wait for, or on anyone. Was there a Mister Scheyer? I wished I had asked her.

The telephone bell tinkled — one long and three short rings.

My brother, George, answered it. In a moment he was saying, "Oh, hi .... Sure, she's right here. Hey, Sis, it's for you."

Raising and lowering his eyebrows suggestively, my brother handed me the receiver as he whispered, "It's Mickey."

"Hello," I said into the mouthpiece.

"There you are, Sugar. No one answered your phone in town so I figured you'd be at Kahana. Are you pretty well settled in now?"

"Very comfortable. Everything works, and the weather is marvelous. We all got here after school today and won't go back to town till Monday."

"Shucks. I was hoping to see you tomorrow evening for a movie or something. You wouldn't want to come in, would you?"

"No, not this weekend. But why don't you drive over here tomorrow morning and stay till Sunday?"

"Gee, Sugar, thanks. Okay, look for me early in the day."

Saturday morning dawned clear and sunny. I went down to the beach to sunbathe. Mickey would make the day even brighter. He would restore my self-esteem after some of those clods I'd been out with lately, especially that Major Rankin. Why did I go out with such jokers? In a crowd they were all right, but alone — gosh — all they thought of was getting drunk and necking. I didn't *have* to date them, of course, but I guess I wanted to show how popular I was. Among certain girls, there seemed to be a tacit rivalry to see who was most sought after. How vain. How futile. And how blind!

I remembered Maile. She was only sixteen, going steady with that nice university fellow, Craig. Suddenly she left school. Craig married her, and they moved to the mainland. It happened the year I was in Berkeley. Charlotte told me about it when I got back. Actually, she whispered it. "Maile became ... you know ..." Pronouncing the word was taboo, so she defined a swollen belly with her hands.

Maile was lucky. Many girls in her position would be abandoned. Craig quit studying and got a job in his father's business in Oakland. His plan had been to become an engineer. Instead, he would now have to support a family before he was ready. I could imagine his disappointment.

To me it was cruel and uncivilized. The majority, however, agreed with the Puritan mentality of those missionaries who first came to settle in the Islands, and who established Punahou School way back in 1841, and who ordained local morality ever since. No one could defy them with impunity.

Their technique for keeping the rest of us in check was simple and effective: If we stepped out of line, we would find that doors didn't open to us. Rather than be isolated, most people conformed.

I'd had enough sun on my left side and was turning over when I heard a car drive up and come to a stop in the parkway. The horn sounded lightly: One long and three short honks, and I knew who it was.

I stood up and waved. "Hi, Mickey!"

Already wearing his swimming trunks, he jumped out of the car, ran toward me, clasped my outstretched hand, and together, we flung ourselves into the incoming tide.

"Boy oh boy oh boy," was all Mickey could mutter whenever he caught his breath between dives through the waves. We swam a while and horsed around like a couple of sea colts, then sat on the beach.

"When I die and go to Heaven," Mickey said, "I'm going to find it very much like this. Portsmouth, Virginia, will be quite different. I'm going to miss swimming in the warm, salty water. Are you aware that it's much saltier here in the middle of this great ocean than along any seaboard?"

"No. I had no idea."

"It's true. And — you know what? I'm gonna miss you, too, Sugar. You're a helluva lot saltier than any girl along any seaboard."

"Okay, you rascal. You have just earned your lunch. Let's go up to the house. I've some pickled herring for the likes of you."

That was the start of an indelible day. We shared lunch with my mother, three brothers and Joan out on the lanai, facing the ocean. The menu was simply chicken salad and milk. As Mickey served himself, he sent me a glance from the end of the table that said, "What? No herring?" I explained with only a wink, and got a loaded smile in reply, while Mama chattered in her inimitable vernacular about Joan's latest achievements.

Suddenly George said, "Look out over there near the mouth of the bay, to the left. They're fishing."

We looked. In three small outriggers a half dozen bronzed men paddled their craft in a half circle and dropped something overboard.

Dick said, "They're setting out their long *hukilau* net. Later on, when they pull it in to the beach, they'll have a good catch for the whole valley."

"How do you know it'll be good?" Mickey asked.

"Because — up on the cliff side, as you go into Kahana Valley from here, there's a natural ledge. Every so often some guys climb up to it to survey the sea. It's pretty high and, of course, their eyes are trained to spot a school of fish. They can even tell what kind. Then they signal down to the valley and the fishermen take the net out. One day, Harper and I climbed up to the lookout and, boy, the water was so clear, we could see the sand bottom and coral reefs and patches of purple and turquoise ... but there were no fish that day."

"Can anyone go up there?" Mickey asked.

Dick laughed. "Sure, anyone who's part goat. It's a rough climb."

I said, "Let's go have a look at it, at least, Mickey."

"Vell," Mama said, "you better vear shoes."

Mickey and I walked along the highway that curved into the bay, and after a few minutes, turned onto the narrow dirt road leading to the valley. Hardly visible from the main road stood a few unpainted wooden houses of simple construction. Mostly Hawaiians lived there, many intermarried with Orientals and Caucasians. Chickens clucked between the houses and pecked at the hard-packed earth. A couple of dogs of no distinct breed, accompanied by a grunting pig, came to welcome us. Not far behind the houses, past a grove of banana trees where the taro patch began, a man with a shock of white hair stood leaning on a hoe.

"There's Ehu," I told Mickey. "Ehu's his nickname. It means 'white' or 'foam' or any light-colored thing. His hair turned white early. We buy our booze from him. He makes it from taro root."

The old man saw us and grinned. "Whea you guys goin'? You like buy some moa *okolehau*?"

"Naw," I said. "My brudda been get some yestaday."

I never missed an opportunity to practice pidgin English with qualified experts. I liked the versatility of our local dialect. Because its grammar and vocabulary were limited to bare essentials, emotions had to be expressed by the inflection and tone of the voice, with the help of gestures. Color was added by the borrowing of appropriate terms from languages of the Pacific: Japanese, Chinese, Philippino and Hawaiian. Each language had its own idioms but, as communities made liberal use of one another's words, the distinction was not always clearly defined. Hawaiians, for example, didn't pronounce the "g" in the suffix "ing" or "th" or the letter "r." They formed the past tense by using "been" with the present. Instead of "will" or "shall" in the future, they used "gonna" with the present verb.

Ehu said we were crazy when we explained we had come to see the lookout ledge on the cliff side and maybe climb up to it.

"Wassa matta you? You *pupule*? You like fall down break youa neck? Why you no go look da valley? You neva been go dea befoa."

His suggestion was far more alluring than the prospect of fracturing our limbs scaling that precipice.

Ehu advised us to follow the stream a ways, and indicated where to find the best trail and what to expect. He reminded us that it rained every night, and the vegetation grew rapidly, sometimes a foot a day.

He did not tell us about the abundant wild ginger, nor did he describe the rich fragrance of decaying flora, or how, when we crawled through the undergrowth, we would hear the rustle of startled mongooses scooting out of our way, and birds chirping messages of possible danger to their kin. Had Ehu ever noticed how the sunshine played with the wind to make designs as the leaves and branches cast dancing shadows? I believe he knew it all, and more. Hawaiians always lived close to Creation and felt its heart beating, so Mother Nature was good to them. She gave them the breadfruit thriving untended, the bananas and guavas, and even the pineapples that still came up long after commercial planters had abandoned the valley as unprofitable. The equally generous sea offered fish and squid, seaweed and lobster. And everything belonged to everyone.

In a clearing where a stream gurgled between black boulders, Mickey and I sat down. Neither of us spoke till Mickey took one of my hands and said softly, "All the islands must have been like this once ... unadulterated by concrete and machines and fences and locks and lawyers and ...."

"Like a Garden of Eden," I whispered, not wanting to infringe on the magic.

Mickey held my face gently between his hands and kissed me. "And romantic ...."

When I didn't reciprocate, he hesitated, then drew back. "You're right, Sugar. We mustn't complicate things. I don't want to risk hurting you. I care too much. Come on, let's go back down to 1928, and to what they call progress."

I knew he'd understand. I wanted to hug him for it. But, to hide my feelings, I skipped ahead of him down the trail.

Ehu was still working in the taro patch. His wife, Kuuipo, who was part-Chinese, and two small grandchildren played close by. The afternoon sun hid behind the mountain. A sea breeze blew in.

The children stayed near their grandmother and peeked at us from behind the skirt of her ample *muumuu*. Kuuipo lifted the smaller child and cuddled him, while Mickey patted the dark curly head of the other and asked her name. Instead of replying, she covered her face with the familiar skirt.

Kuuipo laughed. "Her name Kaiulani."

"It means Top of Heaven," I explained.

"I'm not surprised," said Mickey. "She's beautiful. And the boy?"

"Kealoha," said the grandmother, holding the baby closer and rocking him in her plump arms.

"And that," I said, "means The Loved One."

Mickey would have stayed for the rest of the afternoon if I had not suggested we go to the beach and watch them haul in the fishnet.

"Yeah! Maybe we can help pull in the catch."

But Ehu said, "*Pau hana. Hukilau* all *pau.*"

"He's saying it's all over, isn't he?" Mickey remarked.

So we said our good-byes and returned home for another swim before dinner.

A blue sedan was parked in our driveway. "Oh, Andy's here again," I said.

"Who's Andy?"

"He works at the sugar plantation at Kahuku and often stops in on his way home."

"To see you?"

"Oh, no! He comes to cry on my mother's shoulder. You see, he's been married a couple of years and is still madly in love with his wife, but she seems to be fed up with him, with marriage, and with living so far from town. She has left him more than once already. Kahuku is too rustic, I guess. He wants children and she doesn't."

"So what does your mother tell him?"

"I don't know. Whatever it is, he keeps coming back for more. She never tells anyone what to do, but helps him find his own solution, to see the problem from other points of view. She always says that troubles start when people act and react with their emotions. They can't be objective then, you see, because their egos get in the way."

We were ten at dinner that night. Besides Andy, two of George's friends dropped in. Mickey and I began the conversation, reporting on our expedition to the valley and our visit with Ehu and his family.

"That grandmother seemed to have more patience with those kids than a lot of young mothers I know," Mickey commented.

Andy said, "It's an old Hawaiian custom."

"What is?" Mickey asked.

"Well," Andy said, "until the missionaries got here, there was no wedlock as we know it. Couples mated, and when a young woman had a child, she gave it to her mother, who, by then, was ready to settle down and lavish maternal affection. When the young woman grew old, she, in turn, took her grandchildren to nurture."

"Sounds like a pretty enlightened system," I said.

"But marriage is sacred!" Andy's voice was distressed. "Without it, there would be chaos!"

Mama changed the subject then. It was just as well, because I was thinking that matrimony did not guarantee happiness, and had not eliminated promiscuity or chaos. Saying that, however, would have done Andy no good.

Maile and Craig came back to mind. But I kept my thoughts to myself.

Chapter Five

Charlotte and I spent most of our free time together. After school, we waited for each other to get on the same streetcar, which took us to Paawa Junction where we changed to one marked "Waikiki."

The open-sided car clattered across the trestle spanning the old duck ponds, and turned onto Kalakaua Avenue. Continuing along that broad thoroughfare, we passed vacant lots, small homes, Fort De Russy (which didn't look at all like a fort), the Moana Hotel, larger residences, Waikiki Tavern, Aoki Store, and finally reached Kapiolani Park. At that point, the avenue narrowed, and the tracks followed the rim of the park to where they and the avenue ended.

Charlotte lived a few paces from there, in a great old wooden house at the water's edge.

Our house was a half mile from hers, on Paki Avenue, an unpaved road that curved between the Polo Club with its pastures and paddock on the right, and the park on the left. Only eight houses, each in its well-kept garden, stood on Paki Avenue. Behind us, where the bare brown buttresses of Diamond Head began to slope upward, spread the Gomes Farm.

Sometimes I'd go to Charlotte's after school, or she'd come to my house and we'd swim or make fudge or play grown-ups.

Then, one day we *were* grown up — or almost. Sunbathing one July afternoon, Charlotte said, "Just think — Next year will be our last in high school. What are you going to do after we graduate?"

"Gosh, I haven't decided yet. College, I guess. You know, I sort of would like to go into dress designing. I got the idea the other day after you and I went to that sale at the Liberty House."

Charlotte chortled. "And bought those oversized, out-of-date evening gowns for next to nothing! Gee! Weren't we lucky? We could never afford to buy such fabrics by the yard. I can cut a whole dress out of the blue satin skirt. Have you made over any of them yet?"

"I'm working on the turquoise chiffon," I said. "Do you remember, when we were kids, how we used to dress up in you mother's old gowns? Wasn't that fun? I liked rainy days 'cause then she'd let us go up to your attic and rummage through her ancient trunks. Draping ourselves in those gorgeous things made me feel like a Greek sculptor. You know, it was about then I made my first dress all by myself. I must have been only twelve or thirteen."

"And it was pretty, too, I remember. What are you going to wear to the party Saturday night?"

"I've got to finish the turquoise chiffon."

"Do you miss Mickey?"

"I did, at first. It's better now that I'm back on the old merry-go-round. On Sunday, Bob is taking me to another of those breakfast parties starting no earlier than noon and ending who knows when. Then, next Friday, Margaret is giving a beach party at her Kailua house, and for that weekend, I've invited a crowd to Kahana. I've made a new *muumuu* to wear then. I don't have time to miss Mickey."

We talked nearly every day. Whatever the subject, it was momentous at the time. We bandied secrets of our hearts that others might have thought silly. Encountering certain feelings for the first time meant we were maturing, and comparing notes was comforting. We helped each other understand our changing emotions and curiosity about our developing bodies.

Some years earlier, when puberty caught up with us, my mother was prepared. She answered all my questions in language I could comprehend, and I passed on the information to Charlotte. For some reason, her mother found it difficult, even impossible, to discuss matters such as menstruation, pregnancy and our interest in boys.

During that summer of 1928, I bounded from one romantic euphoria to another and related all in detail to my best friend. It was toward the end of July that I phoned her one evening and said, "Guess what!"

"Tell me, quick!"

"Well — this afternoon I was in the kitchen when the front door bell rang. Stan went to answer it. I heard the door open and a man's voice say, 'Hi. Is George at home?'

"Stan said, 'No, my brother's out now. But won't you come in? Sis is here.'

"Then the fellow said, 'Gee, thanks. You must be Stan. I'm Sito. George and I used to play together years ago.'

"And Stan said, 'Sure, I know you. We often talk about the old days.'"

Charlotte interrupted me. "Did you say Sito? Isn't he the boy who lived next door to you on Center Street when you were little?"

"Yes! Imagine!"

"Golly. So ... What happened? How old is he now?"

"Oh, about twenty or twenty-one, I guess. I was flabbergasted. And I looked simply awful! I dashed to my room, changed my dress, combed my hair, put on lipstick and, trying to look casual, sauntered into the living room. And there he was — tan, tall, husky, and oh, so handsome. He looks just like Richard Arlen."

"No kidding! My favorite movie star. And then what?"

"He jumped up from his chair and clasped my hands and said, 'Gee, Sisi, gee, you sure look swell.'"

"Wow! How long is he going to stay?"

"Just a few weeks — visiting his parents. He's going to the University of Washington now, in Seattle, and most summers he works on one of the beaches up there as a lifeguard."

"Are you going to invite him to Kahana?"

"Of course. Early in August, he'll spend a whole week with us."

"Darn it," Charlotte said, "just when I have to go with Mother to California. We won't be back till school starts in September. But you've never told me where he got the name Sito."

"Oh, I thought you knew. His parents were living in Peru when he was born. They named him Thomas. In Spanish, the diminutive is Tomasito. The Sito stuck."

Chapter Six

The first week of August finally arrived. I guess I didn't hide my excitement very well. Mama noticed how careful I was to tidy up the living room the evening before Sito was expected.

I'm sure she was fishing when she commented, "My goodness, Sito has grown into a fine young man, don't you t'ink so?"

I felt myself blushing, so I turned away as I said, "Sure, he's okay."

"Yust t'ink, he vas only fifteen ze last time ve saw him — a boy — and now he's a good-looking man. It vill be nice talking about old times."

"Mom ... I hope Astrid and Henry aren't coming again this weekend."

"No, I don't t'ink zey vill be. Vy?"

"They'd spoil everything. Henry is such a jerk."

"Henry? But he and your sister yust got married. Give him a chance to get used to zis country. It's different from Norvay, you know."

"He can make Astrid over to suit himself, but he doesn't have the right to judge *me*."

"Vat doss he say to you?"

"He hasn't the guts to tell *me* anything, but what he says to Astrid — that I'm a flapper who will never amount to anything — What nerve! *I'll* not amount to anything! When he made *her* give up *her* singing career after they got married!"

"She vanted to, I t'ink. She says so, anyvay."

"And you believe that, Mom?" I saw a shadow dull the expression on my mother's face.

The house was quiet. Joan was in bed, and there was no one to disturb us. I lit a few pieces of wood in the fireplace, not because it was cold, but to create an atmosphere. I brought a pot of hot cocoa and mugs from the kitchen. It wasn't often I had Mama to myself, but whenever we were alone, our talks had satisfying results.

As though there had been no interruption, I said, "Before she married him, all she ever thought of was becoming a great singer. She used to play those records of Galli-Curci over and over and, with her silvery voice, she'd have made it, I'm sure. Professor Wanrell expected her to. And you did, too, didn't you, Mom?"

Mama's only answer was a sigh.

I went on, "Henry wanted her all to himself, to bake his pies and iron his shirts and build his ego. Now she has no choice. It's either that or admit she made a mistake. What does he know or care about the arts? If she's happy, that's her business. But she makes it *my* business by saying I'll never find a husband unless I can cook. That shows how the level of her values has lowered. If all a man wants is an unpaid servant, he can't have me. Any dummy can cook. To prove it, let me prepare Thanksgiving dinner all by myself this year."

Mama laughed at that, really laughed, though I don't think because she thought it funny. Rather, having shifted the subject ever so slightly, I had opened a release valve.

"You vill soon be eighteen, Sis," she said.

I didn't want her to stray too far from the matter that bothered me. "I know, I *know*! And you're going to tell me I should be thinking of my future. Well, I won't marry a creep like Henry. That's for sure."

"Oh? Have you chosen a husband already? Is he rich and handsome?"

"What's wrong with that? Nope. I haven't picked him out. Are you afraid I'm going to be an old maid?"

She laughed again. "On ze contrary. I hope you'll vait a long time. Have you t'ought about being a professional artist? You draw vell, you know — especially portraits. You should have some work zat is yours, zat no von can take from you — even in old age, ven your children are gone, and your husband is, vell, maybe he's gone, too."

She was back on track, and I let her continue. "All men are not like Henry. Maybe he'll change, maybe he von't. Some men do. But don't count on a person to give you lasting happiness. It must come from somet'ing inside you — from a vork you believe in and do. A talent is given in trust and should not be neglected. Sure — every voman should find a man to love, to give her whole heart to, but maybe she don't have to give him her whole mind and soul, too.

"You know vy I left Bergen young and vent to Sout' Africa? Because my stepmot'er vouldn't let my fat'er get a piano ven I had ze chance to have free singing lessons. I vas so happy ven Astrid had also a beautiful voice, and right here vas living ze professor to teach her."

"Yes," I said, "and after sending her to study in Europe with such high hopes, it all came to nothing."

"I know. But vat can I say? You see, I never told you before, but also it happened to me."

"What did?"

"Ven I vas in Durban, singing in amateur t'eatricals, a fine English yentleman said I had a gifted voice, and vanted to send me to Europe to study. He'd have paid for everyt'ing — even for many years, to make me a career."

I stared at my mother. She looked away, into the fading fire. The recollection was obviously painful.

"But Mama! For Pete's sake — why didn't you accept his offer?"

"Vell, you see, my dear, I vas in love vis your fat'er and ...."

She didn't say any more, and didn't have to. It was the same old story. Women were softies, always giving in. No wonder men could take advantage. I believe it was at that moment I resolved to break the pattern. *I would never be any man's puppet*! Time would tell.

After awhile, I asked if she ever regretted her choice. It was a foolish question, and I got the evasive answer I might have expected.

"If I had done ot'ervise, I vould not have all you vonderful children."

The real answer to my question was, of course, in her advice: Learn something that is yours, that no one can take from you. She didn't want my fate to be the same as hers and Astrid's.

Maybe I would be an artist of some sort? But I was no genius.

Who was going to send me to Europe to study? I couldn't expect my father to do so after he had backed my sister and lost.

Chapter Seven

Sito fit into our family life at Kahana as he had done years ago. We laughed over our childhood pranks while sitting around the kitchen table for a mid-afternoon bite of Mama's home-baked bread and guava jam. We reminisced as we swam and sunbathed. We drove to the movies at Kaneohe, recalling old times on the way. We remembered Sito's pets: the guinea pig and white mice, and his donkey, Betsy.

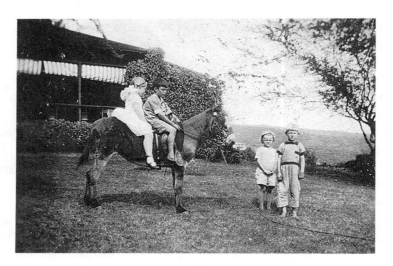

Astrid and Sito on Betsy; Sis and George - 1915

Sito the lifeguard, Seattle - 1928

Mama brought out some old snapshots of us. There we were — just kids then — in our starched Sunday clothes, posing for snapshots with Besty.

Fifty years later, Sito and I would look back with much the same nostalgia to that week at Kahana in 1928. We never forgot the time we sang in barbershop disharmony till late one night on the beach, bellowing out over the Pacific the lyrics of one popular song after another.

Sometimes I wished nothing would ever change. Life was comfortable and predictable.

But was that how I really wanted it? Mama was always telling me to listen to that small voice inside me. I *did* listen but kept getting conflicting messages — one insisted it was safe to be smug, two-dimensional, flat as a painting and limited to what the physical eye could see. The other urged me to explore the third dimension out there, to get beyond things and people and opinions and see other facets. "Take chances!" said the voice. "Don't be intimidated. Be adventurous. The world is enormous. Dare — dare to — to be outrageous!"

My feet began to itch.

Kahana

Chapter Eight

Our senior year began unsensationally. Many new faces and cars, belonging mostly to Army and Navy kids, adorned the campus, but I found none of the new students exceptional. That could change, of course. Sooner or later individual personalities would show, and we would prefer the company of some to others.

But that year, the boys seemed immature. Charlotte joked about it, saying that we must have outgrown them. She had recently met Mark, an Army lieutenant.

"He's older," she said, "and makes me feel like an adult."

We rarely rode the streetcar anymore to get to and from school. When I got my driver's license, Mama lent me her car until Papa gave me a model A Ford coupe. We spent more time at Kahana and, as Dick and Stan were still minors, I had to transport them.

Nevertheless, Charlotte and I always found an occasional hour to tell each other the good and the bad that crossed our paths.

Diane phoned me one day. We had been good friends when she was still at Punahou School. She was now at the university.

"Hi," I said. "Long time no see. What are you doing these days?"

We exchanged the usual banter, then she said, "I'm giving a dinner party next Saturday, and I want you to come. There are some new people in town, and I'm sort of introducing them around."

I said I'd be glad to come.

"Brian will pick you up around seven. Oh, and Sisi, be sure to look your best."

"Why do you suppose she'd tell me to look my best?" I later asked Charlotte. "Don't we always? It's not like her to be patronizing."

"Maybe it was just her way of saying you shouldn't wear dungarees," Charlotte suggested.

Whatever her reason, I chose my sophisticated black lace. It had a beige lining, fit snug down to the knees and then flared out with tulle. After a shampoo, I gave myself a marcel with combs while my hair was still damp. It had grown enough so that, for the first time, I could twist it into a bun at the nape.

"Makes me look older, don't you think, Mom?" I twirled around. "Do you approve?"

"To me you are alvays pretty."

Brian was punctual. As Mama let him in she said, "I don't see your yalopy, Brian. Is zat a new car you have?"

"No, Mrs. Larsen. We're in luck. A friend is driving us."

So Mama kissed me good-bye and wished us a good time.

From the driver's seat of his friend's Chrysler roadster, a tall, slender young man in a white linen suit got out. I had seen him before, on the Punahou campus, in that very car with its top down.

Brian said, "This is John Embree. John, this is Agnes — but call her Sis or Sisi. We all do. She doesn't like Agnes."

We shook hands, and John smiled the same smile I had seen just a week before, that day at school. I was waiting to cross the street to the parking lot, and he slowed down, blocking my way for a moment, and then drove on. And here he was, holding my hand and saying, "How do you do?"

A lyric tremor rippled through me. He released my hand as I blushed and tried to pretend I didn't care who he was.

"You have such a good tan," I said sarcastically. "I'd guess you haven't been here long."

Brian took my arm and ushered me around to the other side of the car. "You don't mind if we all squeeze into the front seat, do you?"

I got in, and John slid behind the steering wheel next to me.

Our shoulders touched. Brian seemed to be no longer there, physically. Only his voice had substance.

I heard it say, "Yeah, John has been here only a few weeks. He's from Chicago ... Came with his two sisters. They go to Punahou. He's at the U., transferred from McGill. Quite a car, isn't it? When he offered to chauffeur us tonight, how could I refuse? The poor guy doesn't have a date," Brian laughed, "so he might as well make himself useful." He laughed again.

Brian did all the talking. I heard only fragments of what he said. "John's mother and Diane's ... old friends ... party tonight for John ... suppose she told you ..." He then changed the subject to football and I heard no more.

Diane greeted us on the lanai of her house in Manoa Valley. As soon as we had said hello to the other guests, she guided me into her bedroom. "Come, Sisi, I'll show you where to powder your nose."

As though I didn't already know. She shut the door behind us.

"I might have guessed — You look fabulous! And you've put your hair up. You see, John told me he wanted to meet you."

"But how on Earth .... ?"

"I've no idea how he knew we were friends. Honolulu's a pretty small world, remember. Maybe he'll tell you one day. You'll find him different from the local men. His family is intellectual. They have famous friends."

"Well, he'll soon learn I'm not in that category."

"I do not allow my friends to belittle themselves. Come on, let's go and have a drink. Dinner is buffet style, and then we'll play bridge. Mother and Dad will join us so we can have two tables."

I was relieved and grateful that John paid no more attention to me than to anyone else. In my one year of French class I had learned the term *savoir-faire*, and in him I saw it exemplified. With rare tact and wit, he made each one of us feel worthy of notice.

On the drive home, Brian slept most of the way while John and I chatted with ease — as though we had been friends for ages.

I awoke early the next morning and lay a long time reliving the evening and wondering if John would want to see me again. I liked him. At about eleven o'clock, the phone rang and I jumped out of bed, but Mama got there first. I couldn't hear what she said, though from her laughter, I assumed it was someone she knew.

Suddenly she called out, "Telephone for you, Sis!"

"If it's Charlotte," I shouted, "tell her I'm not home!"

"No. It's Yohn." And as she handed me the receiver, she lowered her voice and grinned. "He vants to take you to dinner tonight."

John had already won Mama's heart.

Chapter Nine

We chose to have dinner at the Waikiki Tavern, an unpretentious, popular, and sometimes noisy restaurant. By selecting a table at the far end, however, we enjoyed relative quiet and had a view of the beach and some late surfers in the froth-crested breakers.

After the waiter had taken our orders, John said, "You have a charming mother. Her accent is distinctive. I can't place it."

"Probably," I said, "because she was born and brought up in Bergen, where they pronounce the 'r' as the French do. She learned English in South Africa and has lived in this country for twenty years or so. I've been trying to get her to speak like us, but it seems hopeless."

"If you succeed," John tilted his head and shook a finger at me, "I'm afraid you will steal away much of her individuality. To me, conformity is synonymous with mediocrity."

I stared at him. *He was different.* With a sparkle in his voice, he went on, "So — your background is Norwegian. Then you know Ibsen. Have you read his play, *Peer Gynt?*"

"No, but I know the story and Grieg's music very well. My mother sings, you see, and both Grieg and Ibsen were from Bergen."

We talked about Mama and her thwarted aspirations. I told him, too, of the end of my sister's musical ambition.

"For women, the road is still uphill," John said. "And where will your road take you, Agnes? Diane tells me you're the art editor of your yearbook — that you draw well."

"That doesn't mean much," I said. "What I'm doing now isn't important. Portraits are easy. But otherwise I just do pretty pictures."

"Anything wrong with that?"

He was testing me — I could tell by the expression on his face — and expected me to parry. I couldn't let him down.

"Well, no," I began, "there's nothing wrong with it if you like mediocrity."

John's face lit up. Our eyes met and we laughed — like two kids knowing they had discovered a secret treasure. Then, for several moments, neither of us spoke.

The waiter brought our food, and John said, "If you don't fancy making pretty pictures, what kind do you like?"

"The kind nobody here knows anything about." I told him about the boarding school in Berkeley and Madame Scheyer, and how we had called her a "missionary" of modern art.

"And you became an apostle?"

"Well, an avid follower, anyway. Before that, I had no idea there was any art besides the old copying of nature. Believe me, her class was a revelation. She showed us reproductions of abstract work of some painters she knows. The pictures were simply forms, lines, colors — I liked them."

"I like them, too."

"You *do?*"

I've seen some of the originals — in Paris. I spent a year there between high school and university, just looking around, learning the language and getting another culture rubbed off on me. Naturally, I went to museums and galleries — there's one on every block. I'm no expert, mind you, but I was inquisitive. I figured that people who painted like that and those who *bought* the paintings had at least average intelligence, and if *they* thought the stuff was valid, who was I to declare it wasn't?"

"Gosh," I said almost inaudibly.

"Don't be hard on those who can't share your enthusiasm. Give 'em a few decades. So-called modern art will be fashionable by then, and they'll come around. All conformists do when something has been approved by enough of the bourgeoisie. Take Ibsen. When his play *The Doll's House* first came out, the public was furious — said his aim was to destroy marriage. That was fifty years ago. Now the public calls the play a literary milestone. You can't blame them. Most people feel threatened by anything new."

"I see what you mean."

He went on, "I'm going to be a writer some day."

"For the theatre?"

"No. So far, I've experimented with style — short stories and articles. I haven't tried to sell anything yet. I love language, you see. Not only ours, but words in general — their sounds and meanings. I warn you: I'm a purist and might correct your grammar."

"And my mother's, too?"

"Certainly not! English isn't her language, and dialects should be respected and preserved. Maybe you'll help me learn pidgin."

With John I was beginning to feel a secure warmth, a promising friendship.

"And about *Peer Gynt* ..." John said, "Would you care to read it with me? There are lots of things in it I'd like to discuss with you."

"Sure. I'm a born ham."

"That makes two of us. Tell me, how does your mother feel about your leaning against the current?"

"She's on my side, but doesn't want me to get hurt."

"And — she thinks that by conforming, no harm will come to you?"

"I suppose so, though she's not so explicit."

"And what are your hopes and plans for the future, Agnes?"

"To tell the truth, I'm confused. I'll have to face the day of judgment eventually, I guess."

John reached across the table and squeezed my hand. "I'm on your side, too, and rooting for you."

On Monday, I went to school as usual. Some things, however, were not the same. In English class, for example, Miss Porter, with her well-known irony, praised me for at last being aware of what was going on. In Ancient History, I described the difference between the Visigoths and the Ostrogoths with no effort.

It wasn't only the tropical sun that brightened the world that day. The world had never been so luminous, so radiant.

At lunch, Charlotte caught up with me at the cafeteria. "Sorry I haven't called you for so long," she said. "I've been out with Mark every evening lately. What have you been doing? How was Diane's party?"

"Oh, it was ..." No! I couldn't tell her. It was too private. I couldn't. I said, "It was like all the other dinner parties — good food and lousy bridge. What a boring game it is. There must be other, more interesting ways of spending an evening."

Charlotte turned back to the shepherd's pie as she said, "There are. You'll learn."

Chapter Ten

My likeness in the mirror was having difficulty putting up her hair. She wished it were longer and less fine. It might then be more manageable. Of greater concern, however, was her new relationship with John.

"What do you suppose he sees in you?" I asked the reflection, making a face. "You're not beautiful. You have freckles that show even through your tan. Your face is too round to suit me. He says he likes your hair. It is rather nice — unruly, but not bad, especially when the sun has lightened it. But surely that's not why he's taking you dancing tonight? You ought to be someone he can admire for ... for what? Your mind? Oh, come on! But he could be your coach, your guide.

You'd be a willing scholar. You wouldn't let him get tired of teaching you, would you?"

Mama appeared in the doorway. I could see her image next to mine in the looking glass. "Are you ready? Yohn is here."

"Thanks, Mom, I'll be there in a few minutes."

"Don't hurry. I'm have a good time talking vis him."

Saturday night dancing at the Moana Hotel had been a local custom for as long as I could remember. The hotel's L-shaped, broad lanai offered an intimate dance floor. The orchestra played right there in the corner, while in wicker arm chairs along one wall, sat the grey-haired "rocking-chair brigade" smiling or scowling at the dancers, perhaps recalling earlier carefree times, or their misspent youth.

From each wing of the lanai, several steps led down to the flagstoned courtyard. Chairs and small round tables filled the area under the cherished banyan tree, whose vast branches shaded the entire space all year long.

Before choosing a table, John and I walked along the shoreline. Tiny waves lapped the beach, one after another, in silent rhythm, and sank into the sand.

"It still seems unreal," John whispered. "The stars are so bright and close. In Chicago, it's November, too. But even in summer, the lakeshore isn't anything like this." The orchestra started playing. "If that's a fox trot, let's try it. I can't manage anything more complicated."

Our first dance together started clumsily, but by the time the music ended, our steps were in harmony, and the evening continued in a major key ....

When John and I said goodnight at my front door, my mother was still up. I found her in the kitchen preparing bread dough. I slid onto a stool and leaned against the worktable.

"So? You had a good time?"

"Gee, Mama, it was wonderful. He knows so much and makes me feel as though I'm not a complete dimwit. I've asked him to come to Kahana some weekend. Is that all right?"

"Of course it is. You know zat."

"His parents have a vacation house, too ... in Canada."

"And vill he go back in ze summer?"

"No. He might stay here a couple of years. You remember Lorraine?

She was at the Moana, with Willard."

"I know she is your classmate ... but who is Villard?"

"Head of the English department at the U., and he's a friend of John's. I've invited them over, too."

"Vell, zat's nice. Lorraine is Svedish, isn't she? An intelligent girl."

"Mom ... I'm beginning to change my opinion about a lot of things."

"Like vat?"

"Oh, I don't know. Things in general ... seeing with different eyes."

"It's good to change ze viewpoint, so you can be objective. You are growing up."

"For example, Mama, people say we can do whatever we want as long as we don't hurt anyone."

"Zat's right. You don't vant to hurt anyvon, do you?"

"No matter how good one is, it's hard not to offend someone sometimes."

"So vat are you trying to tell me?"

"John says, and I agree, do what you want as long as you're willing to take the consequences."

Mama stopped working and looked at me over her eyeglasses. "Go on — tell me vat consequences?"

"Oh Mom! Nothing! It's just philosophy. It's like I was saying — another way of looking at things."

She sighed audibly. "You had me scared for a minute. Come, we'll have a cup of coffee. I vant to learn more about vat young people are t'inking nowadays."

Mama, in Honolulu - 1916

Chapter Eleven

John and I saw a lot of each other after that Saturday. I was getting used to profound discussions of weighty matters.

Occasionally, in the middle of the week, I'd come home from school to find John already there, talking with Mama. He never tired of asking her about Norway. One day, he had with him a large book with a decorative binding.

"Look what has just arrived!" he said. "The latest addition to my collection of rare volumes. I've been expecting it for weeks."

It was *Peer Gynt*, number forty-seven of a limited edition, illustrated by a well-known artist.

"Do you still want to read it with me?" he asked.

"Any time you're ready," I said.

The following Friday afternoon, John and I headed for the other side of the island in his roadster with the top down and the wind in our hair. We sped up Nuuanu Avenue, through areas dotted with expensive homes, and past miles of woods.

"Have you ever gone hunting for wild fruit?" I asked.

"Not yet. I'm not the Boy Scout type. But I do like to try new foods — just in case you ever offer me some wild guavas. I find all Hawaiian dishes good. All, that is, except poi. Can't swallow the stuff. By the way, your mother told me about your phenomenal Thanksgiving dinner, that you prepared it entirely by yourself."

"Did she tell you *why* I did it?"

"No. You had a special reason?"

"My sister is always badgering me — saying I'll never get a husband if I can't cook. I wanted to prove that any dummy who can read can make a meal. Actually, it was easy. I found a magazine article that told how to do it, step-by-step."

"And now you're qualified to catch a husband, aren't you?"

I laughed out loud. "That's funnier than you think, John. Once upon a time — in fact, a year or so ago — I thought of myself as a chrysalis that would one day be transformed into a social butterfly. That would require getting married, the ambition of every proper girl here."

"You've changed your mind? How come?"

"Because my brother-in-law made my sister give up her singing career to gratify his philistine ego. He doesn't know it, but he's changed my life."

"But what if you fall in love? Most people do, sooner or later."

"I'll cross that bridge when I get to the river. Meanwhile, do you know what Lord Byron said? 'Marriage from love, like vinegar from wine.'"

"Ho, ho! Good for him! Now I'll give you a quotation from John Embree: 'I marriage disparage.'"

Conversation stopped. We had reached the Pali, that slender pass over the Koolau Range. Normally, we'd have parked the car and from the lookout, admired the spectacular view: the valleys far below, Kaneohe Bay, and beyond. But that day, air currents were stronger and noisier than usual. We cringed, held tight, and headed down the narrow winding road of the steep windward side.

As the highway levelled, it became wider and straighter, and the wind gentler. Even at low speed, it didn't take long to drive through the small town of Kaneohe. From there the route ran close to the rugged shore, skirting the bay. John commented on the color patterns in the water, irregular patches of violet, turquoise and blue.

"That little island out there," John said, "is it real or *papier mâché*?"

"It does look artificial, doesn't it? Its shape, and those two swaying coconut palms — like plumes. We call it Chinaman's Hat."

I closed my eyes and leaned my head back so the rays of the sun could tint my face. I was at peace, because of John. I had never felt as happy as that before. Dear John. He had turned my world right side up. "There's no place on Earth more enchanting than this."

"Well now," John said with a chortle, "I wasn't aware you had been to so many places."

He expected a facetious rejoinder, but I couldn't think of one, so I soothed my defeat by making a face.

Enjoying his triumph, he added, "You could start by going to Paris."

"Oh, sure! Papa would never agree to it."

"You can't be certain."

"There are four other children who need to be educated. It costs enough to send us to Punahou. And George is going to the University of California next fall. Besides, Papa's one of those fathers who thinks daughters will get married and, therefore, don't need an education. He says the money he spent on my sister was wasted."

"But your mother doesn't feel that way."

I looked at him sideways. "Do you know something I don't know?"

"Agnes, don't misunderstand. I had to find out where she stood and enlist her as an ally. We've been talking about your talent, that it should be encouraged. You should spend a couple of years in Paris and then — Agnes! What is it?"

I had covered my face with my hands so he wouldn't see the sudden tears. He stopped the car at the side of the road and put his arms around my shoulders, drawing me close to him. He must have understood because he didn't say anything. He just stroked my hair.

"Oh John," I whimpered, "you've no idea ... I've never dared think of it ever since Madame Scheyer ... and then you said you'd been to Paris ... I've dreamed about going. But I couldn't talk to anyone. It was like hallucinating ... not real ... I still don't see how it can be possible."

"You'll see." He didn't release me. "You can make it happen. You, and your mother and I, but mostly you."

And then he kissed me for the first time.

Mama had gone to Kahana earlier in the day with Joan and an old friend, a woman named Tecla, a guest till Sunday. Examining the subject of Paris would, therefore, have to wait till Tecla left. In the meantime, I was eager to read *Peer Gynt*.

John and I dragged two chairs to one end of the lanai. For the rest of that day and all of the next, we took turns reading, stopping only to eat and take an occasional dip in the ocean.

In scene after scene, Ibsen reveals Peer's restlessness, his wanderlust, his egocentricity. As a young rustic in Norway, Peer gets a girl pregnant. Instead of marrying her, he runs off to Africa, then journeys to America, where he makes a lot of money. Finally, in his old age, he returns to Norway, where Solveig, his forsaken sweetheart, still waits for him. Hounding him relentlessly, is a shadowy creature called the Button-Moulder.

The story absorbed us to the end. John admired the style, the prose, and the fantasy of the plot. Peer, the enigmatic hero, entranced me.

"This is uncanny, John. It's weird! We have been reading the biography *of my own father!*"

"What are you talking about?"

"You've met my father, but all you know about him is that he's in his mid-forties, attractive, and, what is called a good provider."

John rubbed his hands together in mock glee. "You mean he has a past that isn't hackneyed and trite? How exciting! Tell me more."

"I'm serious, John. It's spooky. Listen. When my father was a vigorous young blade in Oslo, not yet legally of age, he got his girl friend in the family way. He'd have married her, but his parents felt she was socially inferior and wouldn't give their consent. So he took off and went to South Africa, intending to return in a year or so to marry the young woman he'd wronged."

John listened attentively, so I continued.

"Well, instead, he learned the building trade, and married my mother, a lovely nineteen year old from Bergen. That was in 1905. A year later, San Francisco was devastated by that famous earthquake and fire, and my father saw a chance to rebuild a city and make a pile of dough. But, by then, my mother was expecting. Two months after my sister was born, he sent Mama and the baby to Norway, and restless and chomping at the bit, he got a job on a sailing vessel headed for New Zealand, the first leg of his voyage to California."

"Hold on." John said. "Is all this true or are you making it up?"

"It's not only true, it gets better. When he reported for work on the ship, the skipper had changed his mind, and there was no job. With the help of the crew, however, he stowed away, and gave himself up only when they were well out at sea. By then, of course, the captain had no choice but to put him to work. In New Zealand, he found a job on another vessel, and headed for San Francisco by way of Sidney and Hawaii. They berthed several days in Honolulu. The climate and scenery so enchanted my father, he determined then and there to one day settle in the Islands with his family. He was only twenty-two."

"And how long was it till he did return?"

"About six years, and only after a long string of adventures."

"Yes. I see the resemblance to *Peer Gynt.* He's calmed down now, hasn't he?"

"Hmm ... Calm enough because he has the means to indulge his vanities: another woman and drinking with the boys. My mother pretends she doesn't know — she wants us to think he's working late. I'm afraid she's just like Solveig — she'll be in love with him to the end, no matter what."

"Well, I guess love can't be turned on or off at will. What became of his first sweetheart?"

"She never married. Still waiting, I suppose. She had a boy, named Olaf. My father sent for him some years ago. He's working in California now. You know what, John? I think I've inherited my father's wanderlust. Sometimes my feet itch so much. I do want to get away ... to see all sorts of places ... not as a tourist ... to take risks ... and the consequences."

"And now you will."

"What about the Button-Moulder who follows Peer about?" I asked.

"That's how Ibsen saw the demon of conformity trying to cast Peer in the conventional mould. Your father has apparently succeeded in dodging the Button-Moulder. I'll bet you will, too."

"I'd hate for you to lose a bet."

Chapter Twelve

After breakfast on Sunday, we waved good-bye to Tecla as she drove off in her new sports car.

"A very clever voman," Mama said. "She's been promoted. You remember, Sis. She vas a long time yust a saleslady at ze Liberty House. Now she's a buyer, and vill go to New York several times a year.

"Gee," I said. "I used to think of her as merely another old maid. She's really attractive as well as clever. I'm seeing lots of things with different eyes lately."

"Ya, I've noticed. Come. I'll make a fresh pot of coffee. I can tell you two vant to talk vis me about somet'ing, and I t'ink I know vat it is."

For the rest of the morning, the three of us sat around the kitchen table and talked about Paris. *Why* or *if* I should go were questions that did not come up. John described the cafés that give breath to the City of Light, the splendid vistas and broad boulevards.

"Everyone meets at the terrace cafés," he said. "That's where they read the papers, argue world politics, and have their flirtations. I think I became of age intellectually during that year I was in Paris. I saw for myself the importance of the arts — how they're indispensably fused with every phase of life, and I began to write seriously."

"Sis doesn't know anyvon dere. Von't she be lonesome?"

John smiled indulgently. "It won't take her long to feel at home, Mrs. Larsen. She'll soon make friends with students from all parts of the world. They'll be as poor as she, if not poorer. But in Paris, the quality of life does not depend on the bankroll."

"There's the language," I said. "I've forgotten the little I once learned."

"You'll catch on. In French two negatives don't make a positive. Most adjectives come after the noun. The accent falls on the final syllable. You'll pick up things like that right away."

"So," I said, "that's why you pronounce my name the way you do — Agnès. I rather like it."

John replied, "When I heard you didn't use your name, I guessed why. Then I may call you Agnès?"

I nodded, and Mama said, "Ya, it's soft, like in Norvegian."

John went on, his eyes laughing, "Besides, it means Lamb."

"Go ahead," I said, "that kind of goading is good for me. If I don't end up a human lamb grazing with the herd in a local rut, it'll be thanks to you. I'm going to get a job this summer and save all I earn. Gee! I wonder how long it will take?"

Mama turned on a smile that spread like wild flowers. Behind it was a dazzling idea.

"You know, Sis, your fat'er likes you to look nice. He doesn't know you make your own dresses. Fashions are changing again — skirts are longer and vaist lines are going up. I've been t'inking. Maybe you could ask for a bigger allowance?"

"It wouldn't hurt to try," I said. "How much do you think Papa would give me?"

Her eyes twinkled. "Oh, I vould suggest forty dollars a mont'."

"Wow! A fortune! And I'll put it all in the bank."

"He can afford it. If he doesn't give it to you, he'll spend it viz his drinking friends."

Later that day, John and I took Joan down to the beach. We played with her in the water and built castles in the sand, but our thoughts were never far from the new turn of events.

"I'd like you to make me a promise, Agnès," John said, suddenly looking serious.

"Let's hear it."

"That you will not let anything change your mind, not let anyone prevent you from going to Paris. Will you promise?"

"That's easy. I swear never to marry, or allow anything else to change my mind, to keep me from going to Paris. More than promise ... I'll engrave it on my heart."

"No! Let me." John's index finger traced the pledge on my left chest. "There — graffiti on your heart — it will be there forever."

Joan had been scribbling squiggly lines with a stick in the hard-packed, wet sand. "I wanna write my name, Sisi. Show me how."

John found a twig and printed in large letters, J O A N.

"I can do that," she squealed, and set about copying the characters.

John continued scratching in the wet sand, writing something. I stood up for a better look. "I marriage disparage."

"Ha!" I said with facetious (and prophetic) exultation. "Mine is etched on my heart for always. Yours will last only until there's a change in the tide!"

Chapter Thirteen

By Easter, my savings account thrived. The generous new allowance was secure, and I had accepted a part-time job with an advertising firm. Whenever I could — after school, on Saturdays — I'd go to the shop and find a stack of things to do.

Each of the three young partners who ran the business was expert in his field. Bader managed the finances, and Church found clients, while Erwin was in charge of production and a whiz in lettering. My job was designing show cards, neon signs, letterheads, and anything else that had to do with proportion, color and space.

My self-confidence flourished. I'd had no training. What would I be able to do after a year in Paris? I probably wouldn't stay in commercial art, but it was comforting to know I could earn a living.

After graduation, I had more free time, which I used to design Christmas cards. Most of my orders came from Mama's friends, but business flourished even on a limited scale.

"Prosperity is getting closer," I boasted to John. "I can see her smiling face."

John raised an eyebrow. "How do you know Prosperity is female?"

"How do you know she isn't? The Muses are."

"But isn't business success male territory?"

"Ha! It *used* to be. And I'm going to help it change. Anyway, how would men succeed without the selfless devotion of their women? Even when her man gets rich, he uses her. He gives her jewelry and fine clothes, not for altruistic reasons, but to show the world how wealthy he is. And, to prove he's able to support her, and to keep her subservient, he won't let her work. It's male conceit."

"Well, well! You've been reading Thorstein Veblen."

I nodded. "Fascinating, isn't it? You've read it all, I suppose. I'm only at Chapter Four, where he writes about conspicuous consumption. What an eye-opener! And I couldn't resist peeking at some of the other chapters. I wonder why Veblen isn't studied in high school? It could provoke some lively discussions."

"Because, my dear, in general, schools have a way of teaching *what* to think instead of *how* to think. You'll find that your education is just beginning now that you're out of high school — if, that is, you go on reading and observing and examining and deliberating. By the way, how close are you to setting your departure date?"

"With some luck, I should be ready to leave by the summer of '31."

"So, in the meantime, you can enroll at the U. Not as a regular — you won't need credits — but just to audit a few courses, to add to your education."

"Such as?"

"Oh, fundamental things: History of art, drama maybe, and courses in painting. Huc Luquiens is head of the art department and a friend of ours. He happens to be French, and can tell you a lot about Paris."

John was never far away — a safe harbor. And I was becoming fond of him. Only fond? Was there a more relevant word? Love? What kind of love? What was love, anyway? Was it that unknown component that turned everything to magic, that changed a nobody into a someone? Unreal? Perhaps. But who needed reality all the time? Facts could be banal, and could get stale. Wait a minute. Maybe the true Reality was Love — the fourth dimension — where egoism could not survive? Or was love just a snare and a delusion, another four-letter word? I'd heard it referred to in those terms. But why analyze, when holding someone, and being held, was wonderful?

John wanted to make love. I couldn't pretend I didn't, but then I would remember Maile and Craig. They'd had a son. We also heard Craig was drinking heavily.

I wouldn't let that happen to us. But how could we turn off our feelings? In the age of innocence, life was simple, but who wanted to be a child forever? Like all women of the time, I was a victim of my conditioning. Men had privileges not available to us. It wasn't fair. We had the same needs and emotions. If I looked over my shoulder, would I see the Button-Moulder lurking somewhere, hoping to bag me and drag me into the flock of sheep? The choice was mine. The kind of adult I'd become was up to me. So far, I was sure only of what I did *not* want to be: a lamb, for one thing, or a pampered pet in some man's castle, painting my smile on every day.

My still, small voice kept telling me to do what I wanted, and to take the consequences, whatever they might be. As long as I did, the Button-Moulder would have to keep his distance.

Toward the end of summer, I spent a week at Kahana alone with my family. I needed rest in solitude. Early morning — sunrise — was the time of day I liked best. Precious to me was getting up long before anyone else, going down to the beach, and sitting there, just staring out over the water. At first I'd watch the little fat clouds, half pink in the dawn, glide across the blue, blue sky, and listen to the cadence of the waves. I'd try not to think, and when thoughts came tapping at my mind, I would try not to let them in. It wasn't easy. When I did succeed, I was no longer confined to my physical self. My body melted — timelessly — into my surroundings, cleansing me ... and my spirit. Or so it seemed, for when I would return to work, miraculously, I was full of brand new ideas.

Chapter Fourteen

On a warm evening in late October, John, his newly arrived cousin, Vance, and I finished dinner at the new Chinese restaurant on Kalakaua Avenue.

"Any recommendations on how we might enrich the next few hours?" John asked as we got into his roadster.

"Let's go to your house and discuss it over a highball," suggested Vance.

John drove several blocks along the broad street, turned right on Kuhio Avenue, and parked in front of his rented house. A short, gravel path led us past a few hibiscus bushes to some wooden steps and a small lanai. John's living room, with its wicker armchairs and cretonne curtains, resembled many others in that area. While John got the drinks, I asked Vance if he planned to take a house at the beach.

"Newcomers usually do," I said, "and when they've been accepted by local society, they move up to the valleys."

Vance frowned. "The idea rather underwhelms me. I've been supporting myself since I got my master's last year, and economizing is important. Living at school isn't luxurious, but it's inexpensive, and they do allow me my privacy, which I value."

"Ha!" I said "I've just thought of something. You've already made it. Your school is in Nuuanu Valley."

"Oh, so I can skip living at the beach? Maybe I'll do it in reverse and move to Waikiki later to prove my autonomy."

John returned with three highballs on a tray. "Where are the girls, John?" Vance asked.

"Geoff took them to dinner at that new drive-in. They'll be along soon. Cheers! And, before I forget, here's an advance copy of my father's book. It came in this morning's mail."

Vance looked over the volume John handed him and read aloud, "*Brown Americans*, by Edwin Rogers Embree. Hmm. Rather nice, isn't it, to see one's name on a book cover?"

"Rogers ..." I said. "That's your last name, Vance. All I know is that you two are cousins ... Just how are you related?"

"In the book," John said, "Dad draws a pretty good picture of our families. We both come from rebel stock."

"That doesn't surprise me," I said. "Rebels usually end up being the real patriots."

"I'll drink to that," Vance said. "Our founding fathers were traitors in the eyes of the British. It depends entirely on one's point of view. There's no absolute right or wrong on the human plane; it's subjective. For John's great-grandfather, John Fee —"

"— I was named after him," John said.

"— the seeds for revolt were planted when he attended a seminary in Cincinnati. You see, he was born and brought up in Kentucky, which was a slave state —"

John picked up, "— and when he left the seminary, he turned abolitionist. He insisted that slavery was contrary to the Christian religion and made up his mind to accept the consequences for that belief — no matter what. His father accused him of treason and disowned him. He expected his friends to abandon him, which they did."

Vance broke in, "But wasn't there some wealthy man, a civic leader, I believe, who backed him, and even gave him a piece of land?"

"Yes — a very large tract of land, in fact. The man was Cassius Clay, whom Lincoln later made ambassador to Russia. Clay and my great-grandpa agreed on abolition, but not on how to bring it about. Clay refused to break the law, while old John believed that sinful laws *should* be broken. He founded a bi-racial college in Kentucky, which Clay called mutinous."

Vance stood up and gleefully rubbed his hands together. "At that historical moment, guess who came down from Oberlin College and joined forces with our hero, John Fee?! None other than *my* great-grandpa, Rogers! And his bride's name just happened to be ... Elizabeth Embree."

"And everyone lived happily ever after," I suggested.

"Not so fast," John said. "For years, they and several other families opposed to slavery were persecuted. Their only offense was that they obeyed the commandment, 'Do Unto Others ....' Mobs would have hanged them if they hadn't managed to escape across the Ohio River. Throughout the Civil War, they were hounded every time they dared come back. More than once, John Fee was physically dragged from his home and threatened with death. Eventually, after many more ordeals, and long after the Civil War had ended, they did consolidate their bi-racial college."

"I had a feeling I was in good company," I said, raising my glass. "Long live the rebels, whomever they may be!"

"*Who*ever," corrected John. "Cheers!"

Vance sat down, leaned forward, lowered his bushy, dark eyebrows, and said, "John, I think you have a renegade-in-the-making right here. With her Viking blood and *Peer Gynt* and Thorstein Veblen, she may be a first-rate candidate."

John leaned back and laughed. "In some ways she's ahead of us .... Listen! Do you hear a paperboy out there calling 'Extra! Extra!'?"

We listened. Through the open windows came a distant voice, high-pitched and ominous.

I said, "All I can make out is the word *crash*."

"Oh," said John, "probably another speedster has run his car into a tree. Say — I think the girls are back."

They were, and running up the steps. Cathy opened the screen door, waving the *Star-Bulletin* in the air.

Edwina and Geoff came in, both out of breath, and speaking at the same time.

"The market's crashed!"

"The stock market! The economy's ruined!"

John spread the newspaper out on the floor as we all crowded around to read the details of the financial catastrophe that had pushed other news off the front page.

"What does it mean, John?" asked Cathy. "Are we going to be poor?"

"No, Cathy. Don't worry. I'm sure it won't affect Dad at all, you'll see .... It'll probably blow over in a few weeks. Things will pick up, and the world will go on as usual. Newspapers always sensationalize little events. It's a good way to make money, you know. They sell a lot of papers that way."

Chapter Fifteen

It was several weeks before we realized the significance of the crash. Good news arrived in the meantime.

"Gosh, Mom! My cup has been running over for a long time — and now this ...."

"Vat is it?"

"A letter from Madame Scheyer! Listen! She's been vacationing in Bali and is sailing for home soon. She'll arrive in Honolulu on April 2 on the *Kamakura Maru* from Tokyo. Isn't that keen, Mom? She wants to stop over for a while. She's never been to Hawaii, and says she is looking forward to renewing our acquaintance. Wow! Wait till I tell John! And there's more. She's traveling with an old friend, Madame Archipenko, the wife of the Russian sculptor."

"Do you know who he is?"

"A few weeks ago, I read an article about Archipenko and his work in cubism. He's Ukrainian, in his mid-forties, and teaches in New York."

"Vat is cubism?"

"Picasso started it. He and another artist, Braque, painted objects as seen by the *mind*, rather than the eye ... from different points of view at the same time. The surface of things is broken into angular planes."

"Oh, ya. I know. Not very pretty pictures, if you ask me."

"Sorry, Mama dear, I'm not asking," I said, and gave her a hug. "Your opinion is no different from most people's. If the old way of painting is good enough, why tamper with it? Well, if you were an artist — anyone who wants progress cannot go on marking time in the same old rut throughout life. If you're worth anything, you're bound to experiment, to innovate. You may be a composer, or a writer, or an engineer, or anyone who has an idea."

"All right, all right. Maybe your art teacher, Mr. Luquiens, vould like to meet Madame Scheyer and her friend."

"Say! That's a good idea, too. I can take them to the Academy of Arts for one of their Thursday receptions. I'm sure he'd like to talk to some of his fellow creatures. Luquiens is a good teacher and a competent painter, but conventional. He still looks French — with his graying goatee and beret — so courteous, and a bachelor, besides."

"What does he t'ink of your going to Paris?"

"He said, 'That's fine, but *don't let Paris get you*,' and shook his head sort of sadly."

"Vat did he mean?"

"When I asked, he said, 'Sometimes Americans go overboard for the new freedoms they find, maybe because of prohibition or Puritanism in the States.'"

Mama frowned slightly, "I t'ought in America ve have ze most freedoms?"

"That, Mom, depends on your definition of freedom. John says it's subjective. No two people interpret it the same. If you're rich it's one thing, and if you're poor it's another."

"Vell, I'm learning. You like your courses at ze university?"

"Every one of them. This morning, in art class, we had to do a water color of a group of amber drinking glasses."

"And yours vas ze best."

I had to laugh. "No, Mama darling, it wasn't. But it was darn good for a first attempt. Like anything else, it's easy once you get the knack. I like my Chinese literature, class, too. Especially the poetry. Listen to this ... I think it's beautiful: *Three fragile flowers in a bowl — A mind, a body, and a soul.*"

I greeted Madame Scheyer and Madame Archipenko on the pier when the *Kamakura Maru* docked early in the morning. At noon, I deposited them at the Moana Hotel.

"I'll leave you now," I said. "You must be tired."

"Not at all," insisted Madame Scheyer. "You vill join us for lunch. Ve had enough rest on ze ship."

It was easy to accept the invitation. I didn't ever want to stop looking at Madame Archipenko. About forty years old, she was tall, though not slender. The intense blue of her eyes matched the silk turban that framed her serene, oval face. No hair showed and, of her ears, only the lobes were visible. Dangling from them — bizarre, silver earrings.

Both women were exotic, even eccentric, from my unworldly point of view, each captivating in her inimitable manner. Madame Scheyer's clothes, much like her personality, were flamboyant — of singular cut, and made of fabric clearly handloomed in some foreign land.

Could living in Paris make me one of a kind? Easier there than in Honolulu, where everyone idolized the *typical* American girl with *her* wholesome beauty. Each American girl had a paragon she dreamed of becoming: a certain actress, or a sportswoman. Consequently, there were millions of lovely, gregarious, splendid creatures with the same hairdo, same smile, same eyebrows, same shirtwaist dresses — millions caught annually by the Button-Moulder.

Madame Scheyer interrupted my musing. "How fortunate you are to live in zese magnificent islands. It's heavenly — ze climate and ze flowers!"

We were in the hotel dining room, overlooking Waikiki Beach and the ocean. Oh, if I could think of something outlandish to say.

"Yes," I began, and hesitated. The temptation was irresistible. "It's good for flowers and vegetables, too. But I'm not yet a vegetable and no longer a flower. And besides, I'm going to Paris next year."

The effect was close to what I had counted on. Madame Scheyer nearly choked on her shrimp cocktail. Madame Archipenko's exquisite chin dropped, and both women stared at me while I beamed. We spent the next hour talking a lot more than we ate — nourishing talk that fortified me, that encouraged my converted views. I could feel excitement in my heart — or was it the graffiti, now etched more deeply? Could anything stop me from going to Paris?

Before we said *au revoir*, my two friends agreed to accompany me to the reception at the Academy of Arts the following evening. I couldn't wait to tell everyone about the latest rung on my climb toward the Great Venture. Because there was work waiting for me at the shop, I headed the car in the direction of downtown. My three bosses were as keen as anyone to follow developments. I stepped on the gas pedal. The car sped along the avenue while I expounded my thoughts out loud.

"It *can't* be merely luck. For three years, things that have happened to me — things I didn't initiate — have fit together like pieces of a jigsaw puzzle. The timing has been flawless, choreographed by a veteran strategist someplace. So far, there have been no snags; I haven't stubbed a toe, or missed a cue. I must have a guardian angel directing my debut. That's the only explanation."

I glanced upward and saluted with an energetic wave of my hand, "Thanks, Maestro!"

As usual on Thursday evenings, both sides of Beretania Street in front of the Academy, as well as neighboring cross streets, were lined with parked cars. From them, couples and groups of people, many in evening dress, strolled into the well-lit building. Madame Scheyer commented on its harmonious Chinese architecture and the garden that surrounded it. In the entry, I nodded to several people I knew, and suddenly at my side stood Huc Luquiens.

"I'm glad I found you so soon, Mr. Luquiens," I said, and introduced him to *mesdames.*

Mr. Luquiens shook hands with both women but didn't take his eyes off Madame Archipenko. He offered to show her some of the interesting exhibitions. She thanked him, and they were gone, speaking French. I wouldn't see them again till the end of the evening.

Then I spotted Katy McLean. "Hello," I said. "I want you to meet an important person, Madame Scheyer. Madame, this is Miss McLean, the director of the Academy."

I explained to Katy who Madame Scheyer was, and they immediately became so absorbed in conversation, neither noticed when I went off on my own. In the large courtyard, I found John and Vance at the refreshment table chatting with acquaintances. Almost immediately, Erwin came up and said hello to me. I introduced him to my friends.

"Erwin is one of my employers. He's teaching me the fine art of calligraphy."

"Not all that fine, I'm afraid," he said. Then, in a stage whisper, he added, "I must confess, my motive for coming this evening was to have a look at your foreign ladies. I only half believed what you told us about them yesterday. You didn't exaggerate one bit. I watched the three of you come in. They're no kids, but they sure are knockouts, all right, especially the one with the turban."

Two hours later, in the car on our way back to the Moana, Madame Scheyer gave us the good news.

"Your Miss McLean is a discerning person. She has invited me to give a lecture on The Blue Four, and to show my collection of zere paintings. Already tonight I must send a telegram to my secretary in Los Angeles so she vill ship zem at vonce."

"What a splendid way to end the evening," I said.

"It's more like a beginning," suggested Madame Archipenko. "So — ve'll extend our stay, and I'm happy about zat."

"I have an idea," I said. "You can do nothing till the pictures get here, and that won't be for a couple of weeks. How would you like to spend the time as our guests on the other side of the island? We have a house there on the beach. You would be alone except on weekends."

"Zat vould be enchanting," said Madame Scheyer. "Ve accept vis pleasure. I vill have my reply from Los Angeles tomorrow, so ve can go ze day after."

There was nothing altruistic about my invitation. If they were comfortable and happy while I extracted what I could from their vast store of experience and knowledge, so much the better — and I wouldn't have to share them with anyone.

Chapter Sixteen

We got an early start on Saturday. I chauffeured my two European passengers and their baggage in my mother's car, and John followed with Mama and Joan. Up at the Pali, we encountered a loaded black cloud and an impromptu downpour that obstructed our view of the windward plain below. While we continued down the other side of the mountain under the squall, wisps of mist drifted up to reveal bits of scenery.

"It is breathtaking," said Madame Scheyer. "Reminds me of an exquisite Japanese print."

No one spoke again till we were on level ground. Then Madame Scheyer asked if I remembered Cynthia.

"The one in our art class in Berkeley? Of course I do. Very attractive and awfully talented. Her home was in Tokyo. Did you see her there?"

"Yes. I vent to her house and met her parents. Her fazer is very rich. Zey live luxuriously."

"And how is *she*? Does she still paint?"

"She does — but her face, not pictures. Vat a pity. So young and already she knows vell all ze frailties of ze human race."

I waited, resisting the temptation to ask more questions.

Madame Scheyer continued. "I spoke vis her alone. She is a most unhappy creature — drinking and smoking ... already faded ... skinny, vis dark rings under her eyes. Ven I asked vy she did not go avay somevere to study somesing, she cried like a baby. She's in love vis a man and is obviously his captive. I even offered to take her in hand personally, but she refused. I vas happy to find you, Agnès, a wholesome American girl."

I winced inwardly, and changed the subject. "Have you any news of the financial crisis? Is it getting better or worse? I don't understand the stock market."

Madame Archipenko said, "My husband writes it is very bad in New York. Banks are still closing. People are losing zer savings and cannot find vork."

"Apparently," Madame Scheyer observed, "no von is suffering here."

"Not yet," I said. "My father has plenty of work. He's in the construction business. That would be the first to show signs of failing. And the display shop where I work has lots to do."

"So you vill go to Paris, neverzeless?"

"Nothing will stop me!"

"And vat about ze young man, John? Vill he allow you to go? He's in love, I sink."

"John's the one who wants me to go. It was his idea in the first place. He convinced me, made me promise. I'm saving my money so I'll be independent."

"An exceptional man, you know zat. Maybe you lose him if you go avay? You vill have to choose."

She was testing me — I was sure. "I'll cross that bridge when I come to the river," I replied.

I could not have known then that when I did come to the river, the bridge would be shaky, and I would have to rely on my own inner stamina to make it across.

We devoted most of the day to swimming and sunbathing. In the evening, we talked about Bali — its people, their culture, and their land.

"Ve stayed outside of ze city, vis friends," Madame Scheyer explained, "so zey could answer all our questions. Ze Balinese are beautiful people and very happy — mostly Muslims, but many Hindus."

"And ze nature!" Madame Archipenko broke in. "Ze vegetation and ze hills ... A vonderful place to take it easy —"

"— Vis no telephones!" Madame Scheyer added. "Ze Dutch don't vant to change ze native customs of ze colonies. In von vay it's good, but on ze ozer hand, cheap labor remains for ze Dutch."

"Did you buy anything there?" I asked.

"Oh my, yes! Batiks mostly, but some native sculpture, too. Zey vork in sandalvood — it has a vonderful fragrance," Madame Archipenko said. "Sorry ve can't show zem to you, but ve mailed everysing home from Batavia."

"But ze carving you made zere," said Madame Scheyer, "vy don't you let zem see it?"

Madame Archipenko protested that it was not worth showing, but finally gave in. She brought out a piece of sandalwood about eight inches long — a stylized female figure. With both hands, she extended it for me to hold. There I was — *touching an original sculpture for the very first time!* As my fingers stroked the surface of the carving, something stirred inside me. In some inexplicable way, I felt the sculpture was an extension of myself!

The next day, it was my turn to show my work. I brought down the drawings and paintings I had stored in an upstairs cupboard. Among them was the woman's head with green and purple hair, the one that had caused me to feel the menace of defeat more than once. Both women liked that one the best.

I knew they would because it was the only one not copied from nature. All of the others were realistic portraits and landscapes.

Madame Archipenko had been looking at my black-and-white drawings with more interest than at the paintings. "I find your charcoals and pencil sketches are sree-dimensional. Perhaps you vould do vell vis sculpture?"

Me? Sculpture? Mortals could draw and paint, but sculpture was done by Olympians. Could I possibly join that rank?

Sometime during the afternoon, our caretaker, Lorenzo, dropped in with his wife, Josephine, who lived with their children in Kahana Valley where Lorenzo grew taro and went fishing with his neighbors. In his spare time, he kept an eye on our house and tended it and the garden with the solicitude of a loyal liege. Josephine, always willing to do any housework we might ask of her, agreed to cook for the foreign ladies and keep the house tidy while we were gone during the week.

John and I were ready to leave for town on Sunday evening. Mama decided to stay over another night. I found her in the garden telling Lorenzo where to plant the new shrubs that would be delivered in a few days. *Mesdames* were with them, asking the English names of plants they recognized.

"Ve saw zem for ze first time in Bali," said Madame Scheyer. "Zey told us only ze names in Dutch."

We went from bush to tree to hedge, then came to a variety of plant about three feet high with large oval leaves growing out directly from its central stalk.

"Vat do you call zis von?" Madame Archipenko asked.

"Gee," I said, "I don't know the English name. We call it *ti*. The root is used for making hard liquor — *okolehau*. Have you heard of it?"

"Vat are ze flowers like?"

"Oh," I answered, "I'm afraid I've never noticed. I don't know."

Madame Scheyer smiled indulgently at me, and I have never forgotten what she said: "Vell, most people look and don't see. Zey are ze poor vons of zis splendid Earth ... I mean poor of spirit. Von day, I'm sure, you vill be aware vis *all* your senses."

The distinguished paintings of The Blue Four arrived on schedule. Katy McLean and I were on hand to help unpack, as well as to set up the exhibit. Jawlensky, Klee, Feininger, and Kandinsky — no longer just names of famous, remote artists. At last, I was on human terms, in intimate contact with their *original* works, not mere reproductions printed by machines.

There wasn't a recognizable shape in any of the frames — only harmonious forms: wavy lines and curlicues and squares and rectangles and stripes, done in bright and subtle colors. Some of them made me think of illustrations for a symphony. Surely these artists were aware with all their senses? Aware ... sensitive ... *all* senses. Don't ever forget that! See ... hear ... touch ... smell ... taste. That was five. And somewhere, was a sixth sense. It had to do with intuition, with insight rather than reason. This was the sense I sometimes contacted on the beach alone, the one that enabled me to turn away those thoughts that cluttered up my conscious mind and tapped on the window at the top of my head.

On opening night, John escorted *mesdames* and me to the Academy. For a while, I circulated independently in order to eavesdrop. I wanted to hear what the public thought of the so-called "lunatic non-art". There was a good supply of derision and irony mixed with some "oohs" and "aahs." Inevitably, someone said, "My five-year-old can do as well."

I stopped close to a group examining a Jawlensky canvas. One of the women consulted her catalog and said, "If these meaningless paintings can sell for such preposterous prices, maybe we should reserve judgment."

"I find them interesting," said her friend.

I moved on and caught up with John. "We're not entirely alone," I told him. "I just heard one person say she thinks the pictures are interesting."

"Interesting, huh?" John took my elbow and guided me through the crowd toward the courtyard. "Let's get some punch. I need a drink. Interesting, you say? In the entire English language, there is no more innocuous adjective in a case like this. The word is without substance! Whenever you want to be evasive and offend no one, just say a thing is interesting."

He handed me two glasses of punch, took out his pocket flask, spiked the drinks, and took his glass from me as he said, "Don't look so downcast. I believe the show's a great success. The place is crammed. That means people are curious. They'll understand one day — some will, anyway, and make this kind of art fashionable. You'll see. At least Miss McLean shares your persuasion."

"Yes," I said. "Thank goodness she's the director. But why are you looking so ... so smug?"

"Because, my dear, I can't wait to tell you my brilliant idea. I have a book that tells all about the making of beer. How would you like to brew a batch with me, Miss Larsen, and give a beer party?"

Chapter Seventeen

Mama didn't like the idea at first. We told her only when Madame Scheyer and Madame Archipenko had left for the States, and our insular life had settled back to normal.

"But it's against ze law, isn't it?"

"No, Mrs. Larsen," John assured her. "The law says we can't buy or sell or transport booze. We won't do any of those things. Nothing illegal, believe me."

"We'll brew it at Kahana," I said, "and drink it there, too — we and a lot of other people."

"Vell, beer is better zan *okolehau*. How long will it take?"

"We figured on some time in September," John said.

"So vat about a birthday party for you, Sis? You'll be twenty in September."

The party in September celebrated other things besides my birthday.

Mostly, it paid honor to our successful brew and every step of the elaborate procedure, made festive thanks to the help of friends.

John and I worked well together — so well, in fact, my mother and others commented that the more time passed, the better we seemed to like each other's company.

One day, while having lunch with Diane, she asked, "When are you two going to announce your engagement?"

"That's ridiculous! I'm going to Paris to study painting. I'll be there a year from now."

Diane raised an eyebrow and gave me a half smile. "Then why is John's mother coming to spend the winter? Could it be to get acquainted with you?"

"More likely, she wants to see her three children and get away from a Chicago winter."

I worried about meeting John's mother. Vance and Edwina, as well as John, reassured me, but couldn't dispel my anxiety. John may have written his parents that I was ... well ... something I couldn't live up to. My family couldn't be compared to theirs. Just because we had no horse thieves among our relatives didn't make us equal. We were not intellectuals, and had no famous authors or philosophers or philanthropists among our friends.

Maybe *one* purpose in her coming was to look me over. Not probable, but possible. She must know I didn't expect to be her daughter-in-law. Naturally, if I *did* think of marriage, I'd consider John.

He and I talked about it one evening while having dinner with Vance and Alice, and laughing about the wagging tongues that presumed John and I were preparing for a wedding.

"I thought about tying the knot once," John said. "It was on the ship coming back from France a few years ago. Every day, I wrote at a desk in the ship's library. The desks were in pairs, facing each other. Opposite me sat a young woman who came there every morning at the same time and wrote so intently, she didn't seem to know I existed. Her serene face, slightly sad, had an expression that made me think it would be nice to sit opposite her every day at our own dinner table. I imagined she would be intelligent, and someone I could feel comfortable talking to. I didn't get up the courage to introduce myself till the last day on board. All I learned was that her name was Ella, that she was Russian, lived in Japan, and was on her way home after a year in Paris."

"How romantic," said Alice.

"Only potentially romantic," Vance commented and, turning to me, asked, "Are you going to top that?"

"Not even close," I said. "But a couple of years ago, I was half-ready to get engaged."

"What do you mean by half-ready?" Alice wanted to know.

"It was apparently one-sided," I said. "I had a crush on an old friend — a boy I hadn't seen since we were kids. He was here for a few weeks in the summer, and we saw a lot of each other."

"When I lived in Seattle recently," Alice said, "I had a near miss."

"Maybe you should say, 'a near Mrs.'" Vance quipped.

Alice laughed. "You're right. The reason I escaped in time was that a friend of my mother's said she'd noticed that all men were different from one another, while all husbands were alike."

"Well, Vance," said John, "it's your turn."

"Sorry, friends. I haven't a thing to say."

We knew he was equivocating, and let him be. The subject of marriage was never mentioned again that night.

My first meeting with Mrs. Embree was brief and unceremonious. John took me to have cocktails with her at the Halekulani Hotel, a block or so from John's house. As we shook hands, her eyes assured me there was nothing to worry about, that I could be myself. It was as though we had known each other a long time. I don't remember what we talked about — nothing important, certainly. After less than an hour, she told us to run along and enjoy ourselves.

"I've been invited out to dinner," she said, "and regrettably have to change clothes. Maybe one day we'll become civilized and get rid of needless formality."

The next time I saw her, she asked how I was progressing with my plans for Paris.

"I'd like to get there sometime in September," I said. "I could be ready to leave sooner, but John has explained that in August, everything stops in France — that all Parisians are out of town."

"Quite right," Mrs. Embree said. "Well, September is only six or seven months away."

"I know," I said, "and I've started packing already. I can't wait to be on my way."

"Well, maybe you *could* leave a bit earlier. John and I have been wondering if you'd like to be our guest during August. We have a vacation house in Canada. We spend the whole summer there."

She waited for me to say something, but seeing I couldn't find words, went on, "You talk it over with your mother. John and the girls, you know, will join us there early in June."

I glanced at John. His face wore that smug expression again. It told me more than words. He had already sounded out my mother and had her approbation. His face brightened. "You'll come, won't you?" he said. How could I refuse? John brought out a calendar, and we studied the possible dates.

On the following day when I went to the display shop, I found my three bosses there.

"You look even more cheerful than usual," Church said. "What's the good news?"

"Guess what! I've set my leaving date. I'll be on the *Empress of Canada* sailing for Vancouver on July 27, spend a month with John's family in Canada, then a few days in New York, embark for France at the beginning of September, and get to Paris about ten days later. There. How do you like that?"

"Yeah, it's great," Bader said, flatly.

"I thought you'd be shouting 'Whoopie!' with me," I said.

The three of them exchanged glances. "Sorry," said Erwin, "you caught us at a bad time. Actually, we were discussing making you an offer. You see .... Here, sit down. Your work has been so good, we want you to have a permanent, full-time job with the company. What do you say? Starting as of tomorrow."

I looked at each man in turn as Erwin added, "I don't hear *you* shouting 'Whoopie' with us.

"Gee," I said, "an offer like that means a lot to me."

"Is that an acceptance?"

"Oh, no. I'm flattered you want me, but ... well ... you see, don't you, I've got to go to Paris. If not, I'll always wonder what it's like ... what I've missed. I'll probably run out of money in a year. May I take a rain check on the offer?"

They all smiled. Church said, "You know, if I were in your shoes, I believe I'd do exactly what you're going to do. You come back next year, and we'll have a place for you."

"Maybe you'll stay longer," Erwin said. "Some Valentino over there could steal your heart and weaken your resistance."

Chapter Eighteen

I shouldn't have done it. Something made me — some little demon sent by the Button-Moulder in another attempt to wreck my plans. It was only a moment, but a convulsive one. The evening was starry. John folded down the top of his roadster and drove us up the road that curved around Diamond Head. On the ocean side of the mountain, the road widened at every bend so several cars could park beside the guardrail. Beyond the rail, the cliff dropped almost straight down to the rocky shore far below. Looking out we could see only placid water and space. That night a young moon hung high in the star-filled vault of Heaven. No street lights shone in our eyes to remind us we were not alone on Earth. The passengers of the other parked cars claimed their privacy as jealously as we.

John drew me to him so my head rested on his chest, "I want to remember this always," he said. "In a few short weeks, I'll be gone, then you'll be off soon after. We may never come here again together. How your hair shines in the moonlight."

"It's only an illusion, John, because of the stars in your eyes."

Silent magic surrounded us, until the car next to ours started its noisy motor, and brought us back to the world once more.

John said, "Have you told your employers you're leaving at the end of July?"

"Uh-huh."

"What did they say?"

"Oh, didn't I tell you? They offered me a full-time, permanent job."

I easily could have said at once that I had refused, but I didn't. The little demon was in command. The stars and moon vanished. The silence burned. John's arms stiffened. Against my cheek his heart pounded. I shivered. At last, after what seemed an eternity, I released myself, sat upright and looked at his face. The demon made off.

"Oh John, of course I refused the offer. I couldn't accept it. Didn't I promise you I wouldn't let anything prevent me from going?"

The hurt in John's eyes was awful. "Tell me the truth," he said. "Did you refuse only because of the promise?"

What had I done? "Of course not, John! The offer didn't even tempt me. I'm sorry. I just ...."

He drew me close to him again. "It's all right. I should have known you just wanted to tease."

It really was all right! The stars were back in Heaven and the moon still hung there. I whispered, "It's engraved here, John — here on my heart. It's my honor, an oath, a covenant. To break it, my heart must first be broken. Believe me."

"I do, and I'm sorry ... it's just that you are very dear to me."

The next day I told Mama about it.

"He's in love vis you, silly," she said with no trace of a smile. "Hearts in love are fragile. Don't tease him about such t'ings. Be alvays your own sveet self."

I frowned then, turned away abruptly, and said in a loud voice, "I'm *not* sweet," and waited for her reaction. There was none. I looked around to see her leaving the room humming a tune. Sometimes she could be maddening, and I adored her for it.

John - 1931

The curtain was dropping on the last scene of the first act. One by one, the protagonists bowed out to the strains of *Aloha Oe*. The plot of the second act had not been revealed. I knew only that the sets would be different, and the cast, for the most part, brand new. I would carry on as *prima donna*, but what about the leading man? Would he still be John — so patient and understanding? If not, how would I manage? Unless he suddenly made it as a writer, he'd have to finish college and get his degree in the States. For that he was dependent on his father. *I was more autonomous than he!* What a twist!

Being footloose and answerable only to myself would be a new experience. Would I get stage fright and turn a serious drama into a farce? I didn't speak French or know a soul in Paris.

My mother reassured me. "I know you vill be all right. I vas barely eighteen ven I vent to Sout' Africa. I von't vorry about you. I'm sure you vill be careful vis your money, but on two t'ings you must not skimp: on food and on laundry. Eat vell and be clean."

"Yes, Mama, I'll remember."

The day before I sailed, she handed me a small parcel as I was closing my suitcases.

"I vant you to have zis. Maybe you vill fall in love and maybe you von't vant to get married ...."

First passport photo - 1931

❖*Part Two*❖

Chapter One

The train clickity-clacked eastward across the Canadian prairie. Dark clouds covered the sun, and a light rain tapped on the windows. Each mile brought us closer to Toronto. In sixteen hours I'd see John. Mr. Tyack came down the aisle and paused beside my seat.

"Looks like we're heading into a storm. Beautiful, isn't it?"

I nodded in agreement.

He continued, "You're probably thinking more about tomorrow than today's scenery."

"Does it show?" I asked, smiling timidly.

"*Rather!*"

I wished he would sit down. I felt the need to talk to someone, as I would an old friend. And his British accent was easy to listen to. He started to leave, but hesitated.

"I'm going to the club car. Come join me in a farewell drink."

Mr. Tyack raised his glass of ale. "To your success in Paris. I'm sure you have enough dedication to make a career of it."

"Thank you."

"There may not be another opportunity, so let me tell you now how enjoyable my trip has been. It was thanks to you and those other delightful passengers who joined *The Empress* at Honolulu. Americans are so warmhearted. Sometimes we British are too formal — especially out there in Singapore."

"Yes," I said, "We *did* have a good time on board. I needed a week like that as a test to see how I'd make out completely on my own."

"I'd say you passed with high marks."

"Don't exaggerate, Mr. Tyack. Without your help getting from ship to train, I'd have lost my way, my luggage, and probably my head. I still have a lot to learn."

"Now *you're* stretching the truth, young lady. But you stretch it well. Don't worry, you'll manage excellently on you own."

"Are you going back to Singapore at the end of your leave?"

"Yes, indeed. I've been working on that rubber plantation for well over ten years now. I went out there when I was twenty-five. I like it immensely. The pay is good, and we live like princes. I'll visit awhile with my mother in Hornsea — that's in Yorkshire — and start back in December, zig-zagging across Europe and through India."

"Gee," I said. "That's what I'm going to do some day — travel all over the world and learn a lot of languages."

"Not alone, of course," Mr. Tyack said.

"And why not?"

"Well ... well, women don't travel alone in the Orient."

"Oh?" I had to chuckle. "I'm going to pretend I didn't hear that."

To me, he was inconsistent. I was about to say so, but just then, several other passengers came into the club car, and the conversation turned to the storm thrashing our train.

The following morning, I couldn't sleep after five-thirty. An hour later, I was ready and counting the infinite minutes till the train would be in Toronto. Finally, I found myself on the platform, in John's arms, both of us whispering, "I've missed you so."

Under the warm August sun, we walked, hand in hand, to his parked car, stacked my suitcases on the back seat, and soon left the city, headed north into open country.

"I'm glad you're wearing that hat," John said. "The yellow straw and broad brim make you look like a painting by Reynolds."

"I almost didn't bring it — it's so hard to pack. But I want to hear about you, John. You've sent off your stories, I hope?"

"Yup. A bunch of them. I should have some sort of reply in two or three weeks. Those people are busy. I can't expect them to drop everything else to evaluate my stuff just because they're Dad's friends. But both Wilder and Mencken *offered*, so I took them up on it."

"You'll respect their judgment, won't you?"

"I'll have to. For just a moment, however, let's pretend all goes well, and I start selling. I'll be able to live anywhere I please."

"Even in Paris?"

"Yes, my love. Even in Paris."

"And if you don't sell?"

"Well, then I'll have to enroll at some university in the States. I don't know yet where. As long as I study, Dad will pay the bills. But he's not likely to subsidize a scribbler unless, of course, his writing friends praise me. Edwina has enrolled at Swarthmore."

"Isn't that where students learn at their own speed?"

"Yes. They don't go to regular classes but attend seminars a couple of times a week and take oral and written exams every two years. How's Vance getting along?"

"With ants in his pants. He wants to go away and study anthropology, but has no money. Enjoying your roadster, however, as you might expect. When Alice went back to Seattle, he started dating Eve. You remember Eve?"

"Oh, yes. Bright girl, but a bit too rich for her own good. Things come too easily to them. How's your mother? I'll bet she misses you. You're the apple of her eye, aren't you?"

"It may have seemed so to you. No. Mama has no favorite. She has a way of making each one of us feel like her pet. It's mighty good for our self-esteem."

"What a wonderful woman. And your father?"

"Still the same, charming Peer Gynt. Maybe when I'm older, I'll be able to see him objectively and appreciate his good qualities. He must have some, or Mama wouldn't be still in love with him. He gave me a big hug and his blessing when I left. How far are we from your house?"

"It's about ninety miles from Toronto to Bala — that's our village."

"Beautiful country," I said. "I'm going to like it here. How's your family?"

"Everyone's fine and looking forward to seeing you. Guests have been coming and going for weeks. At the moment, there are only four in residence. You've heard me talk of Howard — my old roommate at McGill. He's now an unemployed architect. We were calling him Poor Howard, but that seemed an unnecessarily long title, so we've shortened it to Poho."

"And who are the other three?"

"There's an anthropologist friend of Dad's, named Houghton, and his twin daughters. They're your age, and were born and raised in China. Poho was brought up in Japan."

"Gosh, and now you're bringing them a bumpkin from the sticks."

"Sorry. I don't allow anyone to denigrate my number-one friend."

John slowed the car and clasped one of my hands. "You know, I had no idea you meant so much to me. These two months without you have been awfully lonely, in spite of a house full of people."

He stopped the car and took me in his arms. "And now we're going to have four whole weeks together under the same roof."

Chapter Two

At High Cliff, I was on top of the rainbow, exactly half way on my journey from Honolulu to Paris, an appropriate setting for an interlude — an *entr'acte*, as the French would say. The sprawling house that crowned the bluff seemed suspended between the real and the unreal, between Earth and Olympus, and inhabited by mortals and gods who easily alternated roles whenever the script so required.

The nearest neighbor was well out of sound and sight. From the living room and front porch, we looked out over Lake Muskoka, its uneven shoreline and small islands. With no effort, I could pretend we were in limbo — a limbo blessed by Nature through thickets of birch and maple and evergreens, where the wild fauna thrived. Thoreau and Hiawatha were close by. As I looked down from the summit of the rainbow, ordinary events were transformed, acquiring an aura of the exotic, of the poetic, as they do in a drama.

Between meals and other major happenings, I sketched the islands and sailboats and woods, and members of the cast while they read or conversed. I did an odd drawing of John as he lay at my feet on the living room floor, looking at me upside down. The startling and disconcerting result motivated Mr. Embree to make an observation I have never forgotten.

"We are so accustomed," he said, "to viewing a familiar object or idea in a determined way that, if it's turned around, it appears distorted. In fact, it is *we*, and not the object, who are disoriented and deformed; we're not prepared to alter our point of view. And that applies to everything: politics and religion, as well as to the drawing of people who aren't right side up."

Near a stream one day, we found some clay, and I modeled a small portrait of Cathy. What a revelation! *It was easier than drawing!* I remembered Madame Archipenko saying I saw in three dimensions.

And there were rides in the Embrees' launch. Steep, narrow steps zig-zagged down the bluff from High Cliff to the beach and boathouse. The handsome mahogany craft had been aptly christened *Highfalutin*.

"We like our names to go together," Edwina told me. "Even our dog, Jack, was renamed Hijack after he swiped a piece of meat off the kitchen table."

"Daddy balked," Cathy said, "when we started calling *him* High Chief."

With John as pilot, we sometimes cruised around the lake with no objective other than enjoying the sun and wind. Once in awhile, we packed a lunch and picnicked on an island. If John and I ever happened to lose the others, no one seemed to notice.

Was it reality or make-believe? What on Earth was the difference, anyway?

One morning, we started out through the woods on our way to the post office in the village of Bala. How long it took or how far we walked was never recorded because we had important things to do, such as investigating the marvels of sprouting fern fronds, and birds' nests. Cathy taught us to make daisy chains, and from Poho, we learned to imitate birdcalls.

We dropped in on Charley, who kept an eye on High Cliff during the winter, to tell him we were almost out of ice up at the house. He took us to the underground area where he stored, in sawdust, the blocks of frozen lake water he had cut at the onset of spring. He slung a block of ice into a gunnysack draped over one shoulder, with the other arm akimbo, marched away up the hill.

Poho said, "Now let's go and find Charley's cousin. His name is Pan, and I think I hear him playing his pipes behind those boulders."

Cathy ran ahead and disappeared behind the shrub-covered crag. In a few moments, she called, "Come quickly! I can't see Pan but there are elves all over the place!"

We hurried up, but Cathy stood alone, laughing. "They hide from non-believers."

"Who's a non-believer?" Poho demanded, and bounded to the far side of a thicket, from where we heard him say, ever so softly, "So — there you are — you precious little rascals. What are you .... ?"

"— Hey, John!" Charley came running down the hill. "John — your father said to tell you there are two letters for you up at the house. I saw them, John. They're big, fat envelopes."

The rainbow began to fade.

Chapter Three

I didn't see John that evening. He and his father were secluded in the study. No one had to say it. We knew the two fat envelopes contained rejected manuscripts.

I went to bed early and talked to myself a long time in the silence. Could I deny I loved him — loved him more than I thought possible a month ego — his ideals, his tenderness? He had rescued me from those insular visual illiterates. He had made me aware of the beauty and potential of language, of the musical sound of spoken words, and he had taught me there was no absolute truth on the human plane. He made me want to leave a comfortable, middle-class rut to discover other parts of our unpredictable world. And he made me feel secure, and capable of doing *anything*.

If he couldn't go to Paris, did I want to go without him? *Did* I? I stared into the quiet darkness above my bed, and stared and stared, searching for the answer until I fell asleep.

In the morning, I found John alone at the kitchen table eating his breakfast.

"Where is everyone?" I asked.

"Oh, they wanted to go to some flower show and shop for antiques at one of the outlying villages. They'll be away all day. Here — sit down. I'll do our eggs and bacon while you put away your fruit and Grapenuts."

He sounded so casual.

"Dad and I had a long deliberation last night," John said, as he turned the strips of bacon. "It's no secret that I'm not going to be a writer. You've guessed as much by now, haven't you?"

He saw that I didn't know what to say.

"But all may not be lost," he continued. "Come on — finish your cereal. The eggs are nearly done."

How could he be so unruffled when I was about to have a fit? I moved my empty bowl aside.

"I'm waiting," I said, "but not for the eggs and bacon. John —

What *did* the letters say? Why the suspense?"

He divided the contents of the frying pan between our plates, then sat down and hid his face in his hands. "Because .... Because I guess I'm trying to kid myself into thinking I'm not a total reject. Both of them — oh, they were polite, of course — said things like I had 'harmonious cadences and eloquent fluency.' That was to soften the blow. They think I need more life experience." He groaned. "Good Lord! One of them even recommended I fall in love!" His tormented eyes searched mine for reassurance.

I reached across the table and took one of his hands. "John, it may not be so bad as you think."

His face brightened. "Come on! Get your straw hat and let's take off in the launch for one of the islands."

For awhile, all was well with the world. Although the rainbow never reappeared, birds sang and the early September sun shone warmly on the lake. We cruised slowly, causing hardly a ripple in air or water, looking for a place where we would be isolated from all other humans. We tied up at a little cove.

"Give me your hand, Madame," John said as, with a flourish, he helped me off the boat. "But I want more than your hand." He wrapped his arms around me, and I was glad he did, so I could put mine about his shoulders and let him kiss me.

"I was afraid you'd be depressed," I said when we had found a place to sit. We leaned our backs against a large boulder. "Do you want to tell me what you and your dad talked about last night?"

He laughed without humor. "Yes." And then he didn't say any more. I knew I shouldn't push him.

"Have you noticed," I said, "how so many trees are changing color? And a lot of them are losing their leaves."

He looked at me seriously. "And I'm about to lose you. Am I?"

"You *know*, John, I'm leaving soon to get my ship."

He closed his eyes and swallowed hard. "I *know!* And I can't go with you." His voice was almost inaudible. "Don't leave me."

I looked away. What could I tell him?

He went on, "I'll have to finish college. Dad won't give me money for anything else. Stay with me. Two of us can live as cheaply as one. My parents would approve — they've told me so."

"But you're the one, remember, who was so opposed to marriage."

"We don't have to get married. Just don't leave me!"

"Married or not, John, I can't stay. I've got to go to Paris."

"Because it's carved on your heart? But I release you from your promise. We'll go to Paris together later."

I had come to the river. There was the bridge that would take me to the other side. Or would it? It was shaky — no doubt about it. I had to make it across. I *had* to!

I gathered all my courage, looked at him squarely and said, "No! No!"

His eyes actually twinkled. "Do you mean that?"

I nodded.

"Are you aware," he said, "that was a double negative, and that two negatives make a positive? You have just said 'Yes'."

"John, how can you joke when you're making it so hard for me? I'm going to cry."

"You do love me, don't you?"

"I'll always love you. But I *must* go, or in a year, I could hate you for persuading me to give in. My sister was trapped like that."

John cradled me in his arms and stroked my hair. We were silent for a long time.

"I know," he said softly. "I'm getting used to rejections. And because I love you, I must let you go. You will forgive me, I hope, if I try to forget you. If not, I don't think I'll be able to bear the emptiness." His voice broke, and he couldn't go on.

The day of my departure, Cathy helped me pack.

"There," I said, "I've checked the bathroom and I think I've got everything. Now I can lock my suitcases."

Cathy opened the closet door. "Oh, no. Your straw hat's here." She put it on and strutted across the floor.

"I've decided not to take it — there's no room," I said. "Do you want it?"

"Oh, thank you. It's gorgeous! And I have something for you. I got up early and made you a lei of wildflowers. It's in the icebox."

She rushed out of the room. I followed at a slower pace and joined the family on the front porch. It was time to say good-bye.

"We don't like farewells — sentimental or otherwise," said Mrs. Embree. "You know we have loved having you with us. Here is a little memento." She handed me an envelope. "It's a five-dollar gold piece. Now, don't save it. Spend it on something you really want."

She kissed me warmly on the cheek, and I shook hands with Edwina, Poho, and Mr. Embree, who said, "It's *au revoir*, I hope. Charley's putting your bags in the car. Cathy wants to ride with you and John to Toronto. You don't mind, do you?"

Chapter Four

The clock on the wall said it was not yet eight o'clock on the morning of September 6, 1931, when I signed the register at the Hotel Barbizon.

"Welcome to New York, Miss Larsen," said the grinning desk clerk. "Will you be staying long?"

"Only till I can get a ship. I'm on my way to Paris"

"Well, now! How about that? An artist?"

"Art student," I corrected.

"All our guests are students of the arts as well as business and professional women."

"I know," I said. "I saw your ad in *The New Yorker*, and that you charge only two dollars and fifty cents a day."

He chortled. "And nothing extra for the night. Ha, ha. But seriously, Ma'am, we can give you a nice corner room, with two windows. Since today is Sunday, our dining room is closed, but you'll find a coffee shop around the corner. And tomorrow's Labor Day, remember. Offices and most stores will be closed, too."

An hour later, I stepped out onto East 63rd Street. The skyscraper capital of the world towered above and all around me. I looked heavenward and saw a strip of bright blue sky between endless blocks of tall buildings. The sun must have been somewhere up there, too, but the street was in shadow. Half aloud I said, "When I slid down off that rainbow, I thought I'd get back to Earth. But where is Earth in this world of asphalt and steel and concrete?"

Oh, well. I was hungry. More than twelve hours had passed since I devoured those chicken sandwiches Edwina had made for me to eat on the train. At the coffee shop, the buoyancy of the young waitress restored my optimism.

She smiled, took my order and said, "You're new here, ain't you? D'you come from far away?"

"From Honolulu."

"Wow! That *is* far. In the Philippines, ain't it?"

"No. A lot closer. In the Hawaiian Islands."

"Oh, yeah. You see, I ain't been to school much."

"How come? High schools are free, aren't they?"

"Sure, but that din't do me no good. I'm the only one in the family what's got a job. I can't quit workin' just to study."

"Gosh," I said. "People keep saying the Depression's nearly over."

"Oh yeah? Well, it ain't. If you ask me, it's gettin' worse. You don't see it in this neighborhood but .... Excuse me, Ma'am. I'm gonna get your breakfast."

A few minutes later, she returned with my order, smiled, then moved briskly to another table.

I didn't talk to her again till I was ready to leave. As she opened the door for me, she said, "Hope I'll see you again tomorrow, Ma'am."

"Yes," I said, "unless I get lost. Would you face me in the direction of Fifth Avenue? I'm going to take a long walk and do a bit of window shopping."

The people who crowded the sidewalks seemed to know where they were going. Why were they in such a hurry? Was it to get out of town on the last long weekend of summer? I paused often to admire displays in the store windows. What sophisticated fashions — nothing like those in Honolulu. I liked the new hats — silly, but adorable. The *cloche*, which hid every strand of hair, was apparently out of style. I caught a glimpse of my reflection in a window. My own hat would have to go.

I reached Fifth Avenue. Was I truly in New York? Neither my eyes nor ears were large enough to take in everything in that urban bewilderness. I looked up again at the gigantic structures. What was inside them? Wheels that made our country run? Machines masquerading as men from nine-to-five, cranking out money to feed their ambitions and their children, who, in turn, would become anonymous machines grinding our more money in an endless, vain cycle? How many dreams conceived up there were nurtured to maturity? How many were crippled or stillborn?

A lady's gloved hand rested lightly on my arm as a voice said, "Is it really you, Sisi?"

It was my mother's old friend, Tecla Nielsen, stunning in her silly little hat and pale yellow suit. We both exclaimed over the apparent coincidence of our meeting.

"Prophetic," she said. "I'm sure it was in my tea leaves this morning." She took my arm. "Come along, let's make the most of it. We'll ride around the city on the top of a bus while deciding what we're going to do."

As we toured the man-made canyons, she pointed out important landmarks, but I was more eager to talk with her than to look at the sights.

"I'm so glad you made it," she said. "I mean, going to Paris. It's not easy for young women to follow a career."

"But *you* did," I said, "and long ago. You came up from sales clerk at our biggest department store to buyer for their women's fashions."

"That was the easy part. The obstacles came mostly from my relations with people dear to me. Like your mother, you know, I was born in Norway. I left home at eighteen. My prosperous family expected me to marry, have children, and be a good housewife. But I guess I had seen too many Ibsen plays. I went to them all and read them over and over. When I announced I wanted to study at the University, my parents were appalled. 'Do you want to embarrass us?' my father asked. 'What will people say? Why can't you be feminine like other girls, and not cause any trouble?'"

She paused and looked away before going on. "Now, more than twenty years later, I can still remember how betrayed I felt. Even my friends thought I was dotty. But one of my teachers encouraged my hopes. He assured me that being out of step was no crime. So, when I became of age, I got my passport and, with some money my grandmother left me, came to New York."

"That must have taken a lot of courage," I said.

She smiled. "Believe me, it would have taken much more courage to stay back there. I went to school here, learned English, and got a job. Then, in 1917, when I was a war nurse, I met a dashing officer. He happened to be the son of one of the old Island families and talked me into visiting Honolulu. We nearly got married. I was pretty fond of him, but I could see it would mean a social life devoid of what I considered quality."

"And you've never been sorry?"

"Oh, no! I did the right thing. My business life is full of interesting events, and so is my private life."

Her smile was proof of that. "In fact," she added, "a friend is expecting me in Boston this afternoon. I have just decided not to go. I'll phone him from the restaurant where I'm taking you for lunch."

We went to a Danish restaurant that specialized in seafood. Tecla knew the waiter and gave him our order in Norwegian. She then excused herself to make her phone call.

"Tonight," she said when she returned, "we're going to see *Grand Hotel*, and tomorrow, Lynn Fontanne and Alfred Lunt in *The Barretts of Wimpole Street*. I've seen it once, but Fontanne is such a splendid actress, I want to go again. You know the story, I'm sure."

"Yes. We read it in the drama class I took last year at the University. I was impressed how Mr. Browning gave Elizabeth the confidence to break away from her suffocating existence." I hesitated a moment, then said, "She's another woman who made it."

"There are a lot more of us than you might think" Tecla said. "By the way ...." she looked at me sideways, "what happened to that nice young man you were going with in Honolulu? John, wasn't that his name?"

I was glad for the chance to recount how the bond between John and me had intensified and how we had said good-bye at High Cliff. I told her the whole story, knowing she would be sympathetic.

"It's always worse for the one who is rejected, who stays behind," she said. "The new doors that open for you will present distractions. And don't think it's over for you."

I looked at her with expectation.

She continued. "Undoubtedly, you'll face the situation again. Not with him, perhaps. But you're not yet twenty-one, and there are lots of young men out there looking for romance — as you will be, too. Marriage is still considered the inevitable conclusion of a love affair, if not the main purpose of a woman's existence. You break the rules at your own risk." She smiled mischievously. "In Paris, though, you won't be pressured."

Suddenly, it was Monday evening, and Tecla and I were saying good-bye as we walked through the crowds toward the Hotel Barbizon.

"So — I won't see you tomorrow," Tecla said. "I'll be working and you'll be buying your ticket for that ship sailing on Wednesday. It's *au revoir,* then, till we meet again — maybe next year in Honolulu, and you can tell me about some of your adventures."

"These two days have been wonderful," I said. "It sounds like a cliché, but I wish I knew how to thank you."

Tecla squeezed my arm. "When I first came to New York, an elderly couple did all sorts of nice things to help me over the bumps. I couldn't reciprocate adequately and was embarrassed. They told me not to worry, that when I had found my way in the world, I could help young people who were on the road to better themselves."

We reached the hotel. Tecla gave me an affectionate hug. "So you can thank me by giving a hand to the next generation when you are older and able to. Good-bye, my dear. Seeing you again has done me a lot of good. I'm passing you the torch. Don't drop it!"

Even before I got into bed I felt the tears. Soon they spilled over and ran down my cheeks. I dried them but didn't try to stop the flow. Part of me was awfully happy, so why was I crying?

"Because you aren't here, John," I blubbered. "I've so much to tell you. Remember Tecla? You met her at Kahana. I want to be just like her in lots of ways — elegant, with her critical perception and ... and strong."

I found a handkerchief in the dark and blew my nose, clutched the pillow and hid my face in it. Was he thinking of me and hugging his pillow, too?

"Oh, John. I've been only pretending to be strong. I'm not. I miss you. Maybe I should have stayed. What if I fail in Paris?"

From somewhere came Tecla's calm voice. "The only failure is never having dared to try." That made me groan aloud.

"She's right, John, isn't she? If only you'd been here with us. She took me to the Metropolitan Museum, and two plays, and restaurants, and we talked and talked about important things — not petty stuff most women her age are limited to. Like at the Barrett play, she told me to notice how Lynn Fontanne *became* Elizabeth, how her body movements were as eloquent as her words.

"Little nuances of interpretation ... in the voices. Gestures. Costumes. At the museum ... the paintings up close ... from a distance, *I* tried to imagine that I had held the brushes and put the colors on the canvas. For two days I've been on another plane and I never want to leave it."

I blew my nose again and lay thinking a long time about the chance meeting with Tecla.

"You understand, don't you, John? I'll bet the Button-Moulder has been lurking around here, still hoping to persuade me to join his conformist multitude. That's why I wavered. I think he's given up — at least for the time being. I'm stronger now. I love you John, but as I love my mother. Goodnight."

Chapter Five

The boat-train from Cherbourg to Paris sped through the cloudy afternoon countryside. Doris and I were alone in the compartment. She sat opposite me, riding backwards and staring out the window. On the ship, she had chattered with enthusiasm about going to Europe, about all the countries and historical places she wanted to see.

"We've just passed Bayeux," I said. "That's where the famous tapestry is."

"What tapestry?" Doris asked.

"Don't you know about William the Conqueror? Ten Sixty-Six? The tapestry tells the whole story. We're in Normandy."

"Oh? When will we get to France? I can't wait to see Paris. I'm so excited."

If I told her Normandy was a region of France, it might sound as though I was showing off, and she'd be humiliated, so I merely said we'd be in Paris around six o'clock.

"I'm glad you talked me into spending a few days there," she said.

"Are you sure your aunt and uncle won't object?" I asked. "They're expecting you in Wiesbaden tomorrow, aren't they?"

"It'll be okay. I'll send them a wire. They want me to be adventurous — that's why they invited me over. It's my twenty-first birthday present." She frowned a bit and added, "Gosh, what do we do when we get to Paris?"

"We'll see the sights, I suppose," I said.

"No. I mean when we get off the train."

"Are you joking? We'll find a taxi — what else?" I could see she was scared. That was not the Doris I had spent ten days with on shipboard — the self-assured, even blasé young woman. I pretended not to notice and went on, "We'll arrive at the Gare St. Lazare. *Gare* means railroad station. Then a taxi will take us across town to Montparnasse. It won't be hard — you'll see. Leave it to me."

"I thought you hadn't been to Paris before."

"I haven't."

"Then how come you know your way around?"

From my handbag, I took out a slender book that contained maps of the entire city of Paris.

"Look, Doris, this is how I know my way around. See, it shows all the zones, or *arrondissements*, as they call them, and the bus and subway systems. It's awfully easy to follow."

"Where'd you get it?"

"From my friend, John. But all the bookstores have them."

"Oh."

After a few minutes of silence, Doris said, "What a gloomy landscape. It's raining. Back in Los Angeles, it's warm and sunny."

"Are you homesick?" I teased.

"Of course not!" She was not a very good fibber.

The train slowed as it approached the city suburbs. Out in the corridor, passengers moved in both directions, carrying bags, gathering up family members, and saying good-bye to fellow travelers. There was still an hour of daylight when we emerged from the railroad station and found a taxi. I showed the driver a piece of paper with an address on it while, with my best French accent, I read aloud, "*Quatre, rue de Chevreuse.*"

"*Oui, Madame.*" The driver moved the cab out to join the mainstream of traffic.

"Now *I'm* getting excited," I said. "I've been waiting two years for this. Look — isn't it beautiful?"

"There are no skyscrapers." Doris's tone was disparaging.

I stopped listening to her and looked through my own eyes at the city that would be my home for a whole year. I stopped speaking, too, so my emotions wouldn't show. Those trees with most of their yellow and orange leaves already fallen, the drizzle that made the rooftops and streets reflect the grey light, the buildings — none over six or seven stories — with slanting, mansard roofs .... Centuries ago they had all looked much the same.

We drove through the Tuilerie Gardens. There was the Louvre,

just where it should have been. We crossed the River Seine. Oh —
those magnificent bridges, and the barges making their way silently
through the water. And over there the square towers of Notre Dame
Cathedral. How could I explain the joy at seeing the old scenes —
the broad streets with wide sidewalks and fashionable women? Could
I possibly have lived in Paris in some former life?

Montparnasse! Boulevard Raspail ... sidewalk cafés, people sitting
at tables drinking coffee or wine, chatting, laughing. Our driver slowed
at a crossing, and I caught a glimpse of myself wearing a beret and a
turtleneck sweater, standing with a group of young people. I belonged
there. A warm glow somewhere inside me affirmed that I had come
back. Maybe I'd stay longer than a year.

Then we were on rue du Notre Dame des Champs. The taxi turned
right onto a short, cobblestone street and stopped in front of a broad,
three-story building.

"*Voici, Mesdames,*" the driver announced. He got out and unloaded
our luggage.

Both portals of the massive wooden door were closed. On the wall
to the right of the door was a polished brass plaque. "Reid Hall,
American University Women's Club, 4 rue de Chevreuse," I read,
and rang the bell.

In moments, a man wearing a denim apron came out, said "*Bon
soir,*" and loaded himself with suitcases. I paid the driver, and Doris
and I went inside, up to the reception window where the clerk greeted
me.

"Good evening," she said. "You must be Miss Larsen."

"Yes."

"We have your telegram. Welcome to Paris. Your room is ready."
She looked at Doris. "But only one single room. Are you two together?"

"I'm staying only a couple of days," Doris said to the clerk. "Maybe
Miss Larsen and I could share a room?"

The idea did not appeal to me but turned out to be a bonus.

Chapter Six

Doris and I were so tired at the end of that first day, we paid little attention to the others in the dining room and retired early. On the following evening, I met the director, Miss Leet, before dinner.

"We have what we call the 'French table' at meals," she said. "You may sit there, if you wish. No English is allowed, and a French teacher is on hand to help with grammar and pronunciation."

"But I can't say even one complete sentence," I said.

Miss Leet smiled. "So — it will do you good. There are usually eight or ten at the table. And then, after dinner we go into the salon for coffee and socializing. Oh, yes — and once a month we have open house, when you may invite guests for tea and cakes."

So Doris and I joined the "French table." I sat next to a young woman named Anne. I didn't understand much of what anyone said, but I did learn that she came from San Francisco and planned to study painting for a year or so.

Instead of having coffee in the salon, Anne suggested we step out to a café, to Le Dôme, just around the corner.

The small, round tables on the *terrasse* of the café were filled with as many foreigners as Parisians, speaking half a dozen languages. A waiter found us a table in a far corner.

"I'm sorry Doris didn't come with us," Anne said.

"I'm not. She'd find something to grumble about. This morning, when the maid brought in our trays, I commented that having breakfast in bed made me feel like a plutocrat. All *she* said was, 'Gee whiz! No orange juice?' Then we went out and rode all over the city on buses. For lunch, we stopped at a small restaurant, and she was annoyed there was no ice in her drinking water and that everyone didn't speak English."

"How long is she staying?" Anne asked.

"Till tomorrow morning. Then she's off to Wiesbaden. I can take her in small doses only. We were obliged to share a double room because there weren't two singles. At least I saved some money that way."

"She's not an old friend, I gather."

"Oh, no. We met on the ship. There were only seventeen passengers — ten of them young and most from California. It was like being at home. She seemed so sure of herself then. But now ..."

"And now," Anne completed my thought, "she's confounded to see this unsophisticated side of herself and thinks that, by criticizing, she'll hide it."

"You've put it better than I could have," I said. "Poor Doris. She's already homesick. And how long have you been in Paris? You speak the language so well."

"I learned French at home. I got here a couple of weeks ago and have spent the time enjoying the city. How can anyone be homesick with so much to see and do? The natives are beginning to come back from their vacations. In August, you see, most of them go away and tourists take over the town. Tomorrow I'm going to start looking for an art school. Miss Leet gave me a list of them. Perhaps you'd like to go with me? They're all within a few blocks of the Club."

"Gee, thanks. Let's go right after breakfast. Do you know many people in Paris?"

"I didn't when I arrived, but I've become friendly with several at Reid Hall. There's Gertrude. She was born in British Honduras, but her parents now live in Monte Carlo and she's going to the Sorbonne. Then there's Mary, who's a correspondent for *Liberty Magazine*, and Eleanor, who works for Macy's. I'm sure you'll like them — an assorted group, well-informed in many areas — they won't bore you with insipid prattle. And there are constantly new people arriving — women who do interesting things."

How far I had come from Honolulu — and not in miles alone! About us, the babble of indistinguishable words rose and fell as customers came and left — bohemians, students, laborers, gallant men escorting beautiful women — and I was a part of it. I reminded myself to buy a beret the very next day.

"Don't look now, Anne," I said, "but two tables away, on your left, I think that young man is trying to flirt with one of us."

"Some make eyes at anyone in a skirt. You'll get used to it — good for the ego. But sometimes they merely want a cordial chat."

Anne made talking easy, and we had plenty of things to discuss: contemporary painting, how all the creative arts were interrelated, how important it was to experiment with techniques. She had heard of Madame Scheyer and her new way of teaching, of bringing out the individuality of each artist.

In Paris, I would no longer be out of step, no longer bucking the current. My first day was more than satisfactory.

"We've been here over an hour," I said, "and had only a coffee. Don't they expect us to order something else?"

Amused, Anne said, "We could sit here all night without having to order anything more. They'll never ask us to leave. But let's have a liqueur, anyway — a *crème de menthe*, maybe?"

And so we stayed till nearly midnight. A small part of me was afraid that when we left, it would all turn out to be unreal. But it *was* true, and I wanted to savor it for as long as possible.

The next morning, Anne was waiting for me in the lobby after breakfast. Doris was ready to leave. We put her in a taxi and were about to start on our tour of art schools when the clerk said, "Oh, Miss Larsen — about your room — would you like a single one now?"

"Oh ...." I didn't want to spend more if I could help it. I looked at Anne. She was reading my thoughts.

"Would you mind if I shared the room with you?" she asked.

We postponed looking at schools till after lunch and spent the morning moving her in.

Chapter Seven

It wasn't hard to choose a school. La Grande Chaumière offered all I needed, and more than I expected. The concierge escorted us through the many departments. First, she showed us the sketching hall, with a platform for the models and several rows of benches around the platform in a half circle. Afternoon or evening, anyone could bring materials and, for a small fee, draw as one pleased.

In the portrait room, the model had just resumed her pose after a break, and the instructor was commenting on light and shadow. None of the five students paid any attention to us. After visiting several more classes, the last one took my breath away.

"Anne! *This* is what I want to do! I thought I'd be a painter — but look! Sculpture!" In the center of the room the nude model, a middle-aged man, stood on a low turntable. Around him, a half dozen men and women beside their smaller turntables, put lumps of clay onto wire armatures that had been bent into crude skeletons.

We watched one of the women as her glance darted from the model to her work and back. Each time, she added a wad of clay or took one off from a shoulder or a thigh. As someone gave the model a turn, she rotated her work a bit, as the others did theirs, and renewed her glancing back and forth.

"It looks easy," Anne said, "but I bet it isn't."

The woman smiled at us. "You're American, aren't you? I'm from Seattle. Are you going to join the class?"

"*I* am," I said. "Can I sign up any time? Or must I wait for a new term?"

"You may start tomorrow if you want to. You can buy some tools like these at a shop close by, on Boulevard Montparnasse." She showed me her three modeling instruments. "The school furnishes the clay and turntables. Every month, we have a new model, and on Fridays, the professor comes to critique." She spoke without interrupting her work. "Take a look around and see what the others are doing."

After dinner at Reid Hall, many residents and several guests drifted into the salon. I had already met Mary, Gertrude and Eleanor, and they introduced me to other friends and acquaintances. Miss Leet came over and asked if I had found a suitable painting school.

"Not painting," I said. "I'm going to be a sculptor."

Anne and I described how we had spent the afternoon. "And when we left La Grande Chaumière," Anne said, "you should have seen Agnes — so impatient, she didn't know which foot to stand on. We bought our tools, then we each got a beret and went to the Dôme for an *aperitif.* She was so full of enthusiasm I don't know how she can be so placid now."

"It's not easy," I said.

We made a joke of my fervor, but the ferment in my innards was not funny. I had to wonder why changing fields should be traumatic. Was it because I realized how close I came to not knowing about sculpture? Whatever the reason, I felt at last I was where I belonged and feasted on the euphoria.

Day after day, nothing obstructed my buoyancy. At school, I didn't need much help setting up the armature. Somehow, I knew intuitively how to attach the wire to the iron rod, and bend it into a support for the clay. It was easy. From nine to noon every day, I was there, and after lunch, returned to the sketching class for a good three hours.

In long letters to John and to my mother, I revealed every detail — what I did, how I felt, whom I met.

The first and only note I received from John was painful to read. It started out assuring me I had done right by going to Paris, but then, it seemed, John wanted me to suffer as he did.

"... and you forgot your beach robe and shoes in the boathouse. You left your beautiful straw hat behind. I see them walking in the sunshine. Have you no pity? Inside them is not you, but Cathy! Do you realize what this does to me?"

He ended by declaring his determination to forget me.

"I know you will understand and perhaps not care. I may not succeed but I must try."

I reread the letter several times. Yes, John, I understood and re-gretted the hurt I had caused, but not my decision. I owed John a great deal. Without him, I'd never have thought of taking that enor-mous step, much less of fulfilling it. But we had reached a crossroad. He'd soon find someone else, someone who'd console him. My life was full, and I had no time to feel sorry for him. John had done a good job on me.

I was, however, still a chrysalis. Yes, he'd done a fine job. The rest was up to me.

Anne often went out after dinner. Most evenings found me exhaus-ted and asleep soon after darkness fell — even on weekends. I spent Saturdays and Sundays going to galleries to see what contemporary artists were doing, and to museums to study the sculpture of earlier times. At the Louvre, I gazed for hours at the purity of lines of the ancient Egyptians. I remembered the piece Madame Archipenko had made and what it had evoked in me as I stroked the smooth surface of the carving. I had not understood why I felt it was an extension of myself, but now that I was actually working in three dimensions, it was becoming clear.

When the museums and galleries closed, I sat in parks or cafés sketching the people around me — people usually so occupied in discussions or reading, they paid no attention to me.

I had come to the fountainhead, thirsty and ravenous, and wanted to drink of life, and feed my famished soul in the right environment. I looked for nourishment everywhere and, like a desert after a rainstorm, I would bloom.

Over our breakfast trays one morning, Anne said, "The museums will still be here a hundred years from now, you know. Has it ever occurred to you that there's more to life in Paris than sculpture?"

I put down my *café au lait* and stared across the room as though I was seeing my roommate for the first time. Then I laughed out loud.

"Oh, Anne! Of course you're right. I guess I've been afraid I'd wake up one day to find all this wasn't so. What would you suggest?"

"There's a party tonight," she said. "Eleanor has a friend named Jane who's an architect working here for some famous man. She's invited her colleagues — all young fellows — and wants us to come. You will, won't you? She has a studio only a block or two from here."

A party! Just what I needed.

Chapter Eight

That evening, Gertrude and Eleanor walked with us over to Jane's.

"Wait till you see her studio," Eleanor said. "It's one of those classic ones that every artist dreams of having. You come into one large room with a high ceiling. The north wall is mostly of glass panes, so there's plenty of light. At one end of the room is a kitchen sink and a 'john'."

"With a door, I hope," said Gertrude.

"Yes, a door, but no tub or shower. You'd have to use the public baths. That's what a lot of Europeans do, I understand. Indoor plumbing, you know, was invented long after these houses were built. It's a great inconvenience, and expensive, to install it. Anyway — at the other end of the room, steps lead up to a mezzanine that looks down over the main space. She uses it for a bedroom. The furnishings are gorgeous — rugs, paintings and chests of drawers — mostly antiques."

"How did she find it?" Anne asked.

"It belongs to the friend of her older sister. Jane comes from a large family of intellectuals, you see. Her father's a writer, but she's no long hair."

"What are the young men like?" I asked Eleanor. "Have you met them?"

"No. But Jane says they're fun — all about our age, and from different countries — even Japan."

"Any Americans?"

"I don't think so. But one is English."

"And Jane's the only girl in an office full of men?"

"She's too intelligent to let that go to her head. Architecture is important to her. Le Corbusier wouldn't have let her work with him if it weren't."

"Who's Le Corbusier?"

"He happens to be about the best-known architect in Europe — with revolutionary ideas on city planning and construction."

"I see. So he doesn't let just anybody work for him."

"Well — here we are," Eleanor said. "It's the second studio."

We went through a gate into a courtyard that, on the right, had a row of *ateliers* attached to each other. From Number 2 came outbursts of laughter. We pulled a cord that rang the doorbell. Jane welcomed us in and told us all to introduce ourselves, which we did with unabashed informality — all ten of us, shaking hands and telling our names. There was Alex, Gordon, Saka, François and André. André — with that tall, lean body, the brown hair and eyes, with one eyebrow raised. His resemblance to John unsettled me, but no one noticed. Jane was pouring wine into little tankards set out on the table.

"Come along," she said in French, "let's have a drink of Bordeaux and get acquainted."

Over our raised mugs, we exchanged glances all around — hopeful glances that ricocheted and plainly liked what they perceived. A half hour later, we knew where everyone came from and what we were doing in Paris. Strangers became friends. Alex and Saka spoke English well. André and François knew my language no better than I knew French, but that didn't prevent us from conversing. I had already learned the importance of facial and body expressions. School, and shopping in a new tongue, had taught me to guess a large part of what people said to me.

André was Swiss. His similarity to John soon vanished. The quality and tone of his voice, as well as his personality, were different, and a potential problem did not materialize.

Gordon had just returned from his home near Liverpool. "Thanks to you, Jane," he said, "it looks like my second year in Paris will be an improvement over my first." He turned to François and apparently said the same in French.

François grinned. "Now we can go dancing on Saturday nights, and Sundays will be sunnier."

Alex was passing a bowl of peanuts. "Is it true that you're from Honolulu?" he asked me. I took a fistful of nuts and nodded as he went on, "Isn't that a synonym for Paradise? How could you possibly leave it to come here?"

"Well, Alex," I said with my tongue in cheek, "I'll tell you. When people *die* they go to Paradise. I'm far too young to give up the ghost."

That kindled a couple of minor chortles and began a discussion on the relative merits of other cities.

"It all depends on one's values," François said. "My home town of Pilsen has only some 50,000 inhabitants and we've had a well-supported opera for generations."

"Gee," I said, "Honolulu hasn't even a symphony orchestra, and we've got more than twice that many people."

Gertrude said, "British Honduras was such a cultural wasteland from our point of view. I didn't hear any classical music till I came to Europe."

Saka said, "But ... for the climate, Hawaii has it nearly perfect all year round. I've been there in winter."

"You see?" Gordon remarked. "Just as François said, it depends on what's important to you. Some people like a variety of seasons."

"And some like a variety of scenery," Eleanor observed. "Europe attracts me because it's so different from the States. Here, you ride a few hours on the train in any direction, and you're in another country with totally different customs, and another language."

The banter continued. Nothing profound evolved, but by midnight, we knew one another as old friends. While saying goodnight, we agreed to meet again after breakfast and take in a museum or exhibit.

As soon as we were in our room, and again after the lights were out, Anne and I took a long look back on the evening.

"I can't get over how well we hit it off — coming from so many parts of the world," I said. "I wonder what they think of us?"

"Well — they want to see us at least once more. François told me we were the first American girls he'd ever met. And I told him he's the first Bohemian I've known. Get it? With a capital 'B.' The part of Czechoslovakia he's from is called Bohemia."

"Hah! Of course. An evening like that would be impossible at home. Without hard liquor, it wouldn't be a party."

"You're right. Maybe Americans drink because they can't be controversial and congenial at the same time. It's considered impolite to disagree with your hostess — or with any of the guests, for that matter."

"And if you dare to," I observed, "you might not be invited again."

"San Francisco isn't *that* bad," said Anne. "We have, of course, conformist areas, but on the whole, I think we're pretty tolerant. That reminds me ... We must insist on paying our share when we go out with the boys."

"Won't they be offended?"

"I don't think so. I've an idea they live on a very tight budget — maybe not Saka and André, but the other three."

"How could you tell? They were such gentlemen."

"Certainly. But I noticed a frayed cuff or two. It's nothing to be ashamed of. But you'll see, we'll all be more comfortable and more independent, as well."

Chapter Nine

When I awoke the following morning, Anne was already dressed and sitting in our easy chair with her drawing pad and pencil.

"Are you working?" I chided. "On a day like this?"

"Sketching my sleeping roommate is entertainment, not work. Besides, I forgot Renée always brings breakfast an hour later on Sundays. I couldn't sit here and do nothing."

There was a knock at the door.

"*Entrez,*" Anne said. Renée came in with our trays.

"Tell her to set them on the table," I said. "I'm getting up. Look at that blue sky out there! Anything could happen on a day like this and, boy-oh-boy, I can't wait."

An hour later, we were at Jane's *atelier,* and found her ready.

"Where are the other two?" she asked.

"Oh, Gertrude wanted to sleep in — she has a heavy date this afternoon, and Eleanor got a call that made her change her plans."

We went out, and Jane locked her door with a wrought-iron key over six inches long.

"Does anyone know where we're supposed to meet the boys?" I asked.

"Over on Boulevard St. Michel," Jane said, "at a café where they usually have breakfast. It's a lovely walk from here. We'll go through the Luxembourg Gardens."

It was, indeed, a lovely walk through the formal grounds of the old museum. Families were already out strolling with their children, dressed for the holy day. Some little boys and girls were sailing toy boats in the shallow pool around the fountain, while others rode tricycles or ran with balloons on strings. The day was warm and brilliant. It had started well.

Jane was saying, "... and so I come over to this side of the Luxembourg often. It's the student quarter — the Sorbonne is here, you see, so the evenings are apt to be more lively than in other parts of town."

"Do the boys live over here?"

"François and Gordon do. The rents are low."

We left the park through a corner gate. Diagonally across the boulevard, seated at a table outside a café, three of our friends recognized us and waved. The traffic was light, so we reached them quickly.

"Sit down," Gordon invited, "and let's have a coffee while we decide how we're going to spend the day."

"Aren't Saka and André coming?" I asked.

"Apparently not," Alex said. "They should have been here a half an hour ago."

"It's good to see you again," François said, and it seemed his eyes rested on me, but that may have been wishful thinking. "We thought we might visit the Cluny. It's not far from here. Then, after lunch, we can stroll along the Seine and browse through the bookstalls."

"What's the Cluny?" I asked.

"A little jewel — architecturally speaking," Alex explained in English. "It's Gothic and Renaissance, built in the 14th and 15th centuries where some Roman baths once stood. A monastery for a long time, then, about a century ago, an antiquarian converted it to a museum and gave it to the State."

"And what's in it?"

"Medieval stuff — tapestries, stained glass, wood sculpture ...."

Gordon interrupted. "— And don't forget the metal work. There are chastity belts the Crusaders put on their wives before going off to fight the Infidels."

"What? You mean there really were such contraptions?"

"Of course."

"Well — I've got to see them!" I said.

We each left enough francs on the table to cover our coffee and tips, and set off. I fell in beside Gordon.

"Where's the Sorbonne?" I asked. "Could we have a look at it?"

"Sure. But it's not, as you may think, a cluster of buildings with a sports stadium surrounded by a campus. The various colleges are in different parts of the neighborhood."

"And no sports?"

"None to speak of. You see — they go to the university to learn, not to play games."

"We have arrived!" François announced, as he took Anne and me by the elbows. "This is not Neo-Gothic — it's the real thing." He indicated the portal and windows. "See the harmony of proportion and line? And look at the detail. In those days, they didn't worry about keeping costs within a budget. Beauty was important, and beauty included material and workmanship."

Guided by our three architects, we spent a couple of hours in the museum, visiting only a few of the twenty-four galleries. François led us first to the metal works. Sure enough, there they were — several original chastity belts of wrought iron. Each consisted of one metal band a couple of inches wide to encircle the body at hip level and another, of the same width, that went between the legs and then welded to the front and back of the belt.

"I'll bet there was only one key," Jane commented, "and that was in the possession of the husband."

Someone observed that he might be away for years. "Think of the physical discomfort the women underwent, not to mention the humiliation."

We moved on to other exhibits, but the subject lingered in all our minds and was verbalized again when we had ordered lunch at a little restaurant in the neighborhood.

"We've come a long way," Anne said.

"You call that a long way?" Gordon asked. "After seven hundred years, most of you are still at the mercy of men. Sure, you don't have to literally wear those iron doodads but, relatively speaking, we're still in the Dark Ages where the treatment of women is concerned."

"But," Alex interrupted, "here we have three young women freely traveling in a foreign country. That's progress, isn't it?"

"A mere drop in the ocean. Worldwide, how many women can vote for the men who make the laws they must obey? None in France or Switzerland — countries we like to think of as enlightened. And in Italy, Mussolini is going backwards."

I had to have my say. "Has anyone ever noticed how they console and flatter us? They're always saying, 'Behind every great man is a woman!' That's supposed to make us proud and happy to be a crutch. A lot of us fell for it. Was ever a man a support for a woman, content in her shadow?"

"You're not going to get an argument from me," said Jane. "I'm not going to fall into that trap, you'll see. If I ever marry, it will be on the condition that I continue my career as an architect. That's providing, of course," and she smiled ironically, "the Depression doesn't eliminate the building trade altogether."

François raised his wine glass. "Brava, Jane!"

"Hear, hear!" came from Gordon.

"Then," said Alex, "we're all agreed, aren't we?" He looked around at us. "Let's drink to the new woman."

"Three of whom," François said, "we're proud to call our new comrades."

"And let's hope we stick to our guns!" Anne said with fervor. "Men make all sorts of promises during courtship and then forget them as soon as the knot is tied. The wife takes his name and disappears as an individual."

"Actresses keep their own names," I said. "Why shouldn't all women — professional or not? And another thing — When we marry, we change from Miss to Mrs. But no one knows if a Mr. is married or not. It's not fair."

"You know," Alex suggested, "when women bear more of the responsibilities, ours will be less. I won't mind that."

Oh, if only John had been there. If only I could have written and told him about those unfettered young people I was spending Sunday with. But he wanted to forget me and wouldn't know we were getting ready to change the world — to be examples for others to follow.

What a way to start life — my adult life! Only six of us around the table, but how many more were out there?

Chapter Ten

People, places, circumstances, events — they all contrive to shape us into what we must one day become. Looking back now over more than half a century, I can see that that Sunday, out there among new friends, was one of the stones, a milestone, that would make up the mosaic of my life. John, of course, was the touchstone, the standard by which I would measure everything and everyone. There were other stones — large and small, rough and smooth, dull or of brilliant color, and of more or less value — placed in a design within an esoteric frame by the Great Creative Artist. Some of them were gems — gifts of love — some thrown at me in anger or envy, and others I would stumble over, or dig out with toil and strain, or find at random on a beach or a walk in the woods, alone or with companions. And on that Sunday, I recognized my lodestone, the magnet that would hold all the others together.

During the two hours we lingered over lunch, we became better acquainted. Alex told us how he and his brother, an engineer, came to Paris in the late 1920s from his native Budapest. His brother found work and a French bride. Alex got a job that enabled him to study toward an architectural degree.

"I have a room," he said, "in the apartment of my brother and his wife. They are like parents to me — in fact, I call them Tatouche and Mamouche. That means Papa and Mama in Hungarian. You all must come to dinner sometime. Mamouche is a superb cook."

"Sounds like she's an old-fashioned housewife," Jane commented.

"Not at all. She runs her own beauty shop. She does everything with apparent ease and always looks attractive."

"I've noticed that about Parisian women," François said. "Take Le

Corbusier's interior designer Madame Perriand. She doesn't lose her femininity just because she's efficient and talented in the office. And, by the way, she's kept her maiden name."

"It's obvious," said Gordon, "that even without the vote, women like her influence politics and have secured lots of freedoms other women only dream of."

"My sister, for example," said François, "is typical of most Czech women. I know she dreams of a more stimulating life but has resigned herself to being only a good mother and wife. Till I came here, I thought there was no other course for a virtuous woman."

After that, it seemed only natural for me to tell how my sister had given up all hope of a career when she married.

Then Anne told us about her sister-in-law. "After she married my brother, she had three children — one right after the other. That didn't leave her any time for painting. I've seen her so frustrated, I'm afraid that one of these days, she's going to do something rash."

It took awhile more to exhaust the subject for that session. We'd come back to it again and again lest I forget the graffiti on my heart.

In the afternoon sunshine, we walked the few blocks from the restaurant, along Boulevard St. Michel, to the river, and crossed the bridge to the Ile de la Cité. There, on the right, soared the twin towers of Notre Dame Cathedral. I stopped and gasped. "It's so beautiful!"

"Have you been inside?" François asked me.

"Not yet. I'm almost afraid to, afraid to be overwhelmed."

"We could go in together — for support."

"No, thanks. Someday I'm going in — alone, just to look, in silence, when there's no service and when I'm not in a hurry."

"Are you Catholic?"

"I think I'm an atheist. When people ask me what my religion is, I always say I was baptized a Protestant and I'm still protesting."

François chuckled. "I like that. You said you *think* you're atheist. Aren't you sure?"

"It's *organized* religion I'm against. I know too many card-carrying Christians who enjoy impiety during the week. It's hard to keep an open mind."

"My feelings run something like that," François said, "not forgetting, of course, that most of the world's great architecture of the past was spiritually inspired. The Pantheon in Rome, for one. It's two thousand years old! I hope to see it one day and touch its walls. I have no proof there is a God, but neither have I proof there is none."

"What about the Taj Mahal?" I asked.

"That was built for love, and love, in my opinion, is spiritual —if it is real. I want to go to India some day, too, and see the Taj."

The others had gone on ahead. Gordon turned and called, "Hey! Are you two coming?"

Chapter Eleven

On Monday morning, I got to class long before anyone else. Under the oilcloth wrapping, the clay of my unfinished figure was still soft. I gave the turntable several quick shoves and stepped back to better evaluate my work. The new model, about thirty-five years old, was a woman from Algeria.

Reproducing her shapely, well-proportioned limbs presented no problem. But what about capturing in clay the dazzling blackness of her skin, the elasticity of her body, the erotic personality? When she finished posing, she usually twisted her torso and stretched her arms like a panther. If she saw anyone staring at her, she'd throw back her head, bellow a capricious laugh, and roll her large dark eyes. A poet could describe her best, and I was merely a sculptor.

Punctually at nine o'clock, she came into the studio followed by several students who exchanged greetings and got to work.

Stella, whose stand was next to mine, was a tall, large-boned American with a head of luxuriant chestnut hair and a face that nearly always frowned. She had come to France in 1917, as an army nurse when the U.S. joined the World War, and decided to stay after the armistice. With her profession, she could easily have earned her living anywhere in the world but chose Paris because the city didn't intrude on her privacy, and the jobs she took were always on her terms, leaving her free to sculpt during the day.

The model tossed her kimono onto a stool, mounted her stand and took her pose: left foot forward, weight on right leg, and right hand on right hip. By any other body, such a pose would have been banal, but this woman lent it divinity — more so, it seemed, on that day than ever before.

The first break came all too soon. The model stepped down and put on her kimono.

Stella gave me a rare smile and said, "I've never seen you work with so much fire. You're downright glowing. It's not the model — she's been here two weeks already. I'll bet you had a sensational weekend. With me, how I feel inside influences my work an awful lot."

Mrs. Potter, the older woman from Seattle, came across the room. "You know, I find that, too!" Her eyes sparkled.

Glad to shift the spotlight away from me, I asked Mrs. Potter how long she had been sculpting.

"Ever since I can remember," she said, with a rakish smile. "But only in my imagination ... till now. I used to daydream about making beautiful statues to decorate the city parks, and humbly accepting praise from everyone who saw them. In those days, the turn of the century, proper girls were supposed to think of nothing but getting married and raising a family. I never told anyone my secret. My husband was a nice enough fellow but would have been scandalized if I'd taken up such a hobby, and my neighbors would have accused me of — oh — all sorts of lurid things."

Stella guffawed. "Envy!" she said. "I know the type. So — did you finally decide to run away?"

"No. My husband died six months ago. By then, since my children were independent, I made up my mind that for the few years remaining to me, I had the right to do as I pleased — especially since I had money of my own."

"What did your children think of it?" I asked.

"They were unanimous. 'Oh, Mother! At your age? What'll people say?' But my granddaughter — she's nineteen — said, 'I wish I had your guts, Granny.' Without her I may not have come to Paris. She was the only one ... " There was a catch in her voice and she turned her head away.

"Oh, *merde!*" Stella said and tossed a wad of clay onto her turntable with indignation. "American women are always being told they're the freest on Earth because they have a lot of household gadgets. The French woman has learned the art being a woman. She knows what she wants and usually gets it one way or another. You can force her to do anything *she* wants to do."

"Brava!" said our model. "You're right!"

Stella grinned with satisfaction and continued, "They have brains and use them with strategy. Sometimes, however, they have to think with their vaginas."

I looked around at the class. Mrs. Potter was obviously abashed. "Oh ..." she said, "well ... it must be time to get back to work."

The others were all smiling to themselves. No one noticed how I blushed. I wasn't sure I quite understood what Stella meant. If I asked, she might give me more shockers, so I said nothing.

The form of address *Madame*, I had noticed, was used when speaking to any woman who appeared to have reached maturity, whether or not she wore a wedding band. Was it taken for granted that by adulthood, a young woman had experienced an intimate relationship with a man? Apparently virtue was not synonymous with virginity.

That thought came to me one afternoon when I was in a pharmacy to buy some toothpaste. As I waited my turn to be served, I spent the time reading labels and signs in the shop to improve my French. There — right there in plain view on top of the counter — was an object that made me stare in disbelief, an object similar to what was in the small parcel my mother gave me the day I left Honolulu. On the counter was a syringe that folded neatly into a little case. Beside it a placard read, "Indispensable to the purse of every woman." *Voilà!* One of the keys to independence. A challenge to the chastity belt.

Out on the sidewalk, I recalled my mother's words: "One day you will fall in love and might not want to get married." She had lived on three continents. Being confined to the insular fold of Honolulu in her middle age had not shrunk her broad, unbigoted outlook. I was blessed with an enlightened mother. Civilized people knew that mating was a form of gravity, a law of nature discovered long before the bureaucracy of marriage, and one that took precedence over any man-made law. Morality? What was immoral about two people loving each other whether it was six thousand years ago or today? Were all marriages moral? Even those contracted for status or for security?

Stella came to mind again as I headed homeward, past the terrace of Le Dôme, telling myself that I understood her better. A familiar face sitting at a central table caught my eye. It was Mrs. Potter, who motioned for me to join her.

"Come sit down," she said, flashing a smile, "and brighten my afternoon. Do you live near here?"

"Yes. I'm on my way home now." I told her about Reid Hall and why I found living there an advantage. "So, you see, I don't have to worry about anything but my work. And besides, my mother needn't fret over me. Our meals are first-rate."

"Oh, yes," Mrs. Potter said. "Mothers! We're an apprehensive lot. When my children went off to college, I used to tell them not to economize on food." She laughed. "And here I am, not taking my own advice. You see, I want to stay here as long as possible. I may live to be a hundred and can't if I throw my money around on luxuries and fancy meals. I've learned that nourishment doesn't necessarily have much to do with the amount of money spent on it."

"Have you an apartment?" I asked.

"No. My home here is nothing more than a small room on the top floor of a tiny family hotel. The French entertain their guests in restaurants and cafés, so I do the same and don't need a large home. Every morning I thank God I don't have to clean house and drive out to do the shopping. Now I have time for living, meeting people, going to concerts and — at last — becoming a sculptor. I'll age much slower this way. And, what's more, I'm richer. I used to think wealth was measured by one's possessions."

"And now?" I asked.

"Oh, here's the *garçon*," she said. "What'll you have?"

The café was getting crowded. Before-dinner groups came for their *aperitifs* and *rendezvous*. I ordered a vermouth, and Mrs. Potter went on.

"And now? Well — I like to think I'm wiser. Wealth has to do with learning and tolerance and other intangibles." She looked around wistfully at the garrulous men and women. "I don't know where we could sit like this in the States — certainly not in Seattle. People would drink too much — they do anyway, even with Prohibition. And the women would be at home cooking dinner. Funny how strong one's upbringing is. I was taught we all need the approval of our neighbors. If we were too different, we were criticized. I've been studying older women here — those my age. They're attractive, darn it. Frenchmen are so gallant. It's no wonder the women try to look their best. Some of them even flirt." She darted me a questioning glance that was not difficult to understand.

"You're not going to get disapproval from me, Mrs. Potter. Why shouldn't you have a fling if you want one?"

I swore she cast off ten years in ten seconds. I giggled, and we both laughed as two sophisticates might.

95

After awhile she said, "Just yesterday I was talking to Gerda — you know, that pretty young German woman in our class. I wanted to hear what she thought of the remark Stella made the other day."

"Was she shocked?" I asked.

"Not at all. And wasn't surprised that I was jolted. She said that was because American films don't show life as it really is, but as Puritans would like it to be — with people who are either all good or all bad."

"She's right, isn't she?" I observed. "Our movies *are* censored."

Mrs. Potter nodded and sighed. "Oh, to think I had to grow old and travel 15,000 miles to find myself. It won't happen to you, my dear." She reached across the table and patted my hand. "It's too late for me to become a vamp, but I'm going to have a good time anyway. You won't let anyone else decide what's right for you, will you? Life is really awfully short, believe me. And it's *your* life."

The sun set long before I started back to Reid Hall. A stiff wind had come up and made me button the collar of my coat. Swirls of fallen leaves danced along the broad sidewalks and crossed the streets in all directions, heedless of traffic. In a few days, the trees would be completely bare. Autumn had settled in and so had I. I took in deep breaths of air — French air — seasoned with its own brands of odors — coffee, tobacco, gasoline and, of course, perfume. Did all cities have their private aromas? New York certainly did, and Honolulu, too. I'd have to check out the theory some day — in London, Rome, Madrid ... even New Delhi, maybe.

I'd fallen in love with not only the scents of Paris, but her beautiful faces, the façades of her ancient buildings, her boulevards lined with trees, and her people. One of the oldest cities in Europe, she was already there when Caesar's army conquered her fifty years Before Christ. Who said old was ugly? The centuries had improved her elegance, her intellect, her culinary talents and her charms. She was unique and did not have to compromise with mediocrity.

What would she do to me? Could she make me a charming and elegant intellectual? Maybe — if I helped a lot. I was working on the chrysalis. The Button-Moulder had been out of sight for a long time — given up, I hoped. A cold wind blew as I turned on to rue de Chevreuse.

"Tomorrow is Saturday," I whispered to myself. "Tomorrow night we'll see what happens. Maybe our architects will take us dancing?"

Chapter Twelve

I took off my coat in the warm lobby of the Club and had started upstairs when Anne called me from the office. She was with Gertrude, who was talking on the telephone.

"It's about tomorrow night," Anne told me. "Dinner with our friends, Henri, Felix and Jacques, and Gertrude, you and I. How about it?"

I nodded, and Gertrude turned back to the phone. "Henri? Yes, both Anne and Agnès accept with pleasure. Of course .... No, really, it won't be any trouble at all — you'll see. All right .... We'll be ready at seven. *Au revoir.*"

She replaced the receiver and turned to us with a mischievous smile. "Come along, I'll tell you about it at dinner."

The others at the French table had finished the first course by the time we arrived. Gertrude soon had everyone's attention. Giggling like a teenager, she began, "*Alors,* we won't be here to eat tomorrow evening because we're going to prepare an American dinner for three French gentlemen."

"Wait a minute!" I said. "Do you mean *we* are going to *cook?* You must be joking."

"Don't worry. Believe me — it will be painless. We'll go to Henri's. I have the menu all planned." She tried to look serious. "I'll explain. Last week, Henri took me to a restaurant where we had an especially delicious meal. As usual, our conversation was brainy, and witty, too. Then he asked if I could cook. I wondered why he wanted to know but, just in case he was thinking of wooing me and hoped I was clever in the kitchen, I planned to demonstrate that preparing meals was not my best attribute."

"So?" asked Mrs. Kimball from across the table. "What are you going to serve them?"

Gertrude cleared her throat. "First course: Del Monte fruit cocktail. Second course: Heinz's corned beef hash and Campbell's pork and beans, with canned Boston brown bread. The beverage will be apple cider and, for dessert, a lemon pie bought at a baker's."

"You're a genius!" said Cecelia, who sat next to me.

"*Brava!*" Anne clapped her hands. "What a coup! I can't wait."

The French teacher, Madame Claudel, was puzzled. "*Je ne comprend pas.* There seems to be a big joke going over my head. Will someone please explain?"

The question obviously tickled Gertrude. "Let me try, Madame. Though I was born American, I've never lived in the States and know almost nothing of that cuisine. The joke? Let's see ... It's that Henri hopes I'd be a domesticated housewife preferring an apron to a fur coat and would never go astray. With this he'll have no illusions."

"And so ... you will be honest, *n'est-ce pas?* But — your menu — is it not savory?"

"Hardly a gourmet's choice. There's nothing original about canned hash and beans."

"I agree," Madame Claudel said. "Now I see the joke. But I wonder if your gentlemen friends will."

Later, while we were having coffee in the salon, Cecelia introduced me to her friend, Sonya, who had dropped in for a chat.

"You're both Scandinavian," Cecelia said. "I thought you might enjoy knowing each other."

Sonya came from Stockholm but, with her black hair and large dark eyes, didn't look a bit Swedish. When I commented on it, she was amused. "It happens all the time. Most Northerners are blonde, of course, but brunettes are not unusual. It shows our ancestors were not racists."

I found her charming, and when, as she and Cecelia were leaving, she invited me to tea on Sunday, I accepted.

We had just said good-bye when the *concierge* called me to the phone. It was Gordon.

"I hope you and Anne are free tomorrow night," he said. "We want to take you dancing."

Oh, no! Why couldn't he have called a couple of hours earlier?

"Gosh," I said, "we have to cook dinner for some French people."

He laughed. "Wow! That should be something. Sorry. What about Sunday? I want to hear how you make out in the kitchen."

"It's not what you think, Smarty. Sunday? I don't know what Anne's doing, but I'm going to a Swedish woman's house for tea."

"Well, well. To make the sandwiches? Maybe you'll save next weekend for us — to dance, Cinderella, not to cook."

"All right, Prince Charming. I'll save the first hornpipe for you."

Chapter Thirteen

4 rue de Chevreuse
Paris
November 3, 1931

Dearest Mom,

The last boat brought me a bunch of letters — from Lorraine and Vance and three from you. Sorry you haven't been feeling well.

My life is getting more and more exciting. I'm doing well at school. The professor, Vlerick, says I have talent. But I'm getting a little tired of merely copying the human body. It teaches me anatomy, and that's important, of course, but it doesn't stimulate my imagination.

There's more to life in Paris than work, however. I'm having fun, too — meeting people and getting acquainted with the city.

Anne and I have become good friends. She's working hard at her drawing. She wants to be an illustrator. We're thinking of moving to an apartment. That would cut our expenses and give us independence. It won't be before spring because the well-heated rooms at the Club are too comfortable on cold days. We like, too, not having to shop or cook. But the food is so good here, I'm putting on weight.

We've made a lot of friends already — both men and women. There's one group we see more than others — six young architects who work for an important firm. Then there are three French businessmen — Henri, Felix and Jacques. One evening, Gertrude, Anne and I got a big kick out of giving them an American dinner that consisted of only canned foods. The men ate it with good humor and, perhaps to prove they held no grudge, took us out to a snazzy place for a late supper.

At a tea party one day I met a French count, a German engineer, a Swedish violinist, a Swiss writer, an English peeress and an American businessman. The American is the "boyfriend" of Sonya, the hostess, and a big shot at the Chase Bank. I didn't feel at all intimidated by the company. We had a discussion about the difference between interpretive and creative art. The Swedish violinist brought the subject up. He said he could never compose anything and was, therefore, an interpretive artist. That's what I am when I copy nature.

Could you send me some silk stockings? They're rather expensive here. Gun metal is a good color. I walk so much, mine need constant darning on the heel and toe. Now I'm mending over the darning.

One day I saw Raymond Duncan walking in the neighborhood. He's the brother of Isadora, the famous dancer. They spent several years in Greece, and now he wears a sort of toga and sandals all the time. I'd like to do the same so I wouldn't have to worry about stockings wearing out.

Yesterday Mrs. Kimball, a painter who has a studio on the top floor of the Club, took me to see a Russian woman sculptor named Chana Orloff. Most of her things are portraits in bronze and stone. We saw one she did of Mr. Kimball last summer. It had just come back from the bronze caster. Mr. Kimball is a professor at Princeton and wears very thick eyeglasses. Orloff resolved the problem in an ingenious and startling way: She made the spectacles and put the eyes, not behind the lens, in the head where they belong, but right on the surface of the lens.

I wonder — was that interpretive or creative — or some of each?

In my sculpture class there's a young Greek, named Athanase, who does good work and is full of enthusiasm. Well, he and his wife have open house every week, and he has asked me several times to drop in. So I did one day last week.

They live in a modest one-room atelier furnished simply in exquisite taste. Their friends, however, are far from simple. A half a dozen people, mostly artists, dropped in while I was there and spent an hour or so discussing intellectual questions. Some were way over my head. I like it this way — I might improve my little mind.

That girl, Doris, who came over on the ship with me and went to Weisbaden, stopped in Paris last week for two days on her way back to Los Angeles. She got so homesick she couldn't stand it.

I assure you I'm not pining for Honolulu. But I do miss a couple of things. You, mainly, Mama — your humor and patience and understanding. Also — sometimes I wish I could look out of my window and see the sun rise over the Pacific. Actually, I like the view from my room: terra cotta chimney pots on roofs that slant in the characteristic French style.

The Autumn Salon is on. That's the big art show held twice a year at the Grand Palais. I went with a young American painter, named Allen. He's here on a fellowship and lives on a small cruiser moored in the river. Last summer, he paddled a canoe up the Rhine, through the canals and down the Seine. Next summer, he wants to canoe down the Danube to the Black Sea.

I was impressed by the exhibits at the Salon: painting, sculpture, interior decoration, and so on, in all sorts of styles. I wonder if a piece of mine will ever be accepted there? It would be an honor.

The French are holding a Colonial Exposition in Paris. Dozens of fascinating displays show the history and cultures of French possessions and protectorates in Africa, India, the Pacific, the Orient and the Near East. I went with a woman who works for the League of Nations in Geneva. We also saw the Belgian royal family. They looked like any average household out for recreation.

I don't think I told you I called the American Hospital a few weeks ago to ask for Mrs. Sedgwick's niece, Madeline. She had already returned to the U.S.

This week we're going dancing again with our architect friends. There are little places called boîtes de nuit (it means "night boxes") that sometimes have no more than an accordion for music, and cost very little.

I think I'm becoming attracted to one of the fellows but am determined to stay away from entanglements of the heart. I try to be nice to everyone so no one will notice.

That reminds me — What do you hear from John? He's mad at me, but I'd like some news anyway.

> *With love to all,*
> *Sisi*

P.S. Miss Porter, the secretary of Reid Hall, has told me I'm not eligible for membership in the Club because I've not done regular college work. She added, however, that I may stay on at the same low rates because I'm so far from home, and that my ten-dollar membership fee will be refunded. Isn't that wonderful?

Chapter Fourteen

When we arrived, the *boîte de nuit* was noisy but not yet crowded. We found a small table and six chairs, ordered some *vin ordinaire*, and got easily into the mood of the evening. *Habitués* drifted in. Some obviously knew one another well. They joked and laughed across tables. We had been there a few times before and recognized several men and women who nodded cordial greetings to us.

At the adjoining table, the accordion player chatted with a young woman. I caught his eye and gave him a big smile as I raised my glass of wine. He acknowledged my salutation with a grin, picked up his instrument with a flourish and drew a long suggestive note that hung in the smoke-filled air and blended with the aroma of wine.

The effect was alchemy. I could feel myself moving to another plane. The lengthy note ended with a burst of sounds in the rhythm of a tango and, couple by couple, the tiny floor filled with dancers.

Gordon took my arm. "Come along, let's try it." On the floor he held me firmly and said, "I don't know a mazurka from a fandango, but this is smashing — as long as we keep time."

"It's a tango," I told him, and he laughed.

"Even if I knew the right steps, I couldn't lead you more than twelve inches in any direction. I don't mind, though. All the other dancers seem happy just hugging and keeping in time to the music."

The *boîte* was less than a mile from the Club but far from any world I had ever known. By mute consent, serious talk was out of order. Between numbers we teased one another and laughed at silly jokes. Even André's usually solemn demeanor yielded to frivolity. The high was real and contagious. Every time the accordionist struck up, the six of us scrambled to be first on the floor.

Once, when I was André's partner, he said, "This is a polka of sorts, like we have in my part of Switzerland. Music of the people comes from the heart rather than the intellect."

During an intermission, Jane wondered aloud, "What do you suppose these people do during the day?"

"I imagine they're laborers and shopkeepers," François suggested.

"Not to mention a few architects and artists," Anne added.

"Sure," said Gordon. "Intelligent folks, who know they needn't spend a lot to have a good time."

"Do you suppose the man can play a Charleston?" I asked no one in particular.

"Ask him. He's settling in for the next round."

I turned to the accordionist with another whopping smile. "You play very well, Monsieur."

The musician bowed his head. "*Merci, Madame.* It's a pleasure to make music for you."

"Do you know any Charleston?" I asked.

"Charleston?" He frowned slightly. "I'm sorry, Madame. I'm afraid my repertoire is too Proletarian for that. But I can offer you a Viennese waltz."

"*Bravo!*" said François and, as the strains of the *Blue Danube* began to flow gently from the accordion, he took my hand. "I know nothing of the Charleston, either. I was brought up under the Hapsburg crown, with their kind of music — that includes the Strausses. Will you waltz with me?"

We had danced together before but not in three-four time. And he had never held me like that. We didn't speak, and barely moved, jammed in by the closely crowded mass. From somewhere inside me, I heard a warning. It would have been easy and wonderful to give in, to show him I welcomed his ... his ... his what? Was I only wishing, imagining he found me desirable — more attractive than the others? I should be on my guard. But not now — later — tomorrow. Tonight, I could pretend it was forever. Tomorrow I'd convince myself that, though François was handsome and princely, I was in no hurry to give my heart away.

Tomorrow came. It began after breakfast with a note from Chana Orloff saying she would be happy to accept me for private instructions in her studio every weekday from nine to noon for sixty dollars a month.

I showed the letter to Anne who read it and handed it back with a shrug. "So? You're disappointed, of course. I *am* sorry. But surely Orloff's not the only sculptor in Paris who teaches."

"I know, I know. But I'm impatient."

Anne looked at me sideways. "And a little impetuous, rash, impulsive ....?"

I tossed Anne a cheerless good-bye and went off to school. On the way, the frown on my brow eased. I knew what I wanted to do. By the time I entered the *atelier*, I was sure of myself.

Everyone else was at work. The new model, a young man, was in his sitting pose on the floor of the turntable, motionless. I looked around at my colleagues, all doing their best to reproduce him. Ha! Let them! I was about to try my wings. Never mind the model. The young Greek's head would be my starting point.

Without uncovering my half-finished sculpture of the sitting boy, I put it on the floor in a corner. Then I got a new block of clay from the lean-to adjoining the studio and plunked it on my turntable. With my large gouging tool, my fingers and my fists, I cut, scraped and thumped the clay into the approximate shape of a head. No one paid attention to me. What if they did? I was in Paris, not Honolulu. I thought of the woman's head with green and purple hair I had painted three years before. She had been a kind of declaration of independence that failed. In Paris she wouldn't have caused even one raised eyebrow. Well ... I was about to make another declaration.

It wasn't till the first break began that anyone looked to see what I was doing. An older Frenchman came across the room, examined my work from all sides. He didn't say anything but offered a few smiles of approbation. Then Stella was there, and Mrs. Potter and Gerda and Athanase and the model ... even the two French students who rarely said more than "*bon jour*" to anyone.

"What's that?" Stella asked. Her tone oozed irony.

"It's a head, of course," the model said. "Anyone can see that."

The older Frenchman folded his arms across his chest, turned to me and said, "My compliments, Mademoiselle. I wish I had your originality. You will complete the work, *n'est-ce pas?* At the risk of sounding impertinent, may I suggest that it resembles Athanase?"

Inwardly I crowed. "It's not a portrait. There's a certain expression of his I want to portray."

Everyone turned to the young Greek, who stood behind me trying to suppress a laugh. He lowered his heavy eyebrows and thrust out his jaw.

"That's it!" I shouted. "That's the statement I want — protest without anger!"

At noon, when we were leaving the *atelier*, Mrs. Potter waited for me. "I'm glad you're not letting Stella bully you, my dear. I think she

104

says outlandish things just to get attention. But I wanted to ask you ...
Do you know the sculptor, Despiau?"

"I've heard his name, but never seen his work."

"Well, he does portraits. I've just heard he's going to be teaching at
another school for a month. Maybe you could learn something from
him. He's conservative, however, but still ...."

"That's a good idea," I said. "Getting another point of view makes
sense. Gee, thanks!"

"Athanase"; Private collection.

Chapter Fifteen

I stayed two weeks at the new school. Despiau was competent, even excellent in his way, but it didn't happen to be *my* way. He saw his work through traditional eyes. I wanted change. Progress required change. Evolution meant transformation, and I was subject to mutation.

Some people, understandably, needed to cling to the familiar. Maybe they felt insecure or were afraid of being displaced. Some even tried to block innovation in others.

One evening, Anne said, "You're a lot more cheerful lately. Ever since you went back to the Grande Chaumière, you've been your old optimistic self — especially the last couple of days. What happened?"

"I'm not sure yet, Anne, but I may have found a teacher. That young Greek man in my class told me about a sculptor named Zadkine. He's contemporary and takes private pupils."

"And what does he charge? Sixty bucks, or more?"

"Athanase doesn't know. The only way to find out is to go and see him. He lives only a block or so away. Anne, will you come with me, to talk to him? Please?"

"Of course I will. I'm as curious as you are. When?"

"This afternoon."

We found 100 rue d'Assas with no difficulty. From the street, a walk led between two buildings to the heart of the block where a bronze plaque on a wooden gate bore the name of Ossip Zadkine.

Beyond the fence, we looked past a sprawling one-story structure to the edge of a garden, from which a man approached only moments after I pulled the bell-cord. He was rather small with grayish-blond hair and a ruddy complexion. Much like an English country gentleman, he wore a corduroy jacket and plus-fours.

"*Bonjour, Mesdames,*" he said, rolling his "r" as Russians do, then shifted to English. "Come in. You wish to see my work?"

We introduced ourselves. He shook our hands and ushered us into the building close by. "This is my small studio, where my students work — when I have any, that is."

The room had a sturdy workbench, a potbellied stove, a stool and a wicker armchair. The north wall was mostly glass and looked out onto a rustic garden.

"And in here," Mr. Zadkine opened the door at the other end, "is where I work."

We entered a large, well-lit *atelier* with a high ceiling. Sculptures of various sizes nearly filled it. Some were tree trunks carved into bizarre human shapes. The grain of the wood, as well as the original contour of the trees, had been respected and elaborated in every case. And there were bronzes and smaller carvings in wood and stone. I couldn't resist pausing to stroke a pair of birds in polished marble.

Zadkine talked on, telling us how he had gone to England before the Russian Revolution and become an apprentice woodcarver, telling about when this or that piece of work was done, and who or what museum had purchased it. However, my thoughts were of one thing only. I saw myself, chisel and mallet in hand, hacking at a chunk of stone in his small studio. I was a sculptor!

Zadkine's question brought me back to the present. "Are you a sculptor, Mademoiselle?"

"Well — I want to be. Would you teach me, Monsieur?"

He took a pipe out of his pocket and tapped it energetically on a nearby stand. Then, unhurriedly, he refilled it, lit it, and took a few long puffs before answering. "What I charge, you may find too much."

To my surprise, I told myself it didn't matter. I'd find a way to pay anything.

He went on, "My fee is twenty dollars a month."

Anne darted me a loaded glance. I couldn't answer for an eternal moment. Then I said, "Well ... I'm sure I can manage that. May I begin soon?"

"What about a month from now — after New Year's? My wife and I spend the holidays in the country. She's a painter."

For several days, I was unable to think of anything but studying under Zadkine. I don't know how many times I described his *atelier,* the garden we looked out on and the rustic cottage beyond it. Arcadia, right in the middle of Paris.

Most of all, I liked to tell about his sculpture — especially the huge, elongated crucifix. He had found a tree that just happened to have two branches growing straight out opposite each other at the right place on the trunk. He carved the branches into arms and made the tilted head out of the continuation of the trunk.

When he asked me why I wanted to study with him, it was easy to answer. I said that, since sculpture would be my profession, seeing his work was a spur. His attitude warmed.

"I will show you how to choose your materials — to choose and use your tools. We'll talk about tastes and styles and the history of the arts and, sometimes maybe, a bit of philosophy will creep in. I cannot teach you to be an artist, only help you to see. If you have talent and enough courage to oppose convention, you might amount to someone worthwhile. If you were a dilettante, my approach would be different."

He was what I needed — someone to get me on the right track so I could steer clear of Cupid — at least till I was on sure ground.

Christmas letters and cards began to arrive. There were messages of love, good wishes and news of family and friends. In one batch, a familiar green envelope stood out. I knew it was from John even before I recognized his handwriting. Two years earlier, when I designed and sold greeting cards, I let John choose one. I had a number of them printed with his name and gave them to him on one of his birthdays. At last he was using the cards.

I hurried upstairs to open my mail in private. Maybe John wasn't mad at me after all? I treasured his friendship. He wouldn't let me down. Not John. I had hurt him, but not beyond repair.

I tore open the envelope, eager to see how he explained his long silence. There was the familiar design, but no note. The folded card was blank — except for his printed name: JOHN FEE EMBREE. In front of the name he had written in ink: *MR. AND MRS.*

That was all. What did it mean?

Chapter Sixteen

Zadkine's approach to sculpture distracted me from John's ambiguous card. What I did and how I did it mattered to my new teacher. We discussed my first project and agreed I would carve a head in stone.

"Remember," he said, "you will develop your own distinctive style. Influences will come from many sides — from artists you admire, from emotions, from music and poems — from anywhere. You will create and, inevitably reflect your ambience. Dare! Take risks! We have no rules. What looks right to you is valid. I shall tell you this again and again, and you will remember it all your life!"

He paused to relight his pipe, then went on. "Some day, you'll be able to carve directly into the material — whether it be wood or marble. But as a beginner, you should first make a model in clay to use as a guide while you learn the technique of controlling your tools."

In a week, I had finished the model head, and Zadkine took me by bus to the edge of town where we picked out the stone at a supplier's. The dealer greeted us and we shook hands. Zadkine explained what we were looking for, while I surveyed the sprawling yard. There were slabs and blocks of all shapes, sizes and colors.

Wasn't it Michelangelo who said that in every stone a sculpture lay imprisoned? All one had to do was remove the outside. I couldn't help imagining a yard full of escaping works of art, gathering at the gate and clamoring to be located about the city. I gave them suitable voices and dialogue until Zadkine interrupted my burlesque.

"This piece of *euville* will do very well — don't you think so, Mademoiselle? It's not a hard stone, you see, and the size is right."

The dealer assured us he would have it delivered the following morning.

"Now we'll buy your mallet and chisels nearer home," Zadkine said.

As we rode back to Montparnasse, I told my teacher all about the escaping statues. He thought it was very funny and said, "*Très bien!* So, you'll be a writer, too."

For the next few weeks, there was no danger I would worry about an aching heart — there was too much pain in the muscles of my arms and hands, and I had to nurse scuffed knuckles on my left hand and blisters on my right. Wielding a heavy mallet took some learning and practice to get the aim right and toughen the parts that clasped the hammer. More than one well-wisher suggested I wear gloves. No. Gloves would lessen the sensibility, separate me from my object — no longer a piece of stone, but an extension of myself. The better solution was small bandages.

I received a letter from my mother toward the end of January, and by then, John's Christmas card had taken a position of minor concern to me. I was halfway through the letter before I came to the explanation of his cryptic communication:

... and last week I answered the doorbell and found John standing there with a strange young woman. By strange, I mean I'd never seen her before. She looked a lot like him, and I said, "Oh, is this another sister?" and he said, "No, this is my wife, Grace."

Well, I tried not to show surprise. They came in and I brought out some port wine — that's all I had — and we had a nice visit.

Grace is a lovely person. I like her. She was a classmate of Edwina's at Swarthmore. She's Norwegian and, it seems, has inherited some money from her grandmother. John doesn't have any, as we know.

Anyway, he still hopes to be a writer. They wanted to rent the house at Kahana because there there'd be few distractions. So, the next morning we drove over. Grace loved everything about it.

You can imagine my surprise when we went upstairs and John said, "Oh — I'll use this room for my studio. I like the view of the ocean."

I suppose I ought to tell you ... it was <u>your bedroom</u> he was talking about.

I don't know what to make of it. It's still too early to tell. He didn't ask even once for news of you. If all were well, it would have been natural, as well as polite, to ask.

Your loving mother

Oh, how my poor arms and hands ached! What a blessing — to have no greater pains than those in my muscles.

Chapter Seventeen

My knuckles healed and the soreness in my arms disappeared in a few weeks — even before I completed the stone head.

"You learn quickly," Zadkine told me one day. He beamed, and then added, "Furthermore, you have talent."

He seemed as proud as I. I had never been so self-confident. That was only the beginning. He didn't know it yet, but I was going to submit something to the Salon, *and it would be accepted!* In almost every letter to my mother, I promised her that. Would I ever let her down? I wouldn't let myself down, either — or John's hopes for me. No matter what he did with *his* life, he was the genesis of these events in mine.

New doors continued to open. Through Sonya's, for example, I met Harry Nash, the gregarious New Yorker and Sonya's fiancé. I went to some function or other at his home several times a month. The first party, on New Year's Eve, was one to remember. It began at eleven p.m. and didn't end till eight o'clock in the morning, 1932.

Sonya phoned to say she'd pick me up in her sister's Hispana Suisa at about 10:30. When the driver came for me, the lobby of the Club was empty except for the concierge who hardly looked up as I said goodnight. She went right on knitting as though liveried chauffeurs were an ordinary part of her life. But then, she hadn't seen the limousine that awaited me outside.

In the back seat with Sonya were her brother-in-law and sister, Hugo and Marta, both of whom I had already met. The chauffeur opened the car door and held one of my elbows ever so lightly while I stepped in and sat on a jump seat facing the others. We shook hands as the car moved silently forward and joined the traffic of Boulevard Montparnasse.

"I hope you had a nap this afternoon," Sonya said. "We won't let you go home before breakfast."

"I know. Harry warned me," I said.

The other two chuckled, and Hugo said in fluent English, "Harry's parties are unique. As a host, he embodies the best of French and American hospitality."

"You'll meet several young people," Marta said. "At the moment, he has a house guest, Bob, an American who was many years at the Rome office of the Chase Bank. Nice young man. He's being transferred to London but is stopping here for some extra training."

"And don't forget Nicolas and his two beautiful sisters," Hugo put in. "They're coming tonight, too."

"Yes," said Sonya. "Nicolas works part time at the bank, while he's finishing his studies at the Sorbonne. His sisters are also getting their degrees. A remarkable family. They're of Russian nobility, you see. Came here a dozen years ago with their parents to escape the revolution, but rolled up their sleeves, as you say in America, and are making the best of it. They had to leave everything behind."

"Everything but their jewels," said Marta.

"Perhaps," Hugo said, "but I'm sure they had to sell them to survive during the first years. France, you may recall, was desolate after the war. I believe *nous sommes arrivés.*"

We had, in fact, arrived in a fashionable residential neighborhood. The driver turned onto Avenue Malakoff and stopped the car at No. 63, a building of some five or six stories.

Up on the fourth floor, a uniformed maid opened the door and took our coats. Mr. Nash appeared. "Hello, Sonya, my dear!" He welcomed each of us in turn while from the living room came an undulating hum of voices.

"Come." He took my arm. "I'll introduce you to the others."

How like a friendly old neighbor he was. I met Nicolas first — tall, distinguished and very handsome — then his lovely sisters. Neither wore a tiara or an emerald necklace. I saw nothing more than modest earrings, but that didn't surprise me. Their poise and classical simplicity didn't require embellishment.

A young man came up and extended his hand. "I'm Bob," he said and took me away from our host. "I'll finish the introductions, Harry. It's almost midnight."

Among the dozen or so guests, someone started singing and was joined by most of the company: "*If auld acquaintance be forgot ....*"

In the dining room, Harry poured champagne. After the usual toasts of "*Bonne Année*" and "Happy New Year" from all sides, Sonya raised her voice. "And thanks for the old one, everybody!"

Marta turned to Bob. "That's what we say in Sweden."

Nicolas was at my side, clinking my glass and wishing me a happy new year. "You are a sculptor, I understand. I would like to hear about your work."

Gee! How did he know I wanted to talk about it?

"I've started studying with a sculptor named Zadkine. Do you know him? He's Russian."

"Not personally. I've seen what he does with wood and stone and like it. Is he a good teacher?"

"He's showing me what to do with tools, to begin with."

"When technique is easy, you'll develop your own characteristics, cultivate distinctive qualities."

"You sound like an artist."

"Everyone is — potentially. It's all that matters, after all. I'm trying my hand at writing plays. The arts endure when everything else turns to dust."

Bob came up, refilled our glasses, said, "Cheers" and moved on.

Nicolas looked down at me and smiled. "Political systems come and go, but the cave paintings of prehistoric man still move us, while the men who did them are unknown. Any *littérateur* can recite ancient Greek poetry, but how many know who ruled during the 5th century B.C.?"

He was obviously thinking of his own country and the overthrow of the Czar. I wanted to ask how he felt, personally, about being expatriated, but I didn't know him well enough. It would be prying, so I just sipped my champagne.

At the other end of the living room, a phonograph played the latest hit, and Bob glided across the floor singing, "Darling, *je vous aime beaucoup, je ne sais pas* what to do ..." He set his glass down, twirled around, took one of my hands and said, "Shall we dance, Agnès? Nicolas will let you go for awhile, I'm sure."

From a million miles away I recognized Anne's voice. "Wake up, Agnes. It's noon — it's a new year — we have to go down to dinner soon. Wake up!"

I opened my eyes and rolled slowly over onto an elbow. "I think I'll skip dinner. Go away and let me sleep."

Anne went on, "Do you know you came in at eight o'clock this morning? That must have been some party."

Between yawns I said, "Uh huh. It was. And you know what? No one got drunk! At Harry's we had a midnight supper and danced. By four o'clock there were only five of us left, and Harry took us to a funny sort of cabaret at Les Halles where we had oysters, onion soup, more champagne, and we danced for a couple of hours. By then, we were hungry again, or Harry was, at least, so we went to the Dôme for breakfast. You know what? If you drink too much, you're not aware you're having a good time. Gee — it sure was a wonderful party."

Feigning sophistication, Reid Hall, Paris - 1932

Chapter Eighteen

Paris
February 20, 1932

Dearest Mom,

No! Please don't worry. Stone carving is not too strenuous for me. I'm not fragile, you know. The exercise is good.

There's a resident nurse at the Club, a Miss Noyes. Besides being a good-fun person, she keeps her eye on my wounded knuckles and on anything else that might bother me.

My block of stone is looking more and more like a human head. The details are coming to life. I often work till 2:00, after which all I can do is eat a bite, take a nap and dress for dinner.

Last week three of us from Reid Hall went to see Lucille's summer collection. Dresses have changed very little; hats are like pancakes worn on the side of the head — still pretty bad.

Spring is getting closer. Four of us are thinking of renting a car over Easter vacation and driving through southern France to see some chateaux and historic places. I want to visit one of the famous caves of prehistoric paintings.

Last week Mrs. Kimball and I went to the Flea Market where all sorts of so-called junk is sold from stalls on a huge open area in the suburbs. One can find genuine antiques as well as useful but valueless stuff. Mrs. K. got a complete set of unused Shakespeare in English for 80 cents. I bought a pair of real gold earrings for two dollars.

One night, several of us went to a theatre, a huge, barn-like place, where people try out things they have created in order to get the public's reaction before releasing them. As we arrived, a young man had just finished playing the accordion. He didn't get much applause. Then a woman mounted the stage and talked about a book she had written, defending the privilege of women choosing their own style of life. The audience argued heatedly for and against her views. I was surprised that so many were still opposed to our having the same rights as men. We left after the next number: a young woman who did the rumba. Suggestions from the audience on how to improve her act were far from flattering.

My social life has been invigorated by Sonya and Harry, their friends, and Richard Wagner. To see "Tannhauser," Jane and I stood in line two hours to get 25-cent tickets for my first opera. We saw and heard very well. The following day, I went to a Wagnerian concert. Have you ever known music to pick up your insides, twist them around, and leave you to straighten them out again? Wagner did that to me. I want more.

Last Wednesday, Bob took me to a Belgian restaurant for dinner. Then we called on the Tutins, who are newlyweds, still billing and cooing. He's English and she's French. She has gorgeous red hair. The four of us went to Dinah's, an American nightclub in the Quarter. A lot of Negroes, including Josephine Baker, settled here after the war because in France, no doors are closed to them. Dinah sang "Love For Sale," with encore after encore. Bob told us it can't be sung in the States because it's sensuous and might stir the base passions. Imagine, in the "Land of the Free" we have censorship!

The next night, I had dinner at Harry's and then drew his and Bob's portraits in charcoal. They were both pleased. I've found it's a good way to repay people for their kindness.

Then on Saturday, the Chase Bank hosted a grand ball at one of the big hotels. I went on Bob's arm but danced mostly with Nicolas. I got home at 4:30 in the morning.

The next day I'd have slept through till evening but had to go to an afternoon concert. It was Maurice Ravel conducting his own compositions. The last number was "Bolero," played that day for the first time. The audience gave him a standing ovation, but I'm not sure how I feel about it.

It started me remembering one day when I was about twelve. I was coming home on the streetcar from a music lesson and an elderly gentleman sat beside me. He saw my roll of music and asked if I was taking lessons. I was so timid, I only nodded.

"And you enjoy music?" he asked.

I nodded again.

"I'm glad you do. Some day you may travel to foreign countries

and you'll understand the full worth of music. Wherever you go, you'll appreciate people's feelings through their music. It's a universal language."

What he said then has meaning for me now, nine years later.

With only a few days left in Paris, Bob has been giving me a whirl: a Russian restaurant, the Sports Palace to see Cossacks in their splendid uniforms riding fabulous horses, and Russian dancers and singers.

He told me Nicolas had asked if it would be all right to invite me out. Bob assured him there were no ties between him and me. Believe me, Mom, I want no ties with anyone.

Thanks for sending me a "Star-Bulletin" every now and then. I like keeping up with the hometown gossip. So many of my former classmates are engaged or married. I hope they enjoy their gilded cages!

What's this I read about race riots in Honolulu? We always took it for granted that we got on well with Hawaiians.

Vance wrote me he had a wonderful Christmas dinner with you. How thoughtful of you to include him. He mentioned John and Grace had arrived but didn't comment.

On Thursday I'm going to quit work early so I can see Bob off.

I'll write again soon.

With love to all,
Sis

The big clock at the Gare du Nord said it was nearly noon. I pushed through the crowds, found track number five and hurried along the platform. Halfway down, I recognized Mrs. Tutin's red hair and then saw Bob surrounded by several friends, preparing to board the train. He turned when he saw me, gave me a fraternal hug, and kissed one of my cheeks. Everyone talked at once.

"*Bon voyage!*"

"Write soon."

"You'll love London."

"Don't forget to come back for a visit."

"*Au revoir!*"

The train moved, Bob waved from a window, and then was gone.

His friends on the platform separated into groups and dispersed. I walked away between Mrs. Tutin and Nicolas.

"John and I will miss him," Mrs. Tutin said. "I hope we won't lose you, too, Agnès, just because he's left. I'll call you soon. Forgive me if I rush off now — my husband is taking me to lunch."

She shook hands with us and said good-bye. Nicolas and I walked on in silence for several paces. Then he said, "May I invite you to have lunch with me? There's a nice little place just a block from here."

His eyes showed surprise and then pleasure when I accepted. We came to the intersection, and he clasped my elbow as we crossed the street. "Have you noticed the pussy willows and daffodils at the flower stalls?" he asked.

"Yes — and it's only February. Isn't it early for them? This will be my first spring out of the tropics, except for one in California."

"The colder the winter," he said, "the more explosive is spring. Here we are. Not very fancy, but the food is good."

In the crowded restaurant, we found a small table away from the entrance. As soon as the waiter had taken our order, Nicolas said, as though there had been no interruption, "Yes, spring in Russia comes suddenly — just when you think winter will never end. It could be as late as May. You wake up one cloudless morning to find the birch trees covered with green. And soon the lilacs bloom. Oh, it's beautiful here, too, but in the far north, it's something else. You see, between Moscow and the North Pole, there are no mountains, so the winds bring with them all the aromas of earth and flowers and grasses." He looked past me into the distance. "Pushkin wrote much of the spring."

"I suppose you have, too," I said.

"No, not I." He smiled. "I only read it. It's in the blood of every Russian. The earth is our mother, and in our relationship there is spiritual harmony. Tolstoy expressed it well in his prose and poems."

"But the Communists have outlawed religion, haven't they?"

"They have, indeed, and good riddance. But let's not confuse institutional religion with spirituality, Tolstoy's faith made him humble. A rumor says he looked in the mirror one day and saw a peasant. He knew then that, rich or poor, we are all kinsmen, and he had no right to be treated with more respect than a low-born *muzhik*. He and Rabindranath Tagore, the Bangali writer, corresponded for years. The two had much in common."

"Didn't Tagore get a Nobel prize for literature?"

"Yes — in 1913. He urged social reform and world unity in all his writings. The Church, on the other hand, excommunicated Tolstoy for expounding the same philosophy." Nicolas shook his head as he added, "There's some irony in that."

"Have you been back to Russia?"

"Not yet. Some day. I can't make plans till I get my degree."

"I've heard material conditions are pretty bad there."

"That's understandable. Give them time. Now they have to spread what they have very thin to reach all the people. You should have seen how the poor lived under the Czar. Today there's more than enough work for everyone. A lot of foreign specialists are going there to help. Good times will come, I'm sure."

"So there's no danger the people will rebel again?"

"Not so long as they don't confuse material comfort with progress."

"I don't follow."

"I mean ...." his gentle eyes looked straight into mine, "I mean, plain living and high thinking. When we moved to Paris, I learned the value of that. Substantially, we arrived with no more than what we carried in our hands. Our wealth is in intangibles — things such as love of the arts, of learning ... anything that enriches the quality of life. Material possessions are useful, of course, but have little meaning if there is no knowledge."

For an hour longer, I encouraged him to do most of the talking. When he asked about my work, what I said sounded inconsequential. How could anything in my life compare with his? He knew established artists. He had seen the Bolshoi Ballet, the experimental theatres in Moscow. And he, Nicolas, had written several plays.

It was almost like listening to John — John in another guise, urging me to accept nothing less than the best the world could offer.

Decades have passed since then, but I have never forgotten that luncheon and don't want to. At one point, when we were getting up to leave, he said, and I couldn't believe it, "Don't let anything stop you from learning, from cultivating your talents. Take your little chisel and mallet and carve *that* on your heart!"

I didn't tell him what John had already engraved there. I just smiled and thanked him. Then he shook my hand and said, "*Au revoir,* Agnessa — that's how we say your lovely name in Russian."

"*Au revoir,* Nicolas." We went off in opposite directions.

Chapter Nineteen

I decided to walk all the way back to Montparnasse. I say *walk* because no one would believe me if I told the truth — that my feet didn't touch the pavement. After spending two hours in another dimension, I was in no hurry to leave it.

Rue La Fayette brought me to the opera house. From there, I glided over Boulevard Capucines and hovered awhile to stare at the façade of La Madeleine, wondering why a Christian church had been made to look like a Greek temple. A wedding party was descending the steps. I didn't join the curious pedestrians but moved on toward the Place de la Concorde, that vast open square with the Egyptian column smack in the middle. From the center of the square, I looked left at the Tuileries Garden and the Louvre, and then right, up the Champs Elysées, a sight that never failed to take my breath away. Nicolas had said poetry was the mother of all great art. Only a poet could have conceived such a vista as this.

I was eager to talk to Anne about that other dimension, but she didn't come home till after midnight and I had fallen asleep by then. In the morning, I was on my way out when she awoke. Oh well ... Zadkine would understand my excitement. When I got to the studio, however, the only person there was a young man whom I had never met.

"*Bon jour,*" he said and extended his hand for me to shake. "I'm Pierre. Monsieur Zadkine had to go out. You must be Mademoiselle Larsen. I'll be coming here every other day to learn sculpture."

"Yes, I see," I replied, scanning the heap of clay on his turntable.

Surely he wasn't serious about being a sculptor? There would be no discussing lofty standards with him. But the world was big enough for all sorts, I reminded myself.

He went on, "I got here yesterday morning after you'd left. Zadkine suggested I begin making a head. I have no idea how to go on." He laughed as though he'd made a joke he knew wasn't funny.

Who was he? What the dickens was he doing there? The answers and more came soon enough. I exchanged my coat for my smock and inspected the chisels I'd be using that day. Three of them needed sharpening.

"How long have you been working here?" Pierre wanted to know.

"A couple of months."

"*Zut alors!* And you've learned so much? I guess you're a real sculptor. I'm going to be a lawyer. We used to live in Haiti. My name isn't really Pierre. I changed it to be safe." He paused, waiting for a suitable reaction from me.

"Why? Is it dangerous there?"

"Dangerous? Everybody carries a gun. You meet someone on the street, and you say, 'Are you my friend? No?' Okay .... Bang! Bang! Bang! 'You're dead.' Sure it's dangerous. Four years from now, when I have my degree, I'm going back and enter politics. If the president won't give me a ministerial post, I'll collect three thousand men in the mountains, get rid of him and take the job myself until someone kills me."

"Are you serious? That's plain anarchy!"

"Well — what do you expect? Haiti's been occupied by foreign troops ever since 1915."

"So? I'd think that would bring stability to your government."

"Not if the troops belong to Uncle Sam."

"You mean my country has occupied yours? But why? I'm sure we're just trying to help."

"Of course!" He laughed. "But help who? We're not the only poor country you're helping in that way. Why? Because where there's chaos, big business, in cahoots with government can run things as it pleases. The U.S. controls our finances; all capital investments are American."

"How do you know that? I don't believe it."

"Don't get upset, Mademoiselle. I know because my father was president of Haiti for eight years. How do you suppose he got rich? Not from his salary. Ha, ha! He made his fortune by playing ball with the occupiers. The position of president is so lucrative, every strongman wants it. A year ago, my father was given the choice of leaving or being killed."

"And you want to go back to that?"

"Why not? I like thrills."

"Then why on Earth are you studying sculpture?"

"Oh ... it's my mother. She thinks a little culture will do me good and maybe change my mind."

"Well, it's better than getting killed, isn't it?"

"Could be — but not half as exciting."

Anne was in our room when I got back to the Club in the afternoon.

"You looked bushed," she said. "When you left this morning, you were on top of the world. And now look at you. Working too hard, I'll bet."

"I suppose so," was all I felt like saying. I stretched out on my bed. I hadn't told her about lunch with Nicolas, then that dialog with Pierre .... lives of people disrupted, turned upside-down through no fault of theirs. How differently those two men had reacted to their crises.

"I suppose so," I repeated.

"Well — I've a remedy. Guess what! Tomorrow there's a party at Jane's. The architects are coming and we're going to make pancakes. Now that Bob's gone, you'll come too, won't you?"

Suddenly I wasn't tired anymore.

Chapter Twenty

I hadn't seen our architect friends for a long time — too long. Would I still find François attractive after Nicolas? The two had much in common, and their views on everything appealed to me. Both looked forward to a changing world — a world where the ordinary person could enjoy what only the privileged once had. They wanted to be a part of the transformation, and so did I.

The more I thought of my conversation with Pierre, the less I liked what he stood for. All he thought of was getting personal power at the expense of anyone who got in his way.

Could the Pierres and Nicolasses ever find common ground? More likely, the opinions and aims of each would be reinforced rather than weakened as each raised his voice. Most people weren't aware of what was at stake, or they didn't care because they felt somehow immune. And there was always that frightened percentage — the sheep — who preferred to overlook flaws and failings. What they didn't see, didn't exist.

So far, my politics had been only lightly brushed by the Right or Left. What if I should want to take sides some day? Absurd! I didn't know anything about the science and art of government and would do well to leave the recasting of society to qualified individuals. That would exclude me. I had discovered sculpture ... and something else. Odd. Why should I be thinking of my gender just because I was going to see François again? I knew very well why!

Anne and I were the last to arrive at Jane's. Gordon opened the door and hugged us both at once. "You're just in time to settle an argument. Jane wants to use six eggs in the batter. Alex says four are enough, and François says six, but to beat the whites separately."

"Don't ask me," I said.

Anne picked up an apron and tied it around her waist. "The more eggs, the better the batter. And beating the whites makes it frothy."

"Go on," Gordon said, "it sounds like the beginning of a song."

From across the room, François laughed with us. He had been thumbing through a magazine. Before joining us, his eyes caught and stayed fixed on mine. I waved him a tacit hello, to which he replied by raising and lowering his eyebrows several times. His smile told me what I wanted to know, and that was all my heart needed to beat a little faster. Nicolas couldn't do that. The evening was already a success.

Alex lifted a bottle high in the air, "Come — sing a song while we may. We're rich for a change — it's champagne! It doesn't happen every Saturday night, and who knows if it will ever happen again?"

The cork popped and hit one of the walls. The wine flowed, and Alex managed to aim almost all of it into the glasses.

"What a cynic you are, Alex," Jane said. "Why shouldn't it happen again?"

"I guess you haven't read the paper today. Let's drink to the fifty million gas masks the government has authorized the pharmacies to sell us."

"He's right," said François.

"Are you serious?" I asked. "What on Earth for?"

"Well — look at it this way — it makes sense," said Alex. "Incidentally, these pancakes are good enough for another helping. May I?"

"You wait your turn, *mon vieux*," François chided. "Instead, tell us what it is that makes sense."

"Well, you know how German economic conditions have been

steadily worsening since the Versailles Peace Treaty. That situation has generated what they call the National Socialism party. Of course, there's nothing socialist about it, but nationalist it certainly is. A number of rich industrialists, not only German, are supporting the party. They call themselves Nazis."

"What's that got to do with gas masks?" Anne asked.

"If the Nazis win the coming elections, they might appoint that young anti-semite as chancellor."

"You mean Hitler," Gordon said. "We have one like him in England, too, named Mosley. They're dangerous. Not only Jews should worry in that case. Anyone with progressive views will be in trouble."

"You don't think they'd invade this country, do you? The French are building the Maginot Line. Fortifications like that should discourage anyone."

"But they can't keep out gas bombs."

"I hadn't thought of that."

"And in Portugal, the dictator Salazar has been elected premiere. Mussolini is flexing his muscles in North Africa, and the Japanese would like to take over all of China."

"My Honolulu paper," I said, "keeps reminding us of the so-called 'Yellow Peril.' But I don't think they'd ever dare attack Hawaii. We have forts all over the Islands."

"You have other problems in Paradise now, I hear," Gordon said. "Quite a scandal — it's making headlines in the international press."

A broadside of questions came all at once: "What scandal?" "Who?" "A Navy wife, wasn't it? Mrs. Massey, or something?"

Oh dear, I groaned inwardly. Why did *that* have to come up?

"Did you know her, Agnès?"

"Not really. I met her at a couple of parties."

"Well — tell us. What was so outrageous?"

What could I do? I drained my glass and told the story.

"It seems that Mrs. Massey walked away from a party one night — probably staggered away — and claimed she was attacked and raped by four Hawaiians. The four they picked up denied it, but were arrested anyway. Her mother, a wealthy socialite, and her lieutenant husband kidnapped one of the Hawaiians, who was out on bail, and took him to the mother's house. There, they killed him in the bathtub, then stuffed his body in the back seat of her car. Their intention was to throw his corpse in the Blow Hole, a lonely, rocky spot on the coast. But halfway there, they were stopped by two cops for a minor infraction and caught red-handed. Even with Clarence Darrow defending them, they were found guilty."

"There — you see," Jane said, "there's justice after all. Hooray for our side."

"Not so fast," Gordon warned. "Wait till you hear the end."

"And what was it?"

"The sentence," I said, "caused the race riots we've been having. What happened? Massey and his mother-in-law were condemned to spend one day — just one day, mind you — in the Governor's palace, and then were deported to the Mainland and set free."

Amid gasps of incredulity, Gordon said, "Doesn't surprise me. The white race has a toehold on all the others so it can do as it pleases with impunity. The same thing happens in India. A few Western imperialists rule the world, with colonies on every continent that are sources of cheap labor and raw materials, and are captive markets for our manufactured goods. 'The white man's burden' we call it."

"Oh, come on, Gordon," I said. "My country has no colonies. The U.S. is not imperialist."

He patted my shoulder. "Patriotism is an admirable attribute, my dear, but it shouldn't keep you from recognizing your country's shortcomings. Let's not talk about what you've done to the Indians and the Negroes. Tell me — who rules China and the Philippines? And what about Alaska and Hawaii?"

"Alaska and Hawaii are American .... We're territories," I said.

"Sure, but can you elect your governor?"

"No. He's appointed by the president."

"And can you vote for the president?"

"No."

"You haven't any representatives in Congress, either." Gordon stood up and paced the floor with mock consternation. "But you pay the same taxes as your compatriots in the States who are allowed to vote."

He paused, looked around and pretended to glower. "A hundred and fifty years ago you rebelled against my government precisely because of taxation without representation. Remember? And yet you let your government get away with the same outrage."

He lowered his voice to almost a whisper. "The white middle class won't complain because it's in the driver's seat with the manipulators of power, obsessed with self-interest. Profit is more important than people. They didn't teach you any of that in school, did they? *Voilà!*"

He relaxed his posture and put his hands in his pockets. "So? D'you think I'd make a good preacher?"

We all applauded. "Bravo!" "Hear, hear!" "You're ready for a soap box at Hyde Park Corner!"

Gordon sat down and refilled his glass. "Seriously, though, I'm worried about where the world is headed. Unemployment is getting worse everywhere. In a year or so, we'll be back in our own countries looking for work. Employers are going broke fast. Where will we find jobs?"

"My banker friend believes the Depression won't last long," I said.

"He may be whistling in the dark, but I hope he's right."

"So do I," François said. "I'm supposed to go back to Czechoslovakia next year and do another stretch of military service. I've *got* to get out of it somehow ... damned if I'll gratify the lords of war. My family lived through the last ordeal. With all the new weapons they're inventing, I dread to think what the next one will be like."

"Do you think it's inevitable?"

"The munitions manufacturers will see to that."

For several long moments, no one spoke. Then, to nobody in particular, I said, "I wonder how much an individual can do to change the world?"

"Depends on who it is," said Alex. "And maybe not the whole world. Look what Dickens did by exposing the flaws in the society of his day. And Florence Nightingale, and in America, Thoreau wrote that famous essay on civil disobedience and even went to prison for refusing to pay the poll tax."

"Gosh, we didn't study *that* side of Thoreau in school," I remarked. "I'd better look him up again. It's easier for writers. But what can a piece of sculpture do, or architecture?"

"Le Corbusier is designing for the future," said Gordon, "where there will be light and clean air for everyone. On our drawing boards now are plans for the 'vertical city' that Marseilles is interested in realizing. Slums will disappear and women's drudgery will belong to history. But governments will have to cooperate."

Jane said, "That calls for another bottle of champagne. Let's toast to no more cynicism."

Chapter Twenty-One

During the next two weeks, I tried not to think of reforming the world. At Zadkine's, tranquil matters occupied me. I completed my stone head, sent it off to be mounted on a marble base, and began the clay model of a new piece: a sitting woman.

Pierre showed up occasionally but didn't speak of Haiti or of anything related to politics.

A third person joined our class, a young English woman named Jocelyn. She had been sculpting for several years. I liked her instantly and, when she invited me home to have tea with her, I knew we were going to be friends.

Her barn-like studio was similar to Jane's, only twice as large, with a real kitchen downstairs and a well-equipped bathroom off the mezzanine upstairs. There was little furniture because, she said, an *atelier* was meant for work, and a sculptor's trade was messy.

We sat on straight wooden chairs at a small table in a corner. About the room were several portraits of friends, cast in bronze. We talked of them for awhile, and then the conversation turned to traveling.

"I'm one of those," she said, "who's curious to see if the grass is really greener on the other side of the fence."

"Have you crossed many fences?" I asked.

"Not yet. I often shuttle between Paris and London, but that's not going far afield. The lawns in both places seem to be the same color. Some money I recently inherited has changed my lot, however. I bought this studio and now can roam the world. One of my sisters lives in Wisconsin and wants me to visit her and her husband next year. How about you? Will you be staying in Paris long?"

"My original plan was for one year, but that's not enough. In just five months, I've discovered so many new ways of looking at ideas and issues. I want to put off returning home as long as possible."

"But everyone says Hawaii is a paradise."

"Sure — if all you want to do is flit about with flowers in your hair and a highball in your hand. It's a mindless kind of existence. I'd rather be poor here than rich there."

"You're exaggerating, I presume, but I know what you mean. Will you be seeing much of Europe?"

"Actually, three friends and I are planning to drive through the south of France during Easter break. We're going down to the Mediterranean and want to stop at a prehistoric cave on the way. If I live frugally, maybe I can see Italy during the summer."

"Splendid. It's easy to economize here. The French are expert at it and don't sacrifice the quality of their lives."

As I walked back to the Club, I put my brain to work. Anne and I could give up our room for the two weeks we'd be away. What we saved ought to pay for most of our share of the trip. Then, when we came back, we could find an apartment of our own and trim our overhead even more. We didn't need the fancy meals the Club served us. I, for one, was putting on weight because I couldn't resist the desserts.

"Listen ...." I told Anne my thoughts. She listened and liked what I said. Later that evening, the Club secretary assured us that giving up our room would present no problem. She even said we could store our suitcases in the basement at no charge.

The next hurdle was not so quickly resolved. We had to have an automobile for our trip. Henri said he would find one, but the first few cars were, for one reason or another, unsuitable. Eventually a friend of his offered us a 1928 Essex. My father had owned the same model, and it turned out to be a lemon. My friends, however, didn't think it a valid reason for refusing the car. They argued that any other car, if we could find one, would cost twice as much, so I withdrew my objection.

We had chosen our departure date: dawn on Tuesday, March 15, 1932. We actually did leave then, but just barely. The day before, I came down with an awful case of the flu. Miss Noyes, the resident nurse, saw me three times that day and suggested we postpone leaving. I refused to consider it.

"Be sensible," Gertrude pleaded. "Jane, Anne and I can go on and wait for you at Blois. In one or two days, you can join us."

But on the morning of the 15th, my temperature was normal, and they gave in. I didn't think it necessary to say that my body still ached. Miss Noyes saw that I was dressed warmly and bundled under a blanket in the back seat.

"Now," she said, "see to it you go right to bed when you get to Blois. Will you promise?"

I promised.

"All right, you stubborn Norwegian," Miss Noyes smiled and patted my cheek, "you'll come out fine if you take it easy."

Gertrude was at the wheel. Neither Jane nor Anne could drive. I shut my eyes and dozed, relieved that we were on our way. It wasn't till we'd left the city far behind that I awoke to exclamations of, "Look over there!" "At last — it's really spring!" "Are those cherry blossoms or almonds?" "Looks like popcorn, doesn't it?"

I turned my head and looked. The brightness of the daylight hurt my eyes, so I lowered my eyelids again. The next thing I heard was Gertrude saying we had reached Orléans.

"Time for breakfast, *mes amies*," she said and stopped the car in front of a café.

Someone, I think it was Anne, brought me a *café au lait* with a croissant. Soon we were off once more. Orléans, the gateway to the fertile valley of the Loire River, is the cradle of much of France's history. To see it was important, and so was listening to Gertrude telling tales of François the First.

"His birth date is easy to recall," she began. "It was two years after Columbus sailed the ocean blue. What I like to remember about him is that he was a patron of the arts. He invited Leonardo da Vinci to his court and bought the Mona Lisa from him. That's why the painting hangs in the Louvre. And he befriended the great satirist, Rabelais, too. We're going to visit one of his chateaux in Blois."

"Whose, Rabelais'?"

"No! King François'. He, the king, helped bring about the Renaissance when he wasn't fighting a war or being dissolute."

"What else are we going to see?"

"Well, there's one castle called Chenonceaux and another one made up of three different chateaux."

"We may need more than two days to see all that," Jane said.

"Even two weeks wouldn't be enough," said Gertrude. "But we have a schedule to keep ...."

Their voices faded to a drone, and I didn't hear anymore till the car jerked to a stop in front of a tiny hotel. A half an hour later, I was in a comfortable bed in a room by myself, listening to a medley of church bells. My three friends had decided to take the adjoining room so I would not be disturbed. They hurriedly freshened up and went off into the bright afternoon. And there I lay.

In slow motion, my eyes examined the furniture — simple, pre-Victorian — obviously not bought at a department store, but made by hand in the days when life was uncomplicated and travelers came by horse and carriage. On a marble-top stand, a pitcher rested in a basin. After supper and in the morning, a maid would fill the jug with hot water for sponge-bathing.

And there were the bells. Didn't they ever stop? From every church, near or far, they chimed on the hour and every quarter hour, some on time and others either fast or slow. How could the faithful of Blois ever know the correct hour? Did it matter? I could do without both clocks and calendars.

Shouldn't I be grateful to the virus for invading my body? I'd have two days of solitude that I could devote to contemplation. I'd been wondering ... was it the virus alone that knocked me down? Usually I could fend them off, but this time ... this time ... could I have lent a hand? Why would I do that? Was it all those conflicting new ideas thrust at me in the past few weeks? Possibly. No. Probably.

Wasn't I still wincing from my display of ignorance the night of the pancake party? I'd been educated at a prestigious private school and yet, I didn't know things about my own country that foreigners knew. I had been cheated. Why didn't they teach us *all* of history? Were we so insecure we couldn't swallow the truth? Would I love my country less because it wasn't perfect?

And then, that business of the Massey trial. I had to sit there and admit that, though we preach liberty and justice, in practice it was quite another situation. The next time I recited the Pledge of Allegiance, I would say, "... with liberty and justice for all the rich and white."

Remember the chrysalis I used to talk about? Well, maybe it was time for it to emerge into its definite form. I would never be a butterfly or a moth. Except for their beauty, which should not be underestimated, butterflies were useful only for pollination. Moths were nocturnal, drab, and ate holes in woolen garments. Could some other insect serve as a model? What about a bee? Bees worked hard, had a purpose in life, could sting when necessary, and ... and they even made honey. Ha! Metamorphosis — I was ready!

I laughed out loud and was still laughing when the door opened.

Jane, Gertrude and Anne stood there.

"I'm well!" I shouted. "Are you going to let me out of bed?"

"Not so fast." Gertrude shook a finger at me. "To what do we owe this sudden recovery — if, that is, you really are well?"

Anne chortled. "If, that is, she really was ill?"

I sat up and stretched my arms. "Behold! My Renaissance! Maybe it was the treatment I got from my good friends and the fresh country air and the endless church bells. What else?"

Chapter Twenty-Two

My three guardians allowed me to get up and dress Thursday afternoon. Sightseeing was out, but when I demonstrated how steady my legs were, they let me have dinner with them downstairs.

On Friday morning, we all set out, with Gertrude at the wheel. We stayed within the Loire Valley, on roads lined with poplar trees, and across flat farm land dotted with haystacks and rustic houses with roofs of slate or thatch.

The route we chose was used mainly by local traffic — bicycles and horse-drawn carts. Autos were so uncommon that people working in the fields stopped and stared at us. Children waved, and we waved back.

Somewhere I had read that certain primitive cultures believed the universal Father first made Earth and water, then created man by mixing the two, modeling a figure, hardening it in fire and breathing His vital spark into it. I liked that. Nature. The countryside ... where Mother Nature and human nature needed each other. Their interdependence was manifest outside of the city. In the fields we saw, it looked warm. I wanted to take off my shoes and run, feel the mud squish between my toes and, when I was out of breath, lie on my back under a tree and look up at the sky through the filigree of branches and leaves.

— What on Earth was Gertrude complaining about?

"Darn this gas pedal — it keeps sticking. And the gasoline gauge doesn't work, either. Oh, well, I'll just have to be careful."

For the first time I noticed something odd. "The steering wheel!" I shouted "Look — it's on the wrong side!"

Above the bursts of laughter, Jane said, "Listen to her! She's with us again. Welcome back, Agnès!"

They explained what I should have guessed, that the car had apparently been adjusted for Britain where they drive on the left side of the road.

"Maybe you'll let me take the wheel tomorrow, Gertrude," I said. "You should be getting tired."

"Not really. I'm used to it. My parents travel between Monte Carlo and Paris often and like me to take over the driving. But sure — I'll cede my place. Tomorrow we'll have a long haul if we want to be in Le Puy the day after. Palm Sunday is a special event there."

We reached the town of Nevers in time to eat and go to bed and were off again early on Saturday. The road started out flat, but later undulated, bringing us into tree-covered hills. The red-tiled roofs of the farm houses sloped less. Around three o'clock, I took the wheel. The sky was cloudless, the air warm, and the road all ours.

"We haven't seen another car for ages," Jane commented. "The world belongs to us, alone." She began to sing, a bit off key, perhaps, but on impulse, and the rest of us joined in.

"Come away with me Lucille,
In my merry Oldsmobile,
Down the road of life we'll fly,
Automobubbling you and I ...."

We lowered the windows and raised our voices. "Meet me in Saint Louis, Louis ...." Then came "My Wild Irish Rose" and "The Londonderry Air."

Anne broke in with a guffaw. "We've *got* to tell Gertrude about the night we were at the Dôme with the boys and ... and the accordion player ambled by, playing old Irish tunes."

Anne stopped to laugh, and Jane went on, "Oh, yes! François liked one of the songs and asked Gordon what it was, and Gordon said, "It's called 'Londonderry air' and François said, '*Sans blag!* Are you joking? I never heard of writing a song about anyone's *derrière!*'"

Suddenly, out of nowhere, a van overtook us on the left — much too close. I swerved to the right, forgetting what side the steering wheel was on, and misjudged the distance. While we were still laughing, our car was off the road, bumping along the shoulder. When we came to a stop, I looked in the back seat. Jane was unconscious.

Anne, sitting next to her, said, "We bounced so hard, she knocked her head. What on Earth happened? What are we going to do?"

The phantom van disappeared over the hill ahead. Our car had apparently suffered no damage. Jane came to after a few minutes, and, after she assured us she was all right, we drove on.

Gertrude succeeded in reviving our wilted enthusiasm. "We'll have to automobubble right along if we want to reach Le Puy before dark." She talked about what we could look forward to: Roman ruins, gourmet dishes, fishing villages, prehistoric caves, lunch with her parents in Nimes ....

The route became hillier, and we found ourselves in the mountains — real mountains — with patches of snow and ice still clinging to shadowy nooks in the evergreen woods. Dusk surrounded us and softened the landscape.

"I guess I was wrong about this 1928 Essex," I said. "She has stood up well. My father had a lot of trouble with the carburetor of his, and couldn't say one nice thing about the car. I hereby apologize publicly to her. She may have some defects, but who's perfect?"

"She'll appreciate your confidence," Gertrude said. "In only six kilometers, she'll have us in Le Puy — Uh oh. Now what?"

The car was pulling to the left and riding unevenly. We had a flat tire. The spare was sound and inflated, but we found the jack useless. We were alone on the road. The only solution was to walk to town and get help. Anne and Gertrude drew the short straws and set out. In the gloom of the gloaming, Jane and I speculated on the outcome and reassured each other that this was another adventure.

While we waited, twiddling our thumbs, a couple of headlights approached from the rear, then stopped beside us. Two angels, masquerading as young Frenchmen, changed our tire effortlessly, and would accept no thanks. They insisted it was their pleasure.

Finally, at nine-thirty, we four wayfarers sat down to the best dinner any of us had ever devoured.

Nimes
Tuesday, March 22, 1932

Dearest Mom,

Here we are, one week into our trip. So far, it's a lot more exciting than we had ever dreamed — and interesting, too. In Blois, our first stop, there were several ancient castles, centuries old. I didn't go out much because I had to nurse a bad cold.

Only Gertrude and I know how to drive, so we take turns at the wheel. The car hasn't given us any real trouble — only minor inconveniences. Gertrude knows the country well — she has lived most of her life in France — so you won't worry, will you? My French is lousy, but the others make up for it.

After Blois, we stopped at Le Puy, a picturesque town in the mountains, famous for lace-making. Above it is the cathedral crowning a slender hill, more like a huge rock. Leading to it a road winds up and up, and a long straight flight of stone steps. We joined the crowds celebrating Palm Sunday and walked in their procession all the way to the top.

Then we drove higher into the mountains with snowdrifts three feet high. We wound in and out of gorgeous scenery, then discovered a bit of paradise called Villefort, where we spent the night.

The Romans built up Nimes over 2,000 years ago. So far we've seen their temple to Diana, the old arena, now used for bull fights, and several other records of their civilization. Many of them are still in fine condition.

Gertrude's parents are here, staying at one of the big hotels. Ours is inexpensive, but clean and central. Actually, traveling like this is cheaper than staying put in Paris.

Thursday, March 24

We're leaving Nimes this afternoon for the Mediterranean coast. Yesterday overflowed with events. We drove out of town to visit a Roman tower on a hill and a great bridge made of a yellowish stone with an aqueduct on top. At first I found the proportions unsatisfactory, but the more I looked at it, the better they seemed, and soon it became beautiful. I wonder if that means my discrimination is maturing?

Another side-trip was to Arles, about 30 km, away, to see old ramparts, an arena and an amphitheatre. Before the Romans made it a commercial nucleus, the Celts had a settlement there. Recently, of course, Van Gogh made it famous. We had our working materials with us and hoped he would be looking down over our shoulders when we sketched and painted.

Not far from there we "discovered" Les Baux on the bare top of a mountain. In the Middle Ages, it was a thriving Roman city of several thousand people, and now less than 100 live there amid sun-bleached ruins. Enough is left, however, to testify to the grandeur that must have been. There are no trees, but a lovely church still stands in what was a square. The streets, paved with huge blocks of stone, obviously haven't been repaired, or needed it, since the Romans made them.

For centuries the inhabitants quarrelled with the Pope and French rulers, and in 1632, Louis XIII reduced the city walls and the chateau to rubble.

Bauxite, the mineral used in refining aluminum, was discovered there in 1821.

In the evening we dressed up in "civilized" clothes for the first time and dined with Gertrude's parents at their hotel.

Friday, March 25

Oh, the thrill of breathing salt air again and seeing ocean all the way to where it meets the sky! The first thing we did when we got to Grau du Roi was run to the beach and lie in the sun for an hour. Later, after finding a hotel, we walked out on one of the piers at dusk to watch the sun set somewhere beyond Spain.

Early this morning we drove to Aigue Mortes, another fishing village. In the 13th century, Louis IX (St. Louis) and his men embarked for the Crusades from there.

We managed to get up early enough to see the boats go out, and then we were on hand in the late afternoon when they returned with their catches. All the men dress alike in wooden shoes and denim suits.

Did you know that our word "denim" comes from the French de Nimes? That coarse blue cotton cloth has been woven in Nimes for centuries.

What I find exciting about this trip is seeing history with my eyes and touching it with my hands.

Next week I'll tell you about the caves.

With love to all,
Sis

Chapter Twenty-Three

Souillac
Easter Sunday
March 27, 1932

Dearest Mom,

We left the coast reluctantly, got back on the main road and headed for Carcassonne, another ancient walled town. Much of it has been reconstructed. It's filled with American tourists and beggars. We stayed only a short time, to take pictures and have tea at a swanky hotel rebuilt in the same style as the town, with turrets, parapets, crenels and embrasures. By 4:00, we were gone.

Some kilometers into the countryside, our motor coughed a few times and sputtered, but brought us safely to Castelnaudary. A garage mechanic there assured us there was nothing to worry about, but it wasn't long before the motor bucked and hiccupped again. Near a dinky hamlet, we had to coax it to the only garage, where I told the mechanic the carburetor was probably dirty. He tinkered for three hours and sent us on our way.

Sixteen miles past Toulouse, the clouds opened, rain raged down, and the motor died. No amount of teasing, urging or threatening could make her heart beat, and no angels were in sight. We pushed her to a phone and called a garage. Eventually a repairman arrived and towed us to town. After listening to our description of the symptoms, he said, "Ah, that must be the carburetor."

Our hotel room here in Souillac is immense, with two huge beds, a stone fireplace, five large wall mirrors and an adjoining "bath." The only piece of furniture in the bathroom is a wash stand with two pitchers and basins. The tub, shower and johnnie are missing because there is no running water. We must use our chamber pots or go down the hall to the little room marked W.C. That stands for water closet, which the French pronounce "vatair."

For 35 cents a head, we're not complaining. We slept like babies.

Sometime today we'll be at the caves, at last.

Brantôme
Monday, March 28

Our Essex brought us to the caves in foul, dirty rain over muddy roads off the main route. On the way we had stopped for coffee and, as we prepared to take off again — I was at the wheel — I pulled the starter completely out of its place on the dashboard. We found a garage, but the serviceman had gone home for lunch and wouldn't be back for an hour.

Meals are sacred to Latins. It's impossible to hurry them, and nothing can keep them from their two-hour respite in the middle of the day. I applaud the custom. Well, we parked in his garage and played bridge till he returned and repaired the damage in no time. But then he went into a long soliloquy about the excellence of Fords and Essexes, and how French starters were not made like ours. We couldn't figure out whether he was being facetious or not. In any case, we've come to love our Essex, faults and all. She has a soul.

Signposts guided us to the caves — over a squishy lane through some woods. At a clearing, we stopped where a board told us we had arrived. Through the misty rain, we saw an arrow pointing to what looked like a flight of steps some distance away. No one else was about, and we saw no information office.

"Now what do we do?" Anne wondered aloud. No one spoke for a long time.

Then Gertrude said, "This is altogether too "formidable." I propose we keep right on driving. What do you all say?"

We exchanged glances. Jane and Anne agreed, but I said we should stay and brave the rain. "We'll never find ourselves here again. It's the chance of a lifetime. This is one of the reasons I came along."

"It's three against one," Gertrude said.

"Okay. You three go on. I'm going to stay. Really, I won't mind. I'll get a ride, somehow, to the train station."

More silence, then they gave in. I'm glad I was stubborn, and so are they, now.

With kerchiefs on our heads, we hurried over to the stairs — a shaky flight of metal, perhaps 100 feet high — up the sheer side of a mountain. At the top of the steps we looked onto a narrow valley, one flank of which had a catwalk, about 100 feet long. Still, no other humans were visible — no guards, no one selling admission tickets. Instead, a sign said we had come to the entrance of the cave of the prehistoric paintings. A small notice informed us that by turning on the electric switch, the interior of the cave would be illuminated, and to please turn off the lights when we left.

From the entrance, merely an opening without a door, a long passage led into the mountain. Every ten feet or so, a light bulb hung from an electric cord strung along the ceiling. The corridor opened into the main chamber where the drawings and paintings, done about 10,000 B.C., decorated the walls. There they were — the very same bison, the deer, the buffaloes and horses that illustrated our history books in high school. There — the originals — in rich earth colors of browns, reds, yellows and black, with bumps all in the right places.

Coming face to face with one of the first recorded artists on this planet exhilarated and disturbed me at the same time. Trying to imagine how they might have lived was unsettling. Could they really have been so primitive as we were taught they were?

We left after an hour or more, careful to turn off the lights. Still, we saw no people.

Not long before dark, we got here to Brantôme and installed ourselves in this charming hotel on an island in the Dronne River.

I must record for history the nine-course dinner that cost us 60 cents apiece. With a flourish, a dignified waiter served us soup to begin with, then an omelette. After that came a sort of patty shell filled with paté de fois gras and truffles, then peas (a separate course). Fifth was steak with truffle sauce, and sixth was fried turkey and endives with cheese sauce. The last three courses were salad, a choice of a dozen cheeses, and fruit with wafers and jam. Wine, of course, was included.

We're wondering how many kilos we'll have gained when we get back to Paris.

Tomorrow it will be two weeks since our last honest-to-goodness bath!

CHAPTER TWENTY-THREE

Tours
Wednesday, March 30

From Brantôme we drove to Poitiers and spent the night. The town is small but has three important churches built between the 11th and 13th centuries. One of the baptistries, St. John's, was already in use in the 4th century.

History, you know, thrives on gossip. Where would it be without scandals? Diane de Poitiers was the mistress of Henry II and became more important than the queen, who was Catherine de Medici. Henry ignored the queen and their eldest son, François II. When another son became Charles IX, she organized with him the massacre of St. Bartholomew's Day in 1572, hoping to rid the world, or at least France, of Protestants.

Between Poitiers and Tours, we stopped briefly at Loches to see its chateau and dungeon with torture chambers and implements. The keeper obviously enjoyed his job and seemed to relive all the terrible events as he described them to us. Cardinal So-and-So was suspended in that cage in this dark room by Charles XII for ten years. In that other cage, a man sat for five years watching someone being tortured everyday.

Another room, completely dark in the old days, had an open well in the center of the floor. Condemned men were sent in blindfolded and that was the end of them.

And they were Christian? For shame! Well, I suppose we're all sinners. We need only confess, be absolved, and go forth and sin some more. Hah! That's convenient. Maybe I'll join the club.

Our hotel is called The Golden Bowl, built in the 15th century. The dining room is still much as it was then, with a spacious fireplace and beamed ceiling. Our bedroom has walls of blue and white plaid. Everything in the room is plain blue or white, except the woodwork, which is polished walnut.

I'll write again from Paris. We'll be there tomorrow afternoon. Anne and I are going to start at once looking for a place of our own.

With love to you all,
Sis

Chapter Twenty-Four

The Sunday after our return to Paris found the four of us having breakfast and reminiscing at Jane's. Laughing at our misadventures in safety and ease, we recast them into treasures. Though no one mentioned it, we were older, wiser, and solid friends. For me the trip had not ended. It was just another rung of a long journey that would be punctuated with changes. Was *rung* the right word? I wanted it to suggest a foothold on an uphill climb, and that I'd eventually reach the top. What if I never got to the summit? So much could happen between here and there. My values would, presumably, alter several times.

What does it take to cause change? Events and issues are the impetus. They touch us, kindly or cruelly, and we react. Cause and effect. How we respond depends on what we're made of. Some avoid confrontation out of fear or weakness, and submit to anything — the sheep who give despots their power.

Only a minority dares to raise its voice against injustice and is seldom honored for its pains. I would never be one of the herd, following a leader with blind loyalty, not asking questions. The old Button-Moulder would never catch me!

When I looked in the mirror, I saw neither a peasant nor a sage. On the outside, I was still the naive demoiselle who left Honolulu less than a year before. It was the inside of me that was changing, that would fit into no one's mold. My transformation would be private, with no fanfare.

But, like the swelling green buds on the trees that lined the boulevards, the vitality in me was rising. I couldn't hide that. It was spring and I was bursting with regenerating vigor.

On my first day back at Zadkine's, I started releasing my Sitting Woman from a block of stone three feet high. The mallet seemed lighter than before, and my left hand guided the chisel with more precision.

Pierre was no longer there. And Jocelyn was out for some reason. I found her at home with a high fever and no proper food, so I ran to the Club and asked Miss Noyes for help. By evening Jocelyn was in the hospital.

Anne and I moved into a modern, tenth-floor apartment: No. 8, rue Blomet, within walking distance of all the familiar places. We and our friends could come and go as we pleased, could eat what and when we chose, enjoy a spectacular view of the city from our terrace, and save money in the bargain.

Harry took me out to dinner and concerts. One Sunday, we went to the horse races at Longchamps. He said that if he lost, we'd walk back to town, but if he won, we'd take a taxi. We not only rode but had a superb fish dinner at Prunier's.

My old friend, Diana, came through Paris on her way around the world with her aunt. It was at her house, a millennium ago, that I had met John and, as I hoped, she had the latest news of him and Grace. They had gone to Japan, she said. She was afraid they were not getting on well.

For two hours, she kept me spellbound with tales of what she had seen in India — temples and palaces, paintings and jewels, incredible wealth and inconceivable poverty. India was another land I'd have to witness for myself.

I saw the Tutins, too. They came to our apartment for dinner, and then invited Nicolas and me to their house, where I recounted for the umpteenth time our automobile trip. Talking about the caves prompted a discussion on the origin of genius and talent.

I said something about its depending on intelligence. Nicolas said he once thought so, too, but that he now tended to support the teachings of pundits in India — that the mind is only an organizer, that all creativity or so-called original thought comes from *above* the mind, and that the universal consciousness is the fountainhead. All a person had to do was tune in to that higher plane and — *voilà* — he was a creative artist.

Mrs. T. said, "Sounds so easy. You mean anyone — just anyone can do that? Are we all potential artists?"

"That's right," Nicolas replied. "But not necessarily artists — could be any field. According to the wisemen, if you get on the right wavelength, you'll find the source. The function of your intelligence is to arrange it in order, for better or worse."

After dinner, Mrs. T. took me into the nursery ostensibly to show off her new baby girl, but really, I thought, to warn me Nicolas was serious in his affection for me.

A week later, Jocelyn had recovered and gone to Holland for a rest. Zadkine went away, as well, to Venice. He was invited to exhibit at the International Biennial, with one room for his work alone.

The best part of that spring was all those evenings and Sundays we spent with our favorite architects. There was dancing at the *boîtes de nuit*, walks along the Seine as the evenings lengthened and grew warmer, and coffee at the Capoulade on boulevard St. Michèle. And will I ever forget the time Jane, Gordon, François and I went to Versailles for lunch, drank too much wine and danced around the statues in the Park? No — never!

Gordon, Jane and François, at Versailles - 1932

There were serious times, as well, when we gathered at Jane's or at rue Blomet and discussed the state of the world. Franklin Roosevelt would probably run against President Hoover in November. The Socialist Party nominated Norman Thomas, and even the Communists had a candidate — William Foster.

Seventeen thousand war veterans marched on Washington, D.C., demanding immediate cash for their bonus certificates. Many of them were among the fourteen million unemployed. The war had been over fourteen years, but the Administration gave them the cold shoulder. Roosevelt promised he would make life more secure for the forgotten man. Wisconsin announced the first insurance for the unemployed. It was high time!

There was a new hit song: "Brother, Can You Spare a Dime?" Everyone talked about Huxley's latest book: *Brave New World.* None of us had read it yet but we knew it was his nightmarish description of Utopia in the 25th century.

One afternoon when I was window shopping downtown, another new song kept running through my head. I didn't know all the words: *"April in Paris .... Chestnuts in blossom ... da da di da da .... Holiday tables under the trees ... da dada .... What have you done to my heart?"*

I couldn't afford any of those clothes, but imagining myself in them cost nothing. I'd get that black satin to match my blasé mask, April in Paris, the pale blue when I painted on my innocent smile, and the red one with sequins that would turn me into a siren.

Behind me a voice said, *"Bonjour,* Agnessa. A pleasure to see you again."

Nicolas! I couldn't hide my delight. And then he asked me to have a cocktail with him. Of course I accepted. April in Paris!

Our conversation stayed on the light side. I told him I liked the Russian sound of my name.

"Agnessa," he repeated. "It's beautiful."

"I've thought of giving my last name a French tone. Instead of "Larsen" it could be "L" apostrophe "Arsèn," with an accent. How do you like that?"

"French, for sure. And while we're at it — did you know that in Hindu mythology the god of fire is called Agni, defender of the altar? Agni L'Arsèn. Certainly one of a kind."

It was easy to laugh with Nicolas. He saw the unclouded side of the world. Not only that ... he looked for nobility where most would not expect to find it. Not till I started to leave did he bring up the subject of bicycling.

"There are many lovely trails around Fontainbleau," he told r "I'm going to take advantage of this weather. Will you go with '

Sunday?"

"Thank you," I said as we shook hands. "I'll call you this evening and tell you definitely. *Au revoir.* See you soon."

My heart sang "April in Paris" all the way home. Anne was sitting on the terrace when I burst in. "Guess what! I'm going to spend all day Sunday with Nicolas. We're going bicycling, and I can listen for hours to his formula for civilized living. I have a thousand questions to ask him and he'll give me answers that aren't over my head. Isn't it marvelous?"

Anne's expression declared it wasn't at all marvelous.

"What's wrong?" I asked.

"Nothing's wrong with bicycling. Only Gordon has suggested we all go out to St. Germain-en-Laye on Sunday. Besides, Nicolas is a mature and sensitive man, and you know he really cares for you. Will going with him send a message that you're ready to make a commitment?"

"But why? I went with Bob and no one thought a thing about it."

"That was different. There was no emotional involvement on either side. I'm not going to tell you what to do. Just be sure you know what you might be getting into. Think it over."

I did think it over ... and over and over. I remembered John. What was that French term? *Déjà vu?* It meant already seen. I had fouled up my friendship with John. Did I want to risk botching this one? And there was François. I didn't need complications of the heart. I had no reason to believe François was in love with me. Better that way. It wouldn't stop me from loving him .... He needn't know. We'd go on being fond of each other. No entanglements. Don't risk hurting Nicolas. Anne was right.

I waited till evening. As I dialed Nicolas's number, I had no idea what words I would use. His phone rang once, and a second time, then he answered. "*Allo.*" I told him who it was. "Ah, *ma chére* Agnessa!"

My throat went dry. "Nicolas ... I can't .... I shouldn't ... go bicycling with you on Sunday ...." I paused. He said nothing, and there was a long silence. My voice tried to go on.

"I ...."

Nicolas broke in. "It's all right, Agnessa. I understand. It's not necessary to explain. Believe me, I understand."

"Thank you, Nicolas. Good-bye." I knew it was not *au revoir.*

Chapter Twenty-Five

That evening Anne went out, and I sat alone on the terrace watching the city lights come on one by one. Occasionally a flimsy cloud appeared, floated westward, and dissipated. No distinct sounds reached me — only an ethereal hum, a conglomeration of distant noises.

Oh, Nicolas! What harm would there have been in a little flirtation? With you it could have been romantic. Maybe that was all you wanted, too? Hungry and tired, we'd have stopped at a little rustic inn for lunch .... How did Europeans court that was different from Americans? With more subtlety, I'd heard. I might have learned. I wouldn't let Anne give me advice anymore.

My year was almost up. I didn't want to leave. Life in Honolulu was dull — much too uneventful to go back to. I was just beginning to savor and relish the way foreigners lived, only it was no longer alien. I had become one of them ... almost.

I closed my eyes and tried not to think. It was peaceful that way. Then, through the hum I became aware of a faint rhythmic tap that grew louder — the clip-clop of horses' hooves approaching at a trot. I looked down on to rue Blomet where a powerful Percheron was pulling a wagonload of empty bottles over the cobblestones. The rattle and hoof beats receded and disappeared, but their cadences clung to the twilight air.

Once more I heard nothing but a tenuous murmur. Was it the song of the universe coming from infinity — that immeasurable space filled with other worlds? Could I reach that higher plane? What did Nicolas call it? The universal consciousness. I liked that. My loyalty would belong to the cosmos, not be limited by a petty terrestrial frame.

When we build fences around our beliefs or material things, we keep others out. Sure, but also we keep ourselves in — captives of our property. Protection was necessary in the limited world we knew. Without some defense, we'd be overcome by the dark forces around us.

All right — but nothing temporal endured. Beyond the mind th would be no problems or discord. Somewhere out past the ephemeral was the womb of creativity. How could I tune in to it? Back there in Madame Scheyer's class ... when we made those wild paintings ... ideas must have come from ... but of course! From out of the blue! Is that what the term meant? Imagine that. Out of the blue. At last — I knew.

On the half-hour ride in a crowded bus to St. Germain-en-Laye that Sunday, the six of us found places on the long bench at the rear. I pulled at Jane's arm so she would squeeze in beside me just as François was about to sit there. It was an impulsive gesture and no one could have guessed my motive — not even I, to tell the truth.

As we arrived, the local firemen, in their elegant uniforms and polished brass helmets, were demonstrating ladder escapes in the park of the chateau. We watched them for awhile along with the villagers, took a couple of rides on the carousel, bought ice cream cones, rambled over to the famous terrace overlooking the broad plain that cradled Paris, and took snapshots of each other. We could easily pick out the Eiffel Tower and the gleaming white church of Sacré Coeur on the hill of Montmartre, but No. 8 rue Blomet was hidden among the mass of low buildings.

"Somewhere," said Alex, "there's a painting Cezanne did of the city from this very spot. I've seen a reproduction of it. Cezanne's been dead twenty-five years and nothing's changed."

"I wonder if it will still look the same twenty-five years from now?" Jane said.

François guffawed, "We've learned how to build skyscrapers, remember. The future will have to be the vertical city. With populations exploding, if construction spreads out horizontally, there'll soon be no more green areas. We'll have only private little boxes covering the earth. The prairies and woods will disappear."

"And before all of it vanishes," Jane said, "I've decided to see Italy this summer. I want to take in as much of the *old* old world as possible before I go back home and join the lines at the soup kitchens."

I couldn't suppress a squeal of delight. "Are you serious, Jane? Anne, what do you say? Shall we go with her? I mean to Italy, not the States."

For the rest of the day, the rest of the month, and all of June, Italy was our main topic of conversation. We would leave early in July,

*Agnès and
François,
St. Germain-en-
Laye - 1932*

spend a whole month visiting the major cities, and end up in Trieste, from where Jane would sail for New York, and Anne and I would return to Paris.

Then Anne got a letter from home that disturbed her.

"What is it?" I asked. "Bad news, huh?"

"Very bad, my sister-in-law has left my brother and their three small children." I waited for her to tell me more. "She's a painter, you see. They had one baby after another and, even though there was plenty of domestic help, she quit painting. It was considered unmotherly or something."

"Same old story," I said. "If a woman's not married, no one takes her seriously. And when she does marry, she's no longer a person in her own right. What's she going to do?"

"She's done it ... on her way to Vienna."

"Do I get the feeling you're going there too?"

"Not exactly, but I might go to Budapest. An old friend lives there and has often asked me to visit her. It's not far from Vienna, so I could pop in there occasionally."

"Maybe you can help her straighten out her feelings?"

"I can try, anyway."

The sun beckoned us out to the terrace. Neither of us could find anything to say. Perhaps we didn't try. I was thinking how unfair society was.

"As for myself," I finally declared aloud, "I'm never going to get married. A woman who wants a career would be foolish to take a husband. Besides, I'd make an awful wife and wouldn't want to do that to a man I cared about."

Anne looked at me sideways. "Here in Europe, no one minds if you live with a man, but back in the States — gosh — a decent woman wouldn't dare."

"That doesn't mean Americans don't live in so-called sin — only they keep it secret .... Zadkine, you know, is married to a successful painter who uses her own name, Valentine Prax. Well, I used to think, gee, it's possible for two artists to marry and live happily ever after. When the warm weather came, they'd have their noon meal in the garden under the big umbrella. They looked so cozy, And then ... guess what?"

"No! Don't tell me."

"That's right. For the past week or more, Zadkine has been in a foul mood, even to the point of slamming doors. Well, last Friday, he told me his wife moved out and that they're getting a divorce. You see? It's not possible for a marriage between two artists to survive."

"Do you think it's because each needs from the other what the other can't give?"

"Yes, I think so. Thank goodness it's not one of my worries. Right now our main one is getting moved out of this apartment. I'm going to miss our lovely terrace and the good times we've had here."

"You're always saying change is progress."

"It is — even if it's temporarily a step backward."

"But you'll have the use of Jocelyn's studio while she's away. That won't be going backward."

"I didn't mean that. It'll be great living there even for three months. But Jane will be back in America, Gordon will be in England, and you'll be in Budapest."

"Oh, well," Anne said, "I'm not going to worry about you being lonely. Every year new people come to Paris. You didn't know anyone when you arrived, remember. And François will be here."

Chapter Twenty-Six

Dearest Mom,

I'm off again to see the world — by train this time, not in an old car with the steering wheel on the wrong side. Third class is clean and comfortable, and the seats are padded leather. We stretched out and slept on them soon after coming aboard yesterday. We can save hotel bills now and then, with no fear of flat tires or engine trouble.

Last night we had our final party and only two hours' sleep. Anne and I stayed at Jane's, and the architects came in and cooked dinner with us. In the morning there were two loaves of bread left over, each a couple of feet long and two inches in diameter. We sliced them lengthwise, and filled one with cheese and the other with ham, for lunch on the train.

The only book I've read in preparation for our trip is "The Romance of Leonardo da Vinci," which Lorraine sent me for X-mas. Now I know all about Italy in the 15th century and almost nothing about the 20th.

Jane feels awful about leaving Europe. She'll have to look for a job in New York. Finding one may not be as hard as she feared — Le Corbusier gave her six letters to colleagues.

Anne is on her way to Budapest to visit an old friend, and planning to stay in Vienna next year. You'll be glad to know I have a place to come back to in a month. My English friend, Jocelyn, is going to the U.S. and has offered me her studio while she is away.

"There — that's enough letter-writing for awhile. I don't want to miss any of this scenery. Odd, isn't it, how small and insignificant the houses and trees seem after France? Had you noticed, Jane?"

Without turning away from the window, Jane said, "Probably because the mountains dwarf everything else. Come look, quickly! See — down there on the lake shore — that modern villa? Corbu designed it."

Obligingly, the train slowed just then.

"What a setting!" I said. "And resting on those slender pillars ... it reminds me of ... of ...."

Jane supplied the word, "Of music?"

"Yes."

"I think so, too. That's what functionalism and sculpture add up to. Corbu's always quoting Schelling, 'Architecture is frozen music.'"

By then, the villa was out of sight. We sat down, and Jane gave me a sketchy biography of her mentor. He claimed to have had only one teacher, the one who taught him drawing and art history at a Swiss school. Painting and writing were his first loves. Travels through Italy and Greece allowed him to analyze firsthand the classical proportions of ancient structures, and to study the use of light and shadow. After the war, he moved to Paris. In 1922, he and his cousin, Jeanneret, opened an architectural studio in a former monastery on rue de Sevres.

They innovated the open floor plan — made possible by using posts for support instead of walls — and the flat roof for a garden. They put parks and playgrounds around their skyscrapers.

Near Bordeaux in 1926, they put up 40 houses for working people, financed by some corporation. The local authorities were so incensed by their unconventional use of color, they wouldn't connect the public water system to the houses for six years.

Jane shrugged. "Corbu has had to buck a lot of old diehards."

"Same old story," I said. "Most people just will not tolerate new ideas! But as Bernard Shaw said, it's good for people to be shocked once in a while. Shakes 'em up. I'm going to practice swimming against the current. It'll make me stronger. Hmm .... Looks like we'll soon be in Italy."

"How quickly the land has changed character — all those grapevines on the hillsides. We'll soon get to Brig. The guide book says the tunnel under the Simplon Pass is thirty-five minutes long. Shall we time it?"

"I thought Milan would be more modern," I said. "There's a lot of the 15th century still left here."

"And very little beyond the 19th," Jane commented.

"I love it. We have enough modern cities in the States. I like those built around a central square, where we can sit at a sidewalk café and, for a nickel, spend the whole evening admiring that incredible cathedral over there."

"Just think — five hundred years ago, it was much like this."

"Do you suppose the young men were as handsome and flirtatious then?"

"Could be," Jane said. "With centuries of practice, no wonder their flattery sounds convincing. The waiter last night, for example. The restaurant was of no consequence and neither were we, but he made me feel like a duchess."

"I'm going to like Italy," I said.

"We'd better keep reminding each other we're here to see the monuments. And don't forget, we'll have to get up early tomorrow if we want to look at Leonardo's Last Supper before we take off for Genoa."

We caught our train with a few minutes to spare. At first it appeared the compartment would be for us alone, but at the last moment, a well-dressed man carrying a briefcase paused in the doorway. He bowed slightly, said *"Permesso,"* and took a seat next to the door. An appropriate silence followed during which we scrutinized him, as he presumably evaluated us. Eventually, Jane said something to me about the passing landscape.

"Ah, *Signorine,* you are English?"

"No, American."

"I am very happy to be in your company, and that you have chosen to visit our *bella Italia.*"

We exchanged pleasantries, and then he said, "I am a publisher in Milano — of a newspaper."

"A fascist paper?" As soon as the words were out, I knew it was a silly question.

"But of course. There are no others." He smiled good-naturedly, opened his briefcase, and took out some pamphlets. "We shall bring back the glory that was Rome. The state is the source of all ethics and power. Here, let me give you this literature .... It is explained for you in English. The strong will govern the weak. You see, half our population cannot read or write. They will follow our Duce, especially when they realize the might of our military. The world will respect us. War ennobles, brings out the best in men and in women, too. Our women will give us many children. Youth belongs to us. We will educate them for combat, teach them to obey, and to hate the Bolsheviks. Strength is power."

Jane and I exchanged glances and I accepted the pamphlets. Neither of us wanted to encourage his discourse. Agreeing or even disagreeing with him would have done that.

"Excuse me," I said, and went out to the corridor. In a few moments, Jane came out, too.

"It's pretty frightening," she said, "how a leader with the gift of gab can control the emotions and minds of a whole country."

"How can we be sure it won't happen in the U.S. some day?"

In Honolulu, I had no idea what Fascism was — didn't remember ever hearing it mentioned. Everyone I knew was well off, blissful in a land of plenty. The Depression was merely a word, something that happened elsewhere.

But issues and events were forcing me to take sides What would I see on going back to the Islands? First of all, I'd look at things with different eyes. The outcome of the Massey case was partly responsible for that. And I'd learned that in a democracy, every adult citizen had the right to vote for those who made the laws we'd have to obey. In Hawaii, as Gordon had pointed out, we paid federal taxes, but we were not represented in Congress. The land I thought was a democracy was not.

I could not go back and pretend I didn't know those things. Would I *have* to return? It appeared so. My father had much less work. Mama wasn't well. My brother, George, was at Cal studying architecture, two younger brothers had to be educated, and little Joan hadn't even started school. Was my profession imperative? Only men's careers were. Women were supposed to marry. That wasn't Mama's philosophy, but it was Pop's, and he was the source of my funds.

The likelihood of another Prince John coming to rescue me in his Chrysler roadster was pretty dim. So, what would be my doom? People wouldn't come right out and call me a rebel, but find subtle ways to punish me if I didn't conform. To pass muster I'd have to become a housewife and mother and, most of all, keep my critical opinions to myself. In that mindless reality, I'd either turn into an alcoholic or abandon my family and run off to Vienna ... or Paris.

But wait! I already lived in Paris. I wouldn't have to desert anyone. I'd have only to find a way to stay there. Others did, and so could I!

Chapter Twenty-Seven

My mind kept repeating, "I'm a free spirit. I don't have to desert anyone. I'll have many Aprils in Paris."

The docks of Genoa lured us down to the busy port to sketch the big ships and small fishing craft. The city towered in the background. Inevitably, we included a few homespun fishermen in the drawings, and they demonstrated their approval by showing us where to have the best dinner of fresh sardines.

Jane and I talked of only lighthearted matters. Even on our visit to the old Genoa cemetery up on the hill the next morning, we couldn't take the sculptures seriously. We meant no disrespect for the departed souls, only for the monuments on their graves. Life-size marble statues immortalized the dead — there they were, sitting in their favorite positions, or playing hide-and-seek with angels, while God and cherubs peeked down from Heaven. Every stone wrinkle, hair, and stitch of a needle was in place.

On the train to Pisa, we asked each other in what pose we would like posterity to capture us. Jane couldn't decide, but I chose to be remembered sunbathing on a sandy beach — in the nude, of course.

Going south to Rome, Jane suggested we stop off at Lucca. "In Etruscan times, it was an important town, full of ancient buildings, but so small we can see it all in one morning. The cathedral was begun 1,300 years ago."

After checking our suitcases at the Lucca station, we walked the hot archaic streets for several hours, peering down cool alleys while Jane pointed out chronologically the many styles of architecture, and I pretended to pay attention. Finally, all the church bells tolled the hour of noon, reminding the faithful that it was time to eat.

"Haven't we seen enough?" I asked. "I'm hungry, tired and awfully thirsty."

"You're right. Everything's closing now, anyway. And there are restaurants everywhere. How about this one?"

Over a door with a bead curtain, a simple wooden sign said *Trattoria Dino*. Inside, the temperature was refreshing — even more so in the shady back garden. How Italian — to linger over our meal and savor the wine with no hurry. Our train for Rome didn't leave till 4:15, so we ordered another carafe of wine. When at last we finished and stepped innocently out onto the sidewalk, the July sun was waiting. Projectiles of white heat struck us pitilessly, blow after blow.

Jane moaned. "Oh, my head! What are we going to do?"

"Over there," I said. "The ramparts with trees. At least we can sit in the shade awhile."

Dragging our shadows behind us, we staggered the fifty yards to the old earthworks that once had enclosed the town and kept out enemies. A park had been laid out on top, some thirty feet above street level, with shady trees and, to our delight, benches on either side of a broad gravel path.

Jane sat down on the first bench we came to and kicked off her shoes. I hobbled to one farther on. Ah! I had found the Garden of Eden. Oh, Bacchus, you seductive rogue, you irresistible knave ... you .... Sleep!

Blessed slumber subdued my prostrate body to restore the depleted energy for an hour, and another ... and then I awoke abruptly. A hand was shaking my shoulder, and a hoarse voice was saying, "*Signorina. Signorina ....*"

An old man with a shaggy beard stood beside me. What did he want? My purse! It was still under my head. "Go away!" I shouted as I jumped to my feet and ran. "Jane, Jane! Wake up!"

We got to our train with only minutes to spare. Still somewhat unnerved, but safe in a compartment, I had to laugh.

"That poor old man. He didn't want to rob me. He was another angel, sent so we wouldn't miss our train. We're in good hands and can finish our naps in peace. We won't get to Rome for four hours."

Pensione Giuliana
Rome
Wed., July 12, 1932

Dearest All of You,

I'll bet you didn't know that our word "travel" comes from the French "travail," which means work. Long ago, getting from one place to another was toil and trouble, but not today.

Italy is all I dreamed it would be, and so are the Italians. We've met only one Fascist — perhaps more — but just one who tried to convert us. I can't imagine these people putting up for long with a leader who glorifies war. They love the gentle pursuits too much for that, are passionate about the arts, and proud of the contributions to culture they've made for over 2,000 years.

Take the Pantheon, for example. Begun in 27 B.C., it's still in fine condition. Until recently, its dome was the largest ever built, and no one yet knows the technique they used to support the enormous vault. Up at the top is a small opening, a 27-foot "eye" that floods the interior with so much light, no other windows are necessary.

Of course we've been to the Vatican and have seen Michelangelo's Sistine Chapel and Raphael's murals. This while dodging guided groups of American tourists. We overheard two girls who discussed the famous ceiling and agreed it was "not so hot."

A mother and young son were visiting the Colosseum while we were there. The boy was saying, "Gee, our stadium at home is much bigger." Imagine comparing his football field with an arena built twenty centuries ago!

Human beings are as varied and edifying as the monuments we travel to see — never two of a kind. We should study people more. It is they who make things, and will write tomorrow's history and legends.

Last evening was a refreshing change. An old friend of Gordon's called on us, Bill Holford, who's here on an architectural fellowship. We went to a rustic wine cellar and talked till late. Too bad we didn't meet him earlier. He's our sort of person. It takes all kinds.... What a lark! One caper after another ....

With love to you all,

Sisi

Chapter Twenty-Eight

When Nature planned the regions of Umbria and Tuscany, she painted the earth lavishly with rich shades of brown, and modeled the hills after the breasts of women so the men would love the land and tend it with devotion.

When I first began spattering with paints, I discovered a mellow brown called "burnt umber" and wondered how it got its name. Near Siena, in Tuscany, the soil was of buff tones called "raw" or "burnt" siena. I had come to the source.

How could such a land not generate artists? The few who didn't sing or paint or sculpt or compose poetry and music, nourished those who did with their encouragement. And I was there, breathing the air Leonardo and Saint Francis breathed, and drinking the fruit of Medici vineyards. Would that make me an artist, too? Assisi, Perugia, Siena. Each, in turn, was my favorite city. I knew why they were cherished by the Muses. Even their names ... the sound of them was poetry. Then Florence stole my heart. There, astride the Arno River, was proof that to be wealthy I didn't have to own the wonders I saw: the jewels on the Old Bridge, the clothes on the via Tornabuoni, the paintings in the Uffizi Gallery or any of the palaces. Luxury was not the possession of money or property. It was *being aware of living with beauty.* What was it Madame Scheyer said to me at Kahana?

"Most people look and don't see. They are the poor ones of this splendid Earth."

In Tuscany refinement was the mother and father of the Renaissance and in the blood that gave Florentines direction.

One day, walking along a bystreet with very narrow sidewalks, a boy of twelve or so came toward me carrying a large basket of wine bottles on his shoulders. One of us would have to give way.

I started to step down onto the street to let him pass. But no, it was he who stopped, backed into a doorway, even bowed slightly and smiled as he said, "*Signorina.*" A prince could not have been more gallant.

Pensione Norchi
Florence
July 26, 1932

Dearest All,

I've been seduced ... by this city. We have to leave for Venice tomorrow, but one day I'll come back here. To live. I know I will, and be a thread of this incredible fabric of history. But not till Mussolini's gone.

Long before Romulus and Remus, the Etruscans were here with their gifted hands. Over the centuries, Italy has been invaded from Spain, from Africa, from the north and the east, by tyrants and benevolent despots. Eventually they died or were conquered while the Muses smiled and bided their time. Mussolini, too, will pass.

(Have you noticed, Mom, how intellectual and even philosophical I'm becoming?)

Jane and I have spent ten days at this pensione in a room overlooking the Arno. The river runs green, like celadon, colored by the clay in its bed. The hills beyond are dotted with buff-toned villas with red-tiled roofs, and rows of cypresses, like a painting of the Middle Ages that changes as the sun moves across the sky.

You may be sure we have been good explorers — talked to a lot of people as well as poked into corners where there are few tourists.

Tomorrow will be one year since I left Honolulu. I'm not homesick yet. I've bought presents for all of you and mailed them this morning.

With hugs and kisses,

Sisi

P.S. Yesterday while sitting at a café, we eavesdropped on two American women going over their guidebooks and maps. Suddenly the older one said to the other, "Tell me, Phyllis .... Venice .... have we been to Venice yet?"

"Of course, Mother! You remember — that's where we had that heavenly omelette."

Venice, July 31

I don't know about the omelettes, but Venice is heavenly. How can anyone ever forget having been here?

There's not much time for writing. Actually, seeing life on the squares and canals, and the colorful sails of the fishing boats, is what we've been doing most.

We took a boat to the Bienniale Exhibition. It's set in a botanical garden that has lots of tropical trees and plants — hibiscus, oleanders, date palms. Zadkine's work is displayed very well. Each of 13 countries has a separate pavilion, showing painting, sculpture and decorative arts.

Early yesterday morning we sailed down the lagoon to spend the day at Chioggia, a little fishing village Corbu recommended. We had paper, paints, bathing suits and a lunch of fruit and cookies. A small boy in rags and yellow curls attached himself to us when we got off the boat and made us understand he wanted to watch us paint. He led us past houses where young women sat in their doorways making lace, to an isolated beach and waited while we had a swim.

The water of the Adriatic was warm and not a bit salty. While we painted, he looked on with intense curiosity and then, when we gave him a bar of chocolate, he was so happy he jumped up and down. Instead of eating it, he ran off, probably to share it with his siblings. We didn't see him again till late afternoon when we started back to the village. He escorted us across the uncrowded streets, saying what we understood to be, "Be careful of the automobiles." Actually, there were very few cars or pedestrians.

The boat trip back was spectacular as the setting sun made more vivid the yellow, orange and brown sails of the fishing craft against the deep blue of the water.

This morning Jane's sunburn is pretty bad. Several blisters developed on her shoulders. Wearing clothes must be distressful, but she never grumbles about anything.

More later.

CHAPTER TWENTY-EIGHT

Trieste
Wed. August 3, 1932

It's all over.

At 5:00 p.m., Jane steamed away on the S.S. Saturnia. I'm going to miss her. Tomorrow morning I'll be on the train heading for Paris. I now have an incurable hankering to see beyond other borders.

Trieste is a commercial town with hills and a modern port. Everyone speaks German as well as Italian. It belonged to Austria-Hungary until 1919 — clean and orderly as they.

The ride back to Paris will be twenty-three hours long — time enough to evaluate what I've seen in terms of what it's done to me.

What survives of a civilization is its culture, and its arts, the mortar that holds us all together through the ages, regardless of wars and pestilence and demagogs. Nations that hope to survive should nurture their creative talents more then their armies.

I've sent Harry a card telling him I'll cook dinner for him on Friday.

There's one Italian stamp left in my purse, so I'll mail this before I leave Italy.

With love to you all,

Sisi

August in Paris was nothing like April. When I arrived, the train station was crowded with people abandoning the city for their annual stay at the seashore, the mountains, or their native villages. Many shops would be closed and tourists would be everywhere. How hot it was! I started to get into a taxi but remembered my budget and took the subway, instead. Henceforth, I'd have to watch every *centime.*

It was still early when I reached Jocelyn's studio. *Madame la concièrge* awaited me with a pile of letters and the key. The morning passed in a few minutes. I unpacked, washed my clothes and myself, rearranged some of the furniture, read my mail, and called Harry.

"I got your card," he said, "and can't wait to see you tonight."

"It's good to be home again, Harry."

"*Home,* is it?"

"You bet. I can't go back to the boondocks after this."

"I see! Now, don't you keep me waiting tonight. My treat, not yours.

159

Come to the bank before closing time, and we'll go some place special. I want to hear all about it."

Good old Harry. But before evening, I had someone else to see — someone I wanted to be with more than anyone. Had he thought of me? Maybe he had made new friends and wouldn't care? When we said good-bye, he had held my hand a bit longer than necessary and said, "Hurry back — I'll be waiting." But any polite person would have done the same. He might have gone away. Le Corbusier was surely out of town and may have closed the office. In that case, what would I do? I knew he had a room in a student hotel off St. Michèle, but I had no idea which one.

Down Boulevard Raspail I walked, thinking I might find myself alone, and having to start over again making friends. Oh well. Zadkine would be back in September, and I could devote all my time to work. But I did not want a life of only work. I knew perfectly well what I wanted and was on my way to find it.

I came to rue de Sevres and, at No. 35, turned down a passage between two buildings that led to a former monastery in the heart of the block. One flight up, Le Corbusier had adapted a wing of the sanctuary to accommodate the needs of his architectural firm. I passed his empty office and came to the studio. The door was open, so I went in. There was no sound of voices in the vast, sunlit room. Several drafting tables in a row, side by side, virtually filled the long narrow space. Was no one there?

Down at the far end, a blond head was bent over a drawing board — François'— but he was not aware I had come in. Cupid's wings fanned my flushing cheeks.

"Bon jour, mon vieux!" I called.

He turned and saw me, dropped his pencil, stood up, and stared, while I waited, not daring to breathe. Then, with arms outstretched, he bounded toward me. I ran to him. Our bodies met and we held each other close for a long time.

At last, in a voice hoarse with emotion, he whispered, "Thank God you're back at last .... You don't know how I've missed you."

Chapter Twenty-Nine

At eight o'clock that evening, Harry and I sat down to dinner at Chez Maurice. The waiter approached us with the wine list, but Harry brushed it aside saying, "For now, just bring us a bottle of your best champagne." Then, with a grin, he turned to me. "That's to celebrate the stars in your eyes. You can't hide them, you know."

I just sat there, blushing, not knowing what to say.

"Come on," he cajoled, "out with it. Cheer up your old Dutch uncle. Do I know him?"

I shook my head. The waiter returned just then and, as he filled our goblets, I tried in vain to put some words together.

Harry clinked his glass to mine and said, "Here's to young love — may it never grow old."

"But he and I haven't even mentioned the word *love*."

Harry chortled. "That's a good sign. It shows the plight is mutually understood."

"Plight?"

"Oh ... just a joke. The Greeks, I understand, offer condolences when two people fall in love."

"But you aren't a misanthrope, are you?"

"I have nothing against love. On the contrary. Only ... sometimes it leads to marriage, and that can be ruinous. You don't know I once had a wife. She didn't like Paris and left me. Probably didn't like me, either. But that doesn't mean yours won't last."

"The question isn't going to arise. I decided long ago that marriage is not for me."

I told him how my sister's stillborn singing career had motivated me, about Zadkine's divorce, and how Anne's sister-in-law had run away to Vienna.

"And how does your young man feel?"

"I've no idea. For now, we're just glad to have each other's company. He's an architect — one of those I saw a lot of. You know, I've told you about them .... But we didn't pair off then. Now the others are gone, and he and I are the only ones left here in Paris. This afternoon,

I dropped in at the office where he works. We had lunch and then took a walk along the river — just talking — mostly about Italy. I've invited him to dinner tomorrow. Why don't you come, too, and meet him?"

"Thanks a lot, but I'm taking Sonya to a concert. Maybe one day next week. Here, let's have some more champagne then we'll order dinner. So — you don't want to settle down and have a family."

"In Honolulu, I'd be expected to, but not here."

"Will your father go on supporting you?"

"Business isn't very good for him. I'll have to economize this year. Maybe I can sell some sculpture soon. The Depression won't last forever."

"As a foreigner, you can't legally get a job in France, you know, but you might find some part-time work. The so-called old-fashioned young lady would get married in order to be supported."

"Ha, ha. Another of your jokes, I suppose. In my opinion, that would be the hard way. Besides, he's even poorer than I."

"Of course, all students are poor. In Paris it's traditional. *La vie Bohème* and all that."

"He's a real one — from Bohemia."

"No kidding. A Czech, huh? How poetic."

"Yes. His home is in Pilsen. His father has a stationery store and a factory that makes bicycle chains. He's tall and handsome with curly blond hair and he's twenty-five years old and passionate about music."

"Of course — all Slavs like music. So, who needs money with all those qualities? How well I remember. Once upon a time, I was young and poor and in love."

He reached across the table and clasped both of my hands. "Go ahead, Agnès, don't ever miss a chance to love. The world has so little of it. There's lots of marriage and fornication, but those things don't necessarily relate to love."

If the waiter hadn't approached then, Harry may have given way to his feelings, and I'd have been crying, too. While he ordered, I wondered what the Fates had devised for him. For the first time, he let me peek through a tiny crack in his heart — a heart that had been broken, perhaps a long time ago, and still had not completely healed. Conferring with the waiter, he was a man in charge — nonchalant and confident.

162

"*Merci, monsieur.*" The waiter bowed and left.

"I hope you're hungry, my dear. I'm famished. You've told a lot about your young man, but not his name."

"It's François."

"But that's French, not Bohemian."

"I know. But his name in Czech is difficult to pronounce. He likes François better, and so do I."

"Besides, who would be able to spell it? So ... you're never going to get married?"

"Not if I can help it. I guess I've become addicted to my independence. I wouldn't like to give it up."

"And you wouldn't mind being called an old maid?"

"Surely you've heard the well-worn pun: Spinsters are born, not made. I object to the double standard. No one calls a *man* names if he doesn't marry, and if a woman goes to bed with someone other than her husband, *she's* disreputable, not he. Men like it that way."

"Not *all* men. Don't include me in that, please."

"You're enlightened, Harry. Have you ever read Thorstein Veblen? You must have!"

"Oh, sure, the fellow who invented the term 'conspicuous consumption.' He explained how husbands want their wives to be unemployed clotheshorses to show off the male affluence. But Max Weber blamed it on Protestant morality. Add guilt, he said, and you keep men slaving at their jobs and women hog-tied to the home. It's all a matter of being conditioned from the cradle. Oh, good, here's the *garçon* with our *hors d'oeuvres.*"

The first course didn't distract Harry from his premise. He went on, "Only when you have learned to doubt what you've been taught to believe, are you on the way to emancipation ...."

Through most of dinner, we stayed on the subject, considering the influence advertising experts had on our daily lives. They glamorized women polishing furniture, changing diapers and greeting their men with a smile when they came home from the office. And all the movies ended with marriage and happiness forever after ....

There was nothing new about what he said, but the fact that Harry, a sophisticated banker, would spell it out for me, for *me*, who was still in the elementary school of life, was significant.

"Today," he reminded me, "each woman has to fight her battle alone. Someday, there'll be so many of you wanting the same thing, you'll join forces, and your granddaughters won't understand what your struggle was all about."

Indeed. Over half a century later, that conversation may sound stale but is still valid. In 1932, I needed the reassurance because I was preparing for the genesis of a love affair that I might be too naive to handle.

Chapter Thirty

Saturday morning I spent thinking of what Harry and I had discussed. I tried not to feel jittery about seeing François again. Just the two of us ... what would we talk about? Yesterday had been easy because he wanted to hear all about Italy, but that subject was pretty well exhausted. Oh well ... no sense in worrying.

Dinner would be simple — a variation of what Anne and I had perfected: soup made of a lot of vegetables cooked with a piece of meat. After that, cheese — Brie, perhaps — and some fruit. *Voila!* We'd go out for coffee, of course, and take a long walk. Paris was made for walking. Her sidewalks were broad, shop windows entrancing, and the people at the cafés more entertaining than some movies.

When I opened the door for François, he waved a bottle of wine in the air, set it down on the coal bin, grabbed me off the floor, and swung me around.

"It's true! You really are back. I was afraid I might have dreamt it." He let my feet touch the floor but kept one arm on my shoulders while he reconnoitered the studio. "What an *atelier!* You have space, light, not too much furniture ... inexpensive, I hope."

"Very. Plus the luxury of a bathroom and kitchen and being right in the neighborhood — near everything. I'm three minutes from Zadkine's and two minutes from the Grande Chaumiere. I'm thinking of going back there for a few weeks, till Zadkine comes home. I'm so eager to get to work again."

"Italy really lit you up. It shows in your eyes. They've never sparkled like that before. Was it as hot there as here? Let me tell you what I've been thinking. How would you like to go swimming?"

"Where? In the Seine? With all that muck and garbage?"

"No. In the nice, clean, salty water of the English Channel."

"But that's hours away."

"So? We could leave next Friday evening, get there at dawn on Saturday and be back early Monday morning. We'll have two full days in the sun and fresh air."

"What about the expense of a hotel? François, if I'm going to spend another year in Paris, I'll have to be very thrifty."

"Who needs a hotel? If the weather's good, we can sleep under the stars, and if it rains, well, maybe a farmer will rent us some space in a barn. Here — have some poor-man's champagne."

He handed me a glass of white *vin ordinaire* from the bottle he had brought. "Shall we drink to next weekend by the sea? You know you want to go."

How could I refuse? Economize? I would become an expert in the art of saving — doing my own laundry, walking more often than riding. Necessity would devise other ways. I wouldn't enroll at the Grande Chaumière. Jocelyn had two turntables right here in the studio. I'd have only to buy some clay, and my imagination would do the rest.

During that next week, François and I became well acquainted. Every evening, we had supper together, coffee at some terrace café, and strolled through the warm night air. He told me of his childhood in Pilsen, when the Great War waged, when Austria-Hungary broke up and Czechoslovakia became an autonomous republic. Even though his father was well off, they didn't always have enough to eat. His mother was beautiful and gentle and played the piano — especially Chopin — with sensitivity. Then she died, and his father remarried. He didn't have sufficient love for his new wife *and* three children, so François' sister drew close to her two younger brothers. When she married, the boys spent more time at her house than at their father's.

"You'd like her," he said, "and my friend, Boba, too. He and I have been best friends since elementary school. All through university, in Prague, we were together, especially in the summer. Every year we used to take our canoes up the Moldau River by train to a place called Budweiser and paddle our way downstream, even over the rapids, camping on the shore at night .... That was great sport — being free in the wilds for a couple of weeks. You'd like that ...."

The nostalgia in his voice told me more than his words. "Will you be going back home one of these days?" I asked, afraid of what the answer might be.

"I don't want to, but perhaps I must. Corbu doesn't pay us enough to live on. We're considered students, you see. Besides, we know he doesn't earn a great deal. My father has been sending me a small allowance. He could well afford to give me more, but at my age, he thinks, I should be in business for myself — as he was. If I go back, I'll have to do a supplementary year of military service, and I'll be damned if I will. I'm against war. It's only the arms manufacturers who win. The people always lose."

"So what'll you do?"

"Well, I don't have to decide just yet. Something may turn up. What about you, Agnès? How long will you be in Paris?"

"My mother is in favor of my staying as long as I want to, but my father is a builder and there's not much construction in Honolulu now. Maybe if Roosevelt is elected in November, business will get better. I'll make it through the winter, anyway."

"I had no idea," he said. "I thought you had all the money you wanted ... private lessons with Zadkine, driving through France, and a month in Italy ...."

"I'm afraid that's all in the past — except Zadkine. From now on, I'm going to tighten my belt. No more trips."

"No?" His blue eyes sparkled. "Not even a weekend on the Channel coast? You wouldn't let me go there all alone, would you? Besides, I want to see if a Hawaiian swims better than a Czech — or if you can swim at all."

Chapter Thirty-One

On Friday, we got the almost-midnight train for Dieppe. At that hour, there were few travelers, and we had no difficulty finding an empty compartment.

"A whole bench for each of us to stretch out on. Are you tired, Agnès?"

"A little. But I doubt I'll be able to sleep much. The nights are so short now, and I want to see the dawn."

"I like the mornings, too," François said. "They remind me that

I'm young — that we're young — and ...." He didn't finish the sentence.

Did I know what he was going to say? "... and have many years ahead of us." ... of *us?* Did he feel as I did? I couldn't ask him, so I changed the subject.

"I was just thinking of where I was a year ago," I said. "It seems like decades since then .... So much has changed in my life."

"Weren't you in Paris?"

"I didn't get here till late September. Last August, I was in Canada for a month, with the family of a friend, the one who persuaded me to come to Paris." I thought François might ask who the friend was, but he didn't. I was grateful for that. John was a private part of my life.

"When did you come to France?" I asked.

"Oh, it was early spring of last year. For the first few weeks, I was a tourist. Then Corbu agreed to let me work with him. Gordon, Jane and Alex were already there in the office. I wonder how it's going to be without them."

The conductor came by then and checked our tickets. *"Merci,"* he said. *"Bon nuit.* Good night."

When he'd gone, I yawned, and so did François. "We'd better get some sleep," he said.

Day was breaking as I awoke. In the corridor, François stood at an open window. "Come, quick," he called to me, "and get a whiff of this salty air. We'll be in Dieppe in a couple of minutes."

At five a.m., in the pale grey of dawn, we saw a bakery near the station, where an old man was unstacking its ovens and loading fresh loaves into a truck. We bought some ambrosial rolls, ate them with coffee at the bar next door, and headed south on a footpath along the cliff.

From a green plateau, we looked straight down to a strip of a rocky strand. Where the outgoing tide exposed large areas of seaweed and reef, several people with sticks prodded for shellfish trapped in shallow pools of the rugged shore. Fishing boats with sails pink in the sunrise, headed into the channel.

At many places, gulches, worn by age-old streams running out to the sea, interrupted the bluff. One of them, a broad ravine, cradled a resort named Pourville with a few expensive-looking hotels, charming and chic, but not for us. We did, however, wade in the river up to our knees before continuing southward.

Six kilometers farther, at the next gulch, we climbed up its slope to the tableland. There a sign indicated that beyond the green fields and woods, we'd come to Varangeville. What went by that name was no more than a crossroads with three houses and one general store. Two other couples said they had been looking more than an hour to find lodging, with no luck.

At least dinner would be a certainty. We could eat there, at the store, the proprietress told us, if we'd come back in two hours.

"I guess we'll have to make a nest in the woods," François said, "Are you good at it, Agnès?"

"You'll have to teach me. In the meantime, let's go and watch the tide come in."

We stayed at the cliff's edge till dinner time. On the way back to Varangeville, it began to rain.

"There goes our reverie of romance under the stars," François remarked. "Now, what'll we do?"

"Look!" I said. "Beyond that clump of trees ... a farmhouse. I'll race you!"

A little out of breath, we reached the rustic cottage and knocked on the door. A husky young man in working clothes opened it. Behind him, at the dining table, his wife and two small children were eating.

François apologized for interrupting their meal, and asked, "Can you rent us a room for the night? We'll get wet if we sleep out of doors and they have no room at the inn."

"*Je regret beaucoup ....*" said the farmer, "I regret very much, but we have no extra space we could let you have."

"A blanket, then?" I asked. "Could you rent us a blanket?"

His wife said something in a dialect, to which he replied, "*Mais, pourquoi pas?* But yes, why not?"

With a sportive smile he turned to us. "If you don't mind being a bit rustic, you may have a blanket and sleep in the hayloft."

Did we mind? He could see we did not.

"*Très bien,*" he said. "Come back before dark, and I'll show you where everything is."

We hurried through the woods back to the store to find it packed with other hungry weekenders. The woman we spoke with earlier fluttered about, using all the spare hands God gives every housewife in such circumstances. It was a simple feast: generous portions of peas, tomatoes, bread, cheese and wine, served with unsophisticated informality by the landlady.

The tables were cleared, but no one left because the rain fell harder. Someone started playing his accordion, and as he played, those who knew the words sang along. All of us drank wine and, before long, were singing even without knowing the words.

Darkness had nearly fallen when the rain finally stopped. François said the farmer would be expecting us. We bade our companions a good night, left the store, and took the path into the woods.

Whether it was the twilight that altered the shapes of certain land-marks, or the wine, or a combination of the two, it didn't matter. We went too far before turning off. Soon, we were trying a dozen paths of the labyrinth with no light — not even a moon. Another adventure. Eventually, we found our way. The farmer greeted us good-naturedly, handed us a blanket, and led the way to the barnyard.

"Here's the well where you will draw water for drinking and wash-ing, and over there is the stepladder." Our host placed it so the top rested on the opening of the hayloft. "I won't need to come up with you," he added. "I'll just wish you a good repose and we'll see one another tomorrow."

We thanked him and climbed up to the loft where the air was warm and hushed and perfumed with farmyard smells — new and exotic scents to me. I had never before been on an authentic farm. And, as though that wasn't enough, I was about to share my idyllic bower with François. François!

"I'll bet you're tired," he said, as we puffed up the hay and spread the blanket over it. "Fatigue makes the most comfortable bed. It's been a long day."

I was more than tired. All that wine must have had something to do with the weight in my head. How good it was to lie down. François was saying what a beautiful day it had been. "... even the rough times — like when we were lost in the woods. Were you afraid?"

"A bit. When it began to seem hopeless."

"Oh, my poor little Gretel." He turned over onto his side and put an arm around my shoulder. "And you didn't tell me. I'd have com-forted you."

I knew he was teasing, but I blushed nevertheless. He drew me closer — as I wanted him to do — wishing we could hold each other even tighter than on that day in his office ... and never let go. But a part of me warned, "Be cautious! Remember Bacchus and the ramparts in Lucca!"

His lips found my forehead, my eyelids, my cheeks and then my lips. I pushed him away gently.

"Please, François, please ...."

"What's wrong?" he whispered. "Why not?"

"Because ...."

"You do care about me, Agnès. You can't deny it."

"It's because I care so much. It's the wine, François. I've had too much. Please ... I'm not myself."

For a few moments he held me closer and kissed my cheeks. Then he released me and took one of my hands in both of his. We didn't say any more. He held my hand in silence till sleep overcame us.

I slept until morning. When I awoke, François stood in the sunlit opening of the loft rubbing his bare arms and chest with a towel.

"Hello, François."

He came over and sat on the blanket beside me. "I've been down to the well. The morning is dazzling." He ran his fingers through my hair. "Like your tresses. Silken threads of gold. I wish you could wear it down all the time — like the Valkerie."

I couldn't help giggling, perhaps to hide my embarrassment.

"I'm glad to hear you laughing. I thought I might have offended you last night. Are we still friends, then?"

"Silly questions deserve silly answers. Here, help me up while I think of one."

He took my outstretched hands and hoisted me to the floor.

It was still early when we returned the blanket, neatly folded, to the farmer's wife. Graciously, she offered us a cup of coffee.

"No, thank you, Madame," said François, "But if you wouldn't mind, we'd like to leave our passports with you while we're at the beach. We're catching a late bus for Dieppe."

"*Certainment,*" she said. "Look, I'll put them here in this drawer of the sideboard. They'll be safe. *Au revoir.* Enjoy yourselves."

In every respect the day was cloudless — at least most of it was. We waded, swam, sunbathed, ate picnic-style, and chatted with other weekenders. From them we learned that the best place to have a fish dinner was in Dieppe, and that was why we decided to get an earlier bus, the one that left at six o'clock.

But when we returned to the farmer's cottage to pick up our passports, there was no one at home and the house was locked.

"This is Sunday, remember," François said as, for the umpteenth time, he peered in through the windows. "They've probably gone off to grandmother's for dinner and won't be back for hours. We did tell them we were taking a late bus. Well, there's only one thing to do."

He took out his pocket knife. "I'll remove one of these small panes of glass by chipping away the putty, put my hand in and unlatch the window, crawl inside, and get our passports. I'll leave a note of explanation with some francs to cover the damage and their hospitality."

While François went through all the steps of housebreaking, his moll nervously stood lookout till he was safely back and had replaced the pane.

François replacing farmhouse window pane, Varangeville, France - 1932; Photo by Agnès.

Chapter Thirty-Two

Because friends of my parents were in town and I was obliged to visit with them, I didn't see François for two days — two entire days that seemed like weeks. But when on Wednesday we talked on the phone, he had not forgotten the seafood dinner we'd been deprived of in Dieppe.

"I'll bring everything else this evening," he said, "if you go to the market and get some fish."

With arms loaded, he arrived after work, and together we prepared the salad, fried the potatoes and steamed the trout. It wasn't till I set the table that I noticed there was no wine. Oh, well. I could live without it and, if he'd forgotten, I didn't want to embarrass him. Candles — they would help. I found four, put two on the table and two on the coal bin, so we didn't need electric lights.

The meal was superb, even grand, with music from Jocelyn's phonograph. François chose Brahms — Symphony No. 1 in C Minor. Every once in awhile, he put up his hand and whispered, "Ssh .... Pay attention to this passage. Isn't it exquisite?" and we'd stop eating to listen.

When the piece was over, he threw back his head and sighed. "Music fuels my heart. Without it, I would wither."

"In Honolulu," I said, "we're at a disadvantage. The only official group of instrumentalists we have are in the city brass band. Occasionally, a famous musician drops in and gives a concert. It has to be held in a school auditorium because we've nothing better. And it's a social, more than a cultural event. When the newspapers write it up, they describe the gowns the elite women wore, and the parties given before and after in honor of the maestro."

François screwed up his face with derision. "Come on. Don't be ridiculous."

"It's true, François!"

"But you're no dummy where music is concerned. You must have heard some before you came to Paris?"

"Of course I did. Don't forget I have a mother and sister who sing classical stuff. And we have a pianola."

"What on Earth is that?"

"It's a regular piano, but with an attachment, a mechanism. You insert a paper roll that has perforations of different lengths and positions, and then there are pedals that move pneumatic gadgets when pumped. Somehow, air is released through the perforations and that makes the hammers strike the keys, or something."

"And how does it sound? Like a circus calliope?"

"Not at all! I'll have you know that, with your eyes closed, you'd never guess it was not a virtuoso playing."

"Hmm .... I see." François stroked his chin. "Well, some invention! You Americans are clever with contraptions. I mean that."

"Every time my mother went shopping, she'd come home with a new roll. Otherwise I'd never have known the great composers. I remember when I was young — about nine or ten — I was determined to be a dancer, so I played Gounod's *Faust* over and over while I made up elaborate routines. I didn't read the story of Faust and Marguerite till years later, but I knew all the music when I was little."

"No kidding! When I was a boy, I wanted to be a conductor. I used to tramp through the house pretending to lead the orchestra of the last concert we'd attended, and whenever I heard my mother at the piano, I was right there directing her.

"I'll never forget one time, years later, when I was doing my military service. I couldn't get to a concert that had Beethoven's 'Seventh' on the program. You may not believe this but, that night in the barracks, while sitting on my cot, I actually heard in my head the entire symphony, from beginning to end. Every instrument, every note, every pause ... everything. When it was over, I fell asleep, exhausted."

François' eyes met mine. For several pivotal moments, we exchanged silent declarations of accord. We knew, then, how the evening would end.

After coffee, François asked if I'd show him the sculpture I'd started. It was under an oilcloth and damp rags — the pair of dancers I began one afternoon to the accompaniment of a jazz record.

He rubbed his hands together. "Gee! The rhythm shows. Brava! You must complete it. But for now, let's make more music. How about a waltz?" From a pile of discs, he selected one of Strauss'.

"And may I have the pleasure of the next dance, Mademoiselle?"

Almost a year before, we first waltzed together in that crowded little *boîte de nuit*. Now, as we held each other in the classical posture, the humble *atelier* was transformed into a marble hall. There was space for the voluminous skirt of my satin gown to ripple as we swept the room in tempo. Surrounding the ballroom floor, splendid gentlemen and bejeweled ladies watched us with admiration and envy from their red plush chairs, as we floated effortlessly under brilliant candelabra in our enchanted world. Finally the orchestra stopped playing, but the magic continued.

In the center of the great hall, my handsome cavalier held me close, oblivious of the onlookers, and whispered, "I have you now, and I won't let you escape. I'm going to kiss you, and this time, you cannot say you've had too much wine. Or didn't you notice I brought none?"

"I noticed ... but .... " I gave in to his embrace. "I'm still not responsible for what I do ... you have intoxicated me ...."

The evening ended at seven o'clock in the morning.

70 bis, rue Notre Dame des Champs,
Paris
August 28, 1932

Dearest Mom and Family,

Summer in Paris is not a bit dull, and I'm awfully happy. I've been swimming in the English Channel and working on a new sculpture in Jocelyn's studio.

Anne is in Vienna and might spend the winter there. Gertrude has fallen in love in Budapest. She was visiting briefly with Anne when she met her ideal man. Isn't it wonderful? I can imagine how happy she is.

Every afternoon from 2:00 to 7:00, I go sketching at the Grande Chaumière. Zadkine told me to keep working from live figures. During the breaks, I often draw the people around me in the class — the sketchers. There are all sorts, and some are strange.

Submissions to the Autumn Salon must be in next month. Each person may present four pieces of which the jury will select no more than two. I'm going to send in my first sculpture — the man's head in stone.

I'm learning new ways to economize — laundry, for example. I wash one sheet at a time in the bathtub and let it drip on a line above the tub. When it's almost dry, I fold it carefully and put it on the seat of the straight chair I usually sit on. In two days, anyone would think it had been ironed. And my hankies and other small flat pieces I plaster dripping wet on the edge of the bathtub and they, too, look ironed when dry.

Having no telephone helps my budget but doesn't isolate me from the world. My friends call the concierge and she either takes a message or, if I'm home, has me come to the phone.

Concierges are ministering spirits. Ours is about forty — fat, jolly and handsome. She and her husband live in a couple of rooms close to the entrance of our block of ateliers. At a decent hour, she locks the wrought-iron gate that separates our garden from the street. Anyone wanting to come in after that time has to pull a knob on the pillar beside the gate. That rings a bell in her quarters and she calls out, "Who's there?" If it's not a resident, she wants to know the person's business and, if she approves, pulls a cord that releases the gate lock. She is also janitor and general trouble-shooter, as well as an artist at discretion. It's said that France would collapse if the institution were discontinued.

I don't feel like a foreigner anymore even though I'm still not expert in the language. After all, my roots are European, remember. I'm reading history and philosophy now as a pastime. Everyone here is so well educated, I'm trying to catch up.

With love to all,
Sisi

P.S. War between Germany and France seems inevitable. The question is not if but when. There are posters throughout the city telling the French to beware of the "Bosches" (their derogatory term for Germans) and recalling how many times this nation has been invaded by them.

Chapter Thirty-Three

The world — *my* world — was changing. Even cloudy days seemed radiant. My work was easier and took on new meaning. Music was everywhere — in the sounds of traffic, in the babble of voices on the street, in the hum of water boiling on the stove.

One morning, the concierge brought me a message from Zadkine. He was home for a few days and would be glad if I'd stop in — any time.

At eleven o'clock, I hurried over to his house. The gate was open, as was the door to the studio, so I went in, expecting to find him at work. He wasn't in either the small or the large workshop, however. Through the big window, I saw him in the garden, sitting under the umbrella. He wasn't alone. Laughing with him was a woman, and he was holding her hands and kissing them. I had seen the woman before. Of course! Valentine Prax, his ex-wife.

I wasn't intruding — he invited me. I went out and around to the garden where Zadkine greeted me with enthusiasm.

"How good to see you again, Mademoiselle. You remember Madame Prax, the painter?" We all shook hands. "Come, Mademoiselle Larsen, we'll go into the *atelier.* Excuse us, Valentine, my dear."

Would he clarify his marital status? It was none of my business, but how could I not be curious? In the large studio, we sat in the comfortable armchairs beside his desk.

"It was obliging of you to come, Mademoiselle. I am here for only a few days and wanted to tell you I'll be back in October. Will you be working with me again?"

"Yes. I've decided to stay in Paris at least another year. I love it here and don't want to go back home."

"I see." He cocked his head and smiled capriciously. "You are looking very well and happy."

I felt myself blushing and said, "Jocelyn will return at the end of summer, and I'll have to find another *atelier.*"

"You are working I hope? Sketching from life."

"Yes. The Grande Chaumière is open all year."

"You should be modeling from life, too. It is important to know the human figure. Here, let me show you my early work."

From the bookcase he took out a large album of photos. "Look at this, my first piece. I did it in 1908. You'll never find anything more academic than this. See — I worked like that for several years, till 1912, in fact. Now — here in these photos you see how my style changed abruptly. I had found myself."

"Yes, I recognize your style. It's much the way you work today."

"By the way, are you submitting something to the Autumn Salon?"

"The man's head in stone."

"Good. They will accept it, you'll see." He chuckled. "I'll never forget the first years I exhibited there. I was so poor, I rented a cart and pushed it, loaded with my sculpture, clear across town to the Grand Palais. You have talent, Mademoiselle. Keep working from life and then go your own way from there."

As I was leaving, he said, "By the way — if you find an unfurnished *atelier,* let me know. I can give you two beds — I'm getting some new ones. In any case, I'll see you early in October, *Au revoir.* Oh ... and take my unsolicited advice, Mademoiselle. Don't get married. It's ruinous."

From Zadkine's I went directly to the Grande Chaumière and signed up for a month of sculpture. The proportions of the young model's body were classic, and I was eager to start the next morning.

When I told François that evening how I'd spent the day, he said, "What do you make of Zadkine? Do you think he's courting his ex-wife?"

"It was obvious to me," I said, "that they're on intimate terms again, but his final comment, 'Marriage is ruinous' convinces me they intend to stay unmarried. They'll probably be happier that way."

"Do you really think so?"

"Certainly I do. They both have careers and need their independence. I've thought for a long time that creative people need space and autonomy. That goes for men *and* women." I busied myself dampening the rags on my unfinished dancing figures.

François said, "But I know several artists who have successful marriages. Le Corbusier for one."

"I'll bet they're all men, and their wives have no other purpose in life but to clear away obstacles that might get in their way. How many women artists do you know who are happily married? It's the double standard, François, that I'm against."

"I agree it's not fair — not at all fair. But what if the ... if the happily unmarried woman artist has a child?"

"Well, in the first place, it would be his child, also, and in the second place, it would not be the only one born out of wedlock. Sarah Bernhardt and Maria Montessori, both creative women and unwed, had sons, and their careers didn't suffer. In backward, provincial environments, women such as they and their children would be outcasts, but the men wouldn't."

"You feel strongly about the issue, don't you?"

"Perhaps because I nearly got ambushed once."

"And you escaped and came to Paris, *n'est pas?*"

"I did, and I won't be trapped again."

"You won't, huh? Not even if you fall in love with a bohemian who loves you?"

With my hands on my hips and chin in the air, I said, "What my heart does, I don't control, but I like to think my good sense rules my head. Does that answer your question?"

"Yes, my darling. If I asked you to marry me, your head would rule, and you'd refuse?"

"That's right."

"Why? Because I'm broke?"

"Oh, François, stop the buffoonery. You're just as much against marriage as I am and for the same reasons, aren't you?"

He laughed aloud, then came over to where I stood and took me in his arms "I wanted to hear it from you, *ma chère.* We both know that what we have is much more than a flirtation and stronger than any official document. What would you say if ... when you have to leave this *atelier* .... I've been thinking .... Let's rent a place together."

His brow furrowed as his eyes searched mine for a positive response.

My answer, with an impulsive hug, was, "Oh, François, you've been reading my mind!"

CHAPTER THIRTY-THREE

70 bis, rue N.D. des Champs
September 30, 1932

Dearest All of You,

Paris is back to normal. The leaves are almost all gone from the trees and the tourists from the streets. The cold and rain have returned, and so have the French from their vacations. This is where I came in a year ago.

Any day, now, I should hear if my "Head" has been accepted in the Salon. Harry says he'll give me a party if it gets in. I've been 22 years old for a couple of weeks. To celebrate, I had several friends in for potato salad, wine and cake. Lorraine sent me "The Philosophy of William James."

I'm back at the Grande Chaumière and have made two torsos almost life size. The first one was easy. I just copied the model's superb, young body as accurately as possible. It looked fine — very academic — but nifty. In fact, an elderly American woman dropped in one day, saw it, and said, "Just last week I bought a torso from a famous sculptor, but yours is more beautiful."

Anyway, I did a second one, putting angles where shadows should start when it's observed from certain points of view. The teacher, Vlerick, came to criticize. He saw the classic torso first and congratulated me. Then, about the other one, he said, "I can't understand it. The balance and proportions are good. I like this detail and that part ... but ... you know, Mademoiselle, I must confess, it's way beyond me."

I'm still laughing. He's extremely conservative, and his reputation in France is established on that. It wouldn't do for him to admit that anything modern pleased him. I think secretly he did like it, however.

Your old friends, Alf and Leslie, are here. They've been living in Oslo for a long time, expect to stay a year in Paris, then go to Japan for awhile, and return to Honolulu in 1934. He isn't composing now, but studying painting. Leslie complains that the local bread is made of chalk, the wine is adulterated, and the French are stingy and arrogant. In spite of that, she's glad to be here. Alf says that when he gets to Honolulu, he's going to try to organize a symphony orchestra. It's about time, don't you think?

On the last warm Sunday of the season, François wanted me to go to Dieppe with him for a final swim but, since I couldn't, he went alone. I said I'd wait supper for him. Around 10:00, he arrived and we had tea, rye bread, cheese and blackberries. In the woods near Dieppe, he found a jungle of bushes loaded with berries. Having no other receptacle, he lined his old felt hat with leaves, picked it full, carried it carefully to Dieppe and guarded it, unscathed, all the way on the train. He said it was a modest tribute to me. Wasn't that sweet?

October 7, 1932

I forgot to mail this earlier, but it's just as well. Guess what? Word has just come that my "Head" was accepted in the Autumn Salon.

With love,
Sisi

Chapter Thirty-Four

The ninth of October was a Sunday, so François and I didn't have to share our day with either his office or the Grande Chaumière. It was a day particularly full of events that made living in Paris exhilarating. It began without distinction when François suggested we have breakfast on the other side of the Luxembourg Garden, at the Capoulade.

"Come on, *Chérie*, the overcast skies of autumn await, and we've a lot to do."

"I know, I know. The concert starts at five and before that we want to see that old church and those new paintings."

"And, don't forget, we ought to pick up the tickets this morning if we want cheap ones, and that means going across town twice. What time will Bill Holford get here this evening?"

"I told him not to come before eight-thirty. We can take them to that little restaurant on rue Brèa."

The day proceeded pretty much as planned. We examined the ancient church and the exhibit of modern paintings. The only inconvenience: When we reached the Salle Pleyel, all the lowest-priced tickets for the concert were sold out. By pooling our loose change, however, we found enough for the next-cheapest ones.

"That's a relief," François said. "I especially don't want to miss the Stravinsky selection. Have you heard much of him, Agnès?"

"I've never heard any of his music. Russian, isn't he?"

"Yes. But he lives here, in a suburb — Saint Cloud, I believe. His music is nonconformist. At a very young age, he began composing — in St. Petersburg. Rimsky-Korsakoff advised him to avoid academic training and to study privately."

"I promise to listen carefully."

"And be sure," François said, using terms not in my usual vocabulary, "to notice how he enjoys investigating the asymmetry of the cadences, and demolishing the traditional. When *Rite of Spring* was first performed nine years ago here in Paris, the music caused a scandal. So I'm eager to hear how it will be received today."

Beethoven and DeBussy, first on the program, got the applause they deserved. With the first notes of Stravinsky, there was dead silence in the theatre. No one rattled a paper, coughed or cleared his throat. Hardly anyone breathed.

As for me, I just sat there immobile, my body abandoned by my spirit, which had taken flight to guide my mind through the unfamiliar association of sounds. My senses perceived the separate parts of my entity: mind, body and soul, and I remembered the ancient Chinese poem about three fragile flowers in a bowl. The experience was one that would recur many times.

When the final note sounded, the audience rose to its feet, roaring and applauding in praise. No longer was the score considered scandalous. François and I joined the acclaim, and I knew I would never again listen to music with only my ears.

Bill arrived at the *atelier* shortly after we returned. The affable young woman with him was tall, slender and blonde.

"I'm Jo Brooks," she said.

It didn't take long for the four of us to feel as comfortable together as old friends. In the ten minutes it took to reach the restaurant, we knew that Jo lived in London with her mother and sister, and was going to Rome to paint a mural. Bill was on his way back there to continue studying architecture on his fellowship.

As soon as the waiter left with our orders, Bill took a note from his pocket. "I've brought a message from Gordon." He cleared his throat ostentatiously and read, "Tell François about Antwerp, the competition, and that we'll expect him and Alex here in June to work on it."

If a bomb had dropped we wouldn't have been more startled. Bill savored François' incredulity for several moments before explaining.

"Antwerp has a large underdeveloped area at a bend in the Schelde River directly opposite the city. An international competition for its urbanization has been announced. Gordon and I want to try for it, but we'll need help. What do you say, François? Maybe Alex will come, too. We'll all be guests of Gordon's parents at their house at West Kirby. That's a little town on the Irish Sea near Liverpool. We should be there in April. It'll take at least a month to complete."

François leaned back in his chair. *"Mon dieu! C'est magnifique!* I'm overwhelmed. Sure!

"But .... I don't know. I might have to report for military service .... Should hear about that in a few days .... And I'll have to talk to Corbu. He's in Moscow now. A building of his has just been completed there. He'll be back on Tuesday."

The news came, not as a bomb, but as one of those skyrockets that shoots up and spreads its colorful lights in a brilliant umbrella.

Jo's eyes reflected the sparkle. "How I wish we could stay a few days to hear what he has to say. Some of our London friends were in Moscow and came back with mixed feelings. Most go with their minds already made up — one way or the other. I want to see the country for myself."

"There are as many opinions as there are people," Bill said "Take Mussolini .... I've been in Italy over a year, and I know people who detest his regime and as many who think it's fabulous. That, however, doesn't diminish the wonder of Italy as a country or a people."

"When I was there with Jane," I said, "Florence captivated me, but that had nothing to do with Fascism. By the way, will someone tell me what Fascism is — I mean, how is it different from Communism — in ten easy words or less."

"Well, Bill," said François, "you're the expert. Tell us."

"Basically, Fascism is government *of* the few, *by* the few and *for* the many. You see, major corporations finance a likely man or men, get them elected to office and, from behind the scenes, make the laws, while they convince the unsuspecting public that it's for the good of the State."

"And the press, of course," Jo put in, "is obliged to be favorable. If not — they're out of business."

"Didn't Mussolini start out a Socialist?" François asked.

"He sure did. In fact, he wrote a book called *God Doesn't Exist.* The party expelled him for corruption, and he joined the Fascist movement backed by the industrialists. In 1925, the wealthy American, Lamont, stabilized the lira with huge loans and spread the rumor that Mussolini saved Italy from the Bolsheviks."

François took a deep breath. "If Hitler becomes Chancellor of Germany, the same will happen there — only worse, I'm afraid. He wants only so-called 'pure' Germans to be in charge."

"Yes," Bill added, "and will label all their opponents Bolsheviks."

"Are Fascists so different from Communists?" I asked.

"Different?" Bill snorted. "I'll say they are. Communists take the means of production, factories and such things, out of private hands so all the profits go into the general kitty."

"Is that good?" I wanted to know.

"That depends. If you're an ambitious industrialist, it's bad. But, on the other hand, the majority benefits. There's health care, no unemployment, low rent, and a lot of other advantages for ordinary people, such as education."

"So everyone's in the same boat?"

"That's what the Fascists keep saying, that everybody's alike under the Bolsheviks. Not at all. There are high salaries and low wages, depending on each person's qualifications. Specialists earn more and, I understand, artists are among the best paid."

"Then why do people say such awful things about the Russians — even English and American papers?"

"Because, my dear Agnès, we're Capitalists. We can't afford not to. When I'm a wealthy architect, I'll be against them, or I won't get any work."

The discussion didn't stop there. We talked till far into the night trying, with our limited information, to fathom the complexities of governments. I didn't realize then what part that encounter with Jo and Bill would play in my not-too-distant future.

Chapter Thirty-Five

Every ten minutes on the evening of the following Tuesday, I put down *The Philosophy of William James* to look at my watch. Time had never passed so slowly. François wouldn't come till after eight o'clock, and the last time I looked, it wasn't even seven. He'd be bringing Le Corbusier's report on Moscow, and I had to tell him my news of the day.

The morning mail had brought two letters. One was from John's cousin, Vance, who, I thought, was still teaching at a boy's school in Honolulu. His letter was postmarked London! I read it several times to make sure there was no mistake. Some unknown benefactor had granted him funds to study anthropology. There was a Santa Claus! Vance was enrolled at London U. and elbow-deep in books. The letter ended:

... and if you come to London in the next year or two, I'll get you a cheap place to stay. I have a room in a modest boarding house in Bloomsbury. Imagine! Bloomsbury — near the university, the British Museum and right in the heart of artistic and intellectual London life. Some of it will, I hope, rub off on me.

Write soon. Aloha,
Vance

The other letter was from my mother. I read it on my way to Zadkine's, excited because he was going to start me on wood sculpture. But wait! What was this?

... building has practically stopped, and money is scarce. Sisi, you may wish to plan on coming home in a few months ....

No! I couldn't go! No! My eyes filled with tears, while my insides turned knots. My heart pounded. My heart! Right there where John had engraved ... and I had promised him ... and then denied him in order to keep that promise. No matter what *he* did, I wouldn't betray his faith in me. I now believed in myself. It wasn't so much that I

resented leaving Paris — I didn't want the confinement of those isolated islands. And that wasn't all ... I didn't want to leave François.

Four hours in Zadkine's company restored my equipoise. He took
me shopping for wood-carving tools and guided my purchase of thirty-
two chisels of the finest Sheffield steel — wide, narrow, flat, curved,
long and short. Then we went to a lumberyard and chose a log of ash
wood, almost five feet long and eighteen inches thick.

I glanced at my wristwatch. Only a quarter to eight. He wouldn't
be early. Alex might come back with him for supper. Might be later
than usual. Talking to Corbu ... there'd be lots of questions.

I took up my book and tried to read or, rather, tried to understand
what I read. The subject was Pragmatism — stressing the practical
results of an idea as a measure in a course of action. That much
seemed clear. I read on. The next sentence was complicated. I read it
again. The meaning escaped me, but my eyes moved along, nevertheless, from word to word, line to line. Mechanically, my fingers
turned the page. Several pages later, it was eight-thirty. My ears picked
up familiar voices in the hall. At last!

François and Alex darted in, both talking at the same time. "*C'est
formidable!* Wait till you hear!"

For the next half hour, no one thought of supper. While I listened,
the two men interrupted each other telling how the entire office crew
stopped working after lunch while Le Corbusier answered questions
about Moscow.

"They have more French Impressionists than France itself — and
Flemish masters, too."

"The ballet and opera and theatres have a special budget and don't
suffer from any shortages ...."

"Lots of Russians, older ones especially, speak French ...."

"Some of the old churches are architectural treasures, and most
have been turned into museums or libraries or clinics."

"And everybody's employed! There's more than enough work to
go around — a shortage of all kinds of engineers —"

" — And architects, and the pay is darn good!"

"Corbu had all the caviar and smoked salmon he could eat, and
good wine from the Crimea. The hospitality was *magnifique* ...."

When we finally sat down to our bowls of humble vegetable soup, the subject changed to Gordon's invitation.

"We'll be a fine squad," Alex said. "All four of us have strong feelings on urban planning and definite opinions on what the ideal city should be."

"The location's perfect," François added. "Usually an old city has to be remodeled while it's still lived in, but that part of Antwerp is, practically speaking, barren land, so we can start from scratch. Gordon wants us in West Kirby in April — about six months from now. I'll write him tomorrow that we'll be there."

Alex went home around ten o'clock, but François still wanted to talk. "Can't sit down," he said, and put on another pot of coffee. "I'm too keyed up. As Alex and I were on our way here, I had an idea. Didn't mention it to him — thought I'd wait and digest the notion. He's not one to take chances." He stopped and faced me. "We ought to think of going to Russia."

"To visit?"

"No! To work! Don't you see? That would solve everything. They need architects."

And what about me? My feelings must have been obvious. François took my hands. "What's the matter, *mon petit chou?* You look utterly dejected. Tell me what the trouble is. Sad news from home?"

"My father's out of work ... and they want me to go back soon."

"*C'est Magnifique!* Don't you see, *Chérie?*"

I could only shake my head.

"Now you don't have to go back. In Russia, there's work for everyone. You *will* come with me, won't you?"

"You mean ... you want me to?"

"I wouldn't dream of going without you."

"But when you said *we*, I thought you meant you and Alex."

"Sure, he can come if he wants to, but *we* means you and I. You should know that by now. It will solve both our problems. In April, we'll go to England, in June visit my family, and in July, head for Moscow .... Oh, *mon amour* ...."

I was in his arms. Words were no longer necessary or even possible — except, of course, for the irrepressible utterances intelligible only to those in love.

CHAPTER THIRTY-FIVE

70 bis N.D. des Champs
Paris
Oct. 17, 1932

Dearest All of You,

The Autumn Salon will open on Monday, 31st. Several friends have said they're going to stand around my "Head" in shifts exclaiming what a magnificent piece of work it is. Meanwhile, I've begun another masterpiece. So far, it's only a large piece of wood, but in a few weeks it'll be a torso — not in the classic style.

Zadkine helped me buy the tools I needed, and choose the wood at a lumberyard. Sharpening my new chisels is rather tedious. First, I grind them to a bevel on one side only — the under side — then, on the whetstone, hone them to a fine cutting edge. On the upper side, there are "whiskers" that must be whisked off and, finally, I strop the edges on a sturdy piece of soft hide.

Every morning I pick out the tools I might use that day. If they're not at their best, I sharpen them. Before going home, I put them all away and sweep up the chips which I save for kindling in my coal stove.

Three or four times during the morning, Zadkine and I take a break. He comes into the small studio, sits in a dilapidated wicker chair, and lights his pipe, while I perch on a stool. Sometimes he sounds like Madame Scheyer. We discuss my work in progress and then get on to some philosophical view of what we're doing — the meaning of the arts in our lives, apart from being a mere livelihood.

My friend, Gertrude, is getting married in Budapest on the 21st, and Anne is coming back to Paris a few days later. She's going to take the studio Jane had.

Jocelyn will return at the end of November, and I have already found a place to move to. It's furnished and rents by the month. It would have been cheaper if I could have signed a lease but I won't be here long enough.

Do you remember the old war song "How Ya Gonna Keep 'Em Down on the Farm After They've Seen Paree?" Well, I've seen Paree. Maybe in my next letter, I'll be able to tell you my plans for leaving.

I love you all,
Sisi

Chapter Thirty-Six

From a corner of the bathroom floor the pile of clothes stared back at me. "All right!" I said aloud. "As soon as I've finished doing last night's dishes, I'll tackle you. There are a dozen things more important than laundry. Any dummy can wash clothes. My life is loaded with fascinating events and people that take up all my precious time. You must admit I wouldn't make an exemplary wife."

An insistent knock at the door interrupted my monologue. "You see how busy I am? Now I have to find out who that is."

"Anybody home?" I recognized the familiar voice.

"Anne! You're a sight for even the best of eyes! But I didn't expect you till tomorrow."

"Oh ... after Gertrude's wedding, there was no reason to stay away any longer. My, you look well. Tell me about you and François."

"We've found a studio, and will probably move in about mid-November."

"Gosh, everyone's getting married. When's the wedding?"

Unprepared for the question, I didn't know what to say, how to tell her I was breaking one of the rules of propriety Americans were brought up with. I didn't expect or need her approval, or anyone else's. If I told her François and I were both against matrimony, her sense of decorum might be offended. But then again, maybe not.

I shrugged. "We're not planning on getting married."

"You're not?"

"No. It's comfortable this way."

"For you, perhaps, but what will people say?"

"If I cared, I'd conform. I can guess what they'd say in Honolulu. Fortunately, I'm here. Harry, for one, thinks it's okay."

"Oh? Anyone else?"

"Sure, Zadkine. After he and his wife divorced, she moved back in with him. And there are those two friends of my parents. She's from an old Honolulu family, and he's a Norwegian composer — staying in Paris for several months. They told me that in Norway, it's not uncommon for a couple to get married when they baptize their first child. In other words, they could have been living together for ages. No one thinks a thing of it in Scandinavia. And obviously the French don't mind.

"Hmm .... I see. Well, you know I just don't want you to get hurt."

"Marriage does not guarantee that a woman won't get hurt! We all know that. Besides, I like him too much. I'd make a lousy wife." I was about to ask about her sister-in-law, but she shifted the subject.

"You wrote me you might have to go back to Honolulu soon. Do you still have to?"

"Nope! My guardian angel has other plans. François and I are going to Russia to look for work."

"You must be joking! But they're Bolsheviks. They throw bombs and will send you to Siberia if you say your prayers ... and they're starving."

"Sure. And they eat babies, too, I suppose. Le Corbusier was there a few weeks ago and didn't find anything of the sort. The point is, Anne, I have no choice. I can't afford to live here with no income, and I won't go back to the Islands. There are no jobs anywhere in the States. Thirteen million unemployed, banks still closing. *That's* where people are starving. Roosevelt keeps saying one-third of the country is underfed and underhoused. Even Jane, with her credentials, hasn't found work yet. How many are buying works of art?"

"What about going some other place? Australia?"

"They're just as bad off — bread lines and failing banks. Most of the world is in a depression. Anyway — I want to see what the Russian experiment is. Seems to me the world is big enough for more than one point of view."

"Hmm .... I can understand that." Anne sat down and looked about the *atelier.* "Gee, did you do those two torsos?"

"Yup. Which one do you like?"

"Both. If I had to, I'd choose the modern one. The forms make interesting shadows. Where are your stone pieces? The 'Head' is at the Salon, I know, but the 'Sitting Woman'?"

"Oh, that. Well .... " I cleared my throat pompously. "A few days ago, a man was here saying the American Women's Club was having an exhibition and would I please let them show something of mine. He saw the 'Sitting Woman' and said, 'How about that piece?' And I said 'Sure.' I asked how he knew about me, and he said he'd seen the 'Head' at the Salon."

"You see!" Anne bounced up. "If you stayed here you'd soon be recognized — your work would sell. Have you thought of that?"

"Who hasn't dreamed of being discovered, made famous and celebrated? Of course I've thought of it. But that's not pragmatic. I must admit I have a pox called wanderlust. The world is so big, Anne. I'm not ready to settle down, I'm curious to see an entirely new environment — a different social system, language, climate .... This is an opportunity I can't ignore. If I'd been brought up in Europe or Asia, I'm sure I'd be doing my darndest to get to the States."

"What does your family think of your daft idea?"

"They don't know yet. My mother will probably have a fit at first, but then she'll come around. The longer I wait, the less time she'll have to try to get me to change my mind."

"You do know, I suppose, the U.S. hasn't recognized the Soviet Union. We have no embassy there. Are you sure they'll let you stay and work?"

"No."

"You're taking quite a chance. What if they don't want you?"

"Don't know. Dig my heels in, probably."

"And take on the Soviet government?"

"If I have to."

Anne chuckled. "You'll be back."

"You think so? Wanna bet?"

70 bis, rue N.D. des Champs
Paris
Nov. 8, 1932

Dearest Everyone,

The newspapers are full of Roosevelt's election. Everyone here is elated. He's going to make drinking legal again, and the common man respected. Both are long overdue.

I've found a furnished studio and will move in ten days. It's smaller than Jocelyn's, on the 6th floor, so the light is good. There's no elevator though the building is modern, and it has no bathroom. Most people go to the public baths, anyway. The toilet is down the hall and shared with the other studio on the same floor. We both have a key to it. I'll keep a chamber pot under the bed. The former tenant installed a bathtub in the kitchen. That's rather common here.

There's central heating and hot water, too. A few days ago, it was François' 25th birthday. I invited him here for dinner, then we went to a concert. He wasn't his usual cheerful self and finally told me why. His father hadn't remembered. When we came back here for coffee, I brought out a cake I had made for him in the morning, decorated with candles. He was so moved, I was sorry I had done it.

Now, here's some real news! The other day, I had to rush downtown before the banks closed because I was out of cash. I got my money, said a quick hello to Harry, and left to do my window shopping. Suddenly, I turned around and there, walking toward me, was Madame Scheyer!

She greeted me warmly, with a hug and kisses on both cheeks, then we went to her hotel around the corner so we could talk while she changed clothes. She was getting ready for an interview with Le Corbusier. What a small world! Tomorrow she'll be off to visit relatives in Germany for a few days and then will come back to Paris to stay several weeks. She's going to take me with her when she calls on the famous artists she knows — all big names — Brancusi, Arp ... Isn't it wonderful?

In the spring, I'm planning to leave for England to spend a month or so. I want to see London, of course, and Vance writes that John's father will be there on business and that Grace will be along.

That's not all. In my last batch of Honolulu mail was a letter from Eve. She and her brother, Eddie, will be in Paris in February after traveling through Italy, and they, too, will go to London in April. From there — who knows what I'll do? I'm seriously considering several possibilities.

With all my love,
Sisi

Chapter Thirty-Seven

"And what do you think of events in Germany?" I asked Madame Scheyer as she entered the *atelier*.

Before answering, she gave me her coat, sat down on one of the straight chairs and shrugged. "For the moment, my family are well."

She hadn't lost her accent, but I hardly noticed it. "I am, of course, worried for them," she went on, "because we are Jewish. In the last elections, the Nazi Party won the most seats in the *Reichstad* — that's their parliament — and now von Hindenburg is obliged to name Hitler as Chancellor. He won't take office till January, but it's only a question of time till he gets, one way or another, absolute power."

"How was it so many people voted for him?"

"He has a personality that appeals to a lot of people. And Germany is in a terrible economic crisis. You think America is in trouble? The German mark is worthless, and six million people are unemployed. He blames it all on the Versailles Peace Treaty and on the Jews and the Communists. After losing the war, you see, Germany had to give up all its former colonies. Now he promises that, if the people follow him, he will lead them to their former greatness, to a Fatherland of *pure* Germans."

"That's similar to what Mussolini preaches," I said.

"Ya. They are two of a kind."

"When the people see what is happening, can't they put him out of office?"

"By then, with his full powers, it will be too late. And besides, the great money trusts in the world are in favor of him. Most people don't know it yet, but the lives of everyone on Earth will be affected and, I'm afraid, there will be much suffering."

Over tea and little pastries, the conversation became more relaxed. I was glad she asked what I'd been doing since we last met in Honolulu. She listened, quietly nodding as I told her about John and our melodramatic parting in Canada.

"You are learning," she said, "that you cannot live your life to please others. Some people think it's noble to be altruistic. They are the timid souls, afraid of life, of being criticized. I'm happy you're not such a one."

She poured herself another cup of tea while I said, "Back there in Berkeley, you were always telling us to *dare* to be ourselves."

"Ah, you remember. Ya! Where would Kandinsky be if he tried to please the public? And Kokoshka and Beethoven and all the great innovators?"

"My teacher, Zadkine, talks to me like that."

"Ah, yes. Zadkine. He is expecting us, yes, this afternoon?"

"In half an hour or so. He lives only a few minutes from here."

"Good. So we have time to talk about your work. I have been looking at the two torsos over there. Both from the same model?"

"Yes."

"Experimenting like that shows you are thriving. Where are your stone pieces?"

"The 'Head' is still at the Salon, and the 'Sitting Woman' is at another exhibition. Here — look at the snapshots I took of them."

Madame Scheyer spread the photos on the table and nodded approvingly. "Well done, my dear. Sculpture seems to be your medium. As far as I know, you are the only one of my former pupils making a career of her art. And it's obvious you are serious."

That evening, I was still glowing when François arrived for supper.

"You've had a brilliant afternoon, haven't you?" he said. "It shows."

I squealed with glee. "From beginning to end. Madame Scheyer was here about an hour, then we went to Zadkine's. They got on well — have many friends in common. She looked at all of his work but spent more time talking about mine. I'm pretty far along on the wood torso, you know. When we left, we walked over to Boulevard Montparnasse where she got a taxi. She said I was doing well, that Zadkine's a fine teacher, but his work is too chaotic."

"And what did you say to that?"

"Well — what you and I have often discussed. I said, 'But if art reflects life, and life is full of ferment and agitation, how can you say his work is *too* chaotic?' And she stopped and looked at me and smiled and said, 'You know, you're right. I will think about that.'"

"Brava, *Chérie*. Will you see her again?"

"The day after tomorrow. She's going to a lot of art galleries and wants me to come with her."

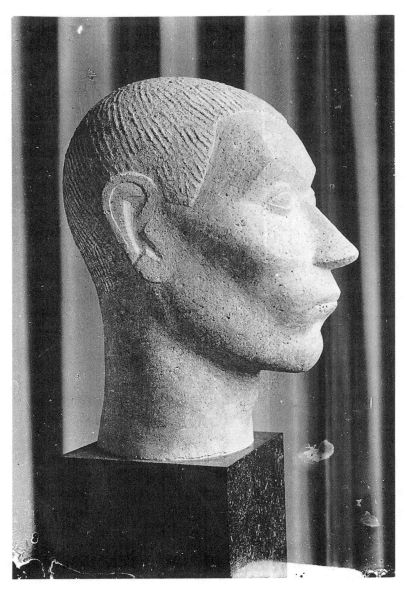

"Head" in stone. Private collection. Photo by Andreas Feininger.

"Sitting Woman"; model for large stone piece.
Photo by Andreas Feininger.

"You're lucky. Her influence will help you separate the genuine from the would-be and the second-rate. What else did she say? What language did you use?"

I had to laugh. "French at Zadkine's, and afterwards she told me I speak it with a Czech accent. How do you like that?"

He darted me a surprised look. "I hadn't noticed. Do you mind? I think your French is darn good."

"Well, I'd rather speak it with a French accent."

"I guess I should try, too. But speaking of foreign accents, there's another American working at Corbu's. His name is Andreas, son of a famous German Painter — Feininger."

"Feininger? My goodness — the world gets smaller every day. He's one of Madame Scheyer's Blue Four. She's his agent in the States. I didn't know he had a son."

"Two sons — both about our age. The other's a painter, named Lux. They have an apartment not far from here. After supper, they're having a few friends in. I told Andreas we'd be there around nine o'clock."

The Feininger brothers looked like many young Americans, and showed no hint of having a prestigious father. Fruit of their own talents, certainly not the work of dilettantes, hung on the faded wallpaper. The photographs, we soon learned, were by Andreas, who told us architecture interested him less than taking pictures.

The three other guests, Katia, Bruno and Phillippe, were European artists. When we arrived, they were discussing the sources of creativity. At such informal gatherings, it was rare not to have some matter to toss around and analyze. The more outlandish, the better. If we didn't explore our own minds and the thoughts of others, how could we sharpen our wits, and think reflectively and clearly?

Back in Honolulu, when John first tried to drag me into a serious discussion, I discouraged him, said I was weary, or changed the subject. Among my friends it was considered impolite to disagree. I still marvel at John's patience, and wonder what he ever saw in me.

Katia said that someone she knew insisted that intelligent people were the most creative. "I don't agree," she stated.

"Neither do I," declared one of the young men. "My best ideas come when I'm not thinking."

"Mine often come from my emotions," said another.

"Emotions and intelligence are two separate things."

"How can we explain a genius? One's creative gift doesn't come from textbooks or teachers. I don't believe the brain invents. If trained, the best it can do is learn to reason and organize, and if relied on too much, it can be conservative."

"And conservatism, as we've all learned, is fatal to creativity."

"Then where does genius come from?"

"Oh, *mon dieu,* who knows? I don't. From somewhere out there in the blue, I suppose. Let's talk about it again in fifty years. If we don't use our brains too much, we may know by then."

Chapter Thirty-Eight

A frigid autumn wind blew on the day Madame Scheyer chose to begin our tour of art galleries. As agreed, I went to her hotel at three o'clock.

"How nice and warm your room is," I said. "My *atelier* is icy."

"I didn't think so."

"I should hope not. When I have guests, I fire up the coal stove. But I must economize this year, and one way to save is to get used to a cold house."

"Ah, how I remember my youthful days. You have, I suppose, a young man to keep you warm."

"Uh-huh. He's an architect at Le Corbusier's."

"Ya? That's good."

"Which reminds me," I said. "The other night we went to the Feininger brothers'. They had a party."

"So? You know already Andreas and Lux? I was going to suggest you meet them. One day you and I will call on the boys together, ya? Talented, don't you think so?"

"Yes. Andreas obviously likes photography better than architecture. He's going to take pictures of my sculpture."

"Nice fellows ... like their father. Where did I put my gloves? Ah, there they are. I'm ready now — shall we go?"

At every art gallery we went to, the manager greeted Madame

Scheyer by name and eagerly had picture after picture brought out for her inspection: drawings, oils, gouaches, watercolors. Some were by older, confirmed painters, and others by young hopefuls. Sometimes Madame Scheyer would say, "Put that one aside, *s 'il vous plaît.* I would like to take a closer look."

She never asked prices.

Once I pointed out a small, abstract canvas that appealed to me.

Madame Scheyer nodded approvingly. "You show good taste. He's a follower of Paul Klee — it's one of his early paintings — poetic interplay of forms and colors. I think you could buy it for about 50 dollars. His name is Miró .... Spanish."

Regretfully, I shook my head. "It's inexpensive, but my budget won't let me."

For the next several afternoons, Madame Scheyer continued her examination of art galleries, tirelessly scrutinizing the works of artists, some of whose names were new to her. I listened to every word she uttered whether praise or criticism, such as, "Much originality, but technically not yet competent," or *"Mon dieu,* he has come a long way — very dedicated," or "Too *façile,* no substance."

What was it Aristotle said about catharsis? Purification of the emotions ... The arts was one way to achieve that. Chrysalis. Metamorphosis. Cleansed of the old. Was I ready to try my new wings? But wait! Madame Scheyer had more to show me.

"A week of galleries is enough for now," she said one day. "Tomorrow we'll go out of the city to Meudon. I want to see the Arps, and also the home a Dutch friend built. He died last year ... van Doesburg ...."

"Was he a painter?" I asked.

"Oh, ya — painter, poet, decorator, art theorist ... avant garde. A great loss — he was only 48 years old. Founded a movement and a review called *de Stijl.* Too young to die."

The Doesburg house was, of course, contemporary. Its interior walls could be shifted to alter the whole plan. A caretaker, who expected us, demonstrated the ease with which areas could be enlarged or reduced.

"One of his convictions," Madame Scheyer explained, "has had a great influence in Europe — that pictures should be a part of the walls they hang on. The Orientals have done that for centuries."

Not far away was the home of Jean and Sophie Arp. As we walked there by a wooded path, Madame Scheyer told me, "I'll be going back to Germany in a few days, and will return in the spring, probably with an auto. Perhaps I shall live in the Doesburg house. I think you will like the Arps.

"Sophie is a painter of considerable talent. I met them through Kandinsky. For awhile he joined *Der Blaue Reiter.*"

"Is that the German name of The Blue Four?"

"No, no. Many people ask that. In English "reiter" means rider. They took the name from a painting by Kandinsky. He and Franz Marc started the group — had no program, only several friends who exhibited together to develop Abstract and Expressionist art. There was Henri Rousseau, Klee, Jawlensky, Vlaminck, Picasso .... Oh, ya... and lots of others.

"When the war came, they broke up, and in 1924, formed another group, a smaller one, and called it The Blue Four because there were only Kandinsky, Klee, Feininger and Jawlensky."

"And they chose you to represent them in the States."

"Ya. When I first showed their work in New York, those people who didn't snub it thought it was comical. Americans are slow to accept modern art because they are conservative and insecure. But those who did approve — my goodness — they went overboard for it, as you say, almost as though they were grasping at a life-preserver in a vast quagmire. There is always a minority that understands the cultural and emotional importance of the arts in our lives. Then I moved to the West Coast. Californians are forward-looking, have more comprehension. Today it's the sanctuary of The Blue Four. I am happy to live there." She threw her arms out in exuberance. "Ya, and now I remember. I had hardly unpacked my belongings when I met you at Anna Head School in Berkeley. That was in 1926, ya? Well — here we are at the Arps' house." She laughed. "We have come a long way, *n'est pas?*"

An attractive woman opened the door to us. "Ah, Galka, it's wonderful to see you again!"

"*Bonjour,* Sophie."

The two friends greeted each other affectionately as Mr. Arp approached, welcoming us both "... and this is your former pupil ...." he said as he shook my hand. "Come — we'll have tea in my *atelier.*"

The afternoon seemed to pass in moments. I could have stayed for days in the placid atmosphere. Surrounded by plain, light walls, the spacious studio urged me to get to work. My hands itched when Mr. Arp showed us his creations. First from his earlier period — shapes carved out of white plaster — audacious, non-figurative contours. Then from his new phase — still abstract — simple slices of white wood, about two inches thick, cut into odd patterns and glued onto plain backgrounds of white, grey or black. The shadows cast were part of the compositions, and changed as the light shifted.

Most people looking at those objects might see merely plaster forms or meaningless wooden shapes. To me, they were points of departure, sending my imagination flying into areas of harmonious chromatic. The lack of original color was an invitation to supply my own. What a feast of invention! In my mind, I rearranged the pieces again and again and made new ones, black or white or polychromatic, in different sizes.

Those days spent in Madame Scheyer's orbit invigorated my emotions. Sometimes I "became" one of the artists she appraised, as though she was assessing *my* work — that work of mine not yet done. I was the observer, observed. Catharsis. Metamorphosis. Brand new wings!

Decades later, in nostalgic moments, I recall that fortnight as a lighthouse secure on a precarious shore, and Madame Scheyer the beam illuminating the life-preserver I clung to.

71 rue Cardinal Lemoine
Paris
Dec. 8, 1932

Dearest Family,

As you see, I've moved. Anne helped me. I rented a handcart, and we pushed it over here loaded with my stuff — all but the sculpture, which Jocelyn is keeping for awhile. She says it embellishes her studio.

From the balcony outside of my two huge north windows, I can see past Notre Dame Cathedral up to Sacre Coeur, which crowns the hill of Montmartre, and to a lot of other church towers rising above the city skyline. I'm now 20 minutes from Zadkine's by the direct route through the Luxembourg Garden.

Madame Scheyer has gone back to Germany to spend the winter. For over a week I went out every afternoon with her visiting art galleries and artists. As a result, several new doors have opened to me.

I've begun another piece at Zadkine's — the head of a girl, in teakwood. And at home I'm doing an unusual sculpture: a fish in water — not real water. If it turns out as I hope, I'll have it cast in bronze. From now on, I'm going to be busier than ever.

We're expecting Gordon to come over for New Year's. He recently won $200 in an architectural competition.

Christmas will be here soon. I hope you haven't sent me any presents. I don't need a thing! Just wrap an old box in fancy paper and put it under the tree with my name on it and pretend I'm there with you.

Merry Christmas and love to all!
Sisi

"Teakwood Head"; Private collection.

Chapter Thirty-Nine

71 rue Cardinal Lemoine
Paris
Jan. 12, 1933

Dearest Family,

The holiday season is over — officially. But for me, I'm still on vacation, if that means a time of recreation. I'm never going to stop re-creating myself! There's so much to learn, and so many places to see, ideas to trade. I won't be left behind. I want to be a part of the changing world and leave it a better one than this — better for everyone. Okay, so I'm Utopian. We should aim high, so if we miss our mark, we won't land in a ditch.

François has been showing me some of Le Corbusier's buildings. We went first to the Swiss pavilion out at University City where many countries have dormitories for their students. After that, we saw two private homes. One belongs to Corbu's brother, a composer. Many of the houses are on pillars with gardens running underneath, leaving only the entrance halls on the ground. Corbu often uses ramps instead of stairs, especially where there are children or old people.

His Salvation Army building is so big, he made it in three sections, with space (less than an inch) between them, to allow for contraction and expansion from cold and heat. It's been written up in several professional journals.

New Year's week was unexpectedly festive. Gordon came over from England. He's teaching at the U. of Liverpool. Bill and Jo came up from Rome, and Anne and Alex joined us.

Besides dancing and eating, we went to art shows. One was a shocker: a Spaniard named Mirò exhibiting his latest phase. The canvases were not startling, but you should see his so-called sculpture. One consisted of an old board as you might find in some neglected back yard, covered with vague drawings and with a few rusty nails stuck in here and there. At one side, a bone was suspended on a string, and on the top of the frame, an old tin can balanced. Can I hear you say, "D'you call that art?"

I won't answer the question directly. I'll only tell you about a style of painting started by the Greeks and revived in the 19th to the late 20th centuries. It was called "trompe l'oeil" and means "deceive the eye." The deception consisted in painting so realistic the viewer could think he was looking at the genuine articles instead of oil on canvas. The painted subjects were, for example, a dead goose hanging by its feet in a kitchen, flowers in a glass vase with dew drops and an insect perched on a petal, playing cards and newspaper clippings. They were considered great works of art Therefore: If those copies of the real thing were art, why is not the real thing art? That is my answer.

In my opinion Miró's present phase is research and should not be judged either "good" or "bad."

We also saw some traditional dancers from India and several interesting movies. We liked a German film, "13 Trunks of Mr. O.F.," a satire on the Depression, and a documentary on the construction of the gigantic hydroelectric dam on the Drieper River in the Ukraine, completed last May. After seeing it, I can't understand why people keep saying the U.S.S.R. won't ever amount to anything. Soviet society is barely fourteen years old and already, a large portion of once fallow land, owned by a privileged elite, has been turned into productive farms. And all this while every other nation is depressed and doing its best to cause difficulties for them. I'd like to work there for a year or so.

Jocelyn's parents left her a lot of money in stocks. The other day, all went down the drain and she has only two hundred dollars a year to live on. Fortunately, she owns her studio, but now will have to earn a living. Our lopsided economic system should be changed.

Anne is leaving in April. She's homesick for San Francisco. I want to go, too, but to exotic places, far away.

I've had a letter from John. He and Ella are happily married and struggling with the wolf in Toronto.

Tomorrow I'm going to call on one of the galleries I visited with Madame Scheyer. The owner is a charming woman named Bucher. More soon.

Love, Sisi

At the entrance to No. 3 rue Cherche-Midi I hesitated. Did I have the nerve to go in? To come there with Madame Scheyer was one thing, but would Jeanne Bucher have any time for me, alone? I really didn't know why I was there. Could I say I was just looking around? No one would ever mistake me for a collector or a connoisseur.

From somewhere a silent voice whispered, "Dare," so I pushed the door open. A bell tinkled. A young woman appeared from behind a screen.

"*Bon soir.* May I help you? Or do you wish to just look around?"

"I came to see Madame Bucher."

"I'm sorry. Madame stepped out for a few minutes. If you care to wait, I'm sure she'll be back soon."

My eye caught a piece of sculpture I had seen reproduced in a periodical. I went over to study it more closely.

"Ah," said the young woman, "you admire Alberto Giacometti's work. So do I. I have followed his progress for many years. Madame knows him well and can give you more information about him."

Just then the bell tinkled again, and Madame came in. "*Mais, voilà, Mademoiselle,*" she said while taking off her coat, "it is a pleasure to see you again so soon."

She remembered me!

Her assistant said, "Mademoiselle is interested in the sculpture of Giacometti."

"Ah, *bien.* You also are a sculptor, *n'est-ce pas?* Madame Scheyer said you have talent."

An hour later I had seen all the pieces she had of Giacometti — about a dozen — and the work of several other sculptors as well. I was about to leave when she said, "Would you like to meet Alberto?"

"But of course, Madame."

"Here ...." She scribbled on a piece of paper. "Here is his address. I shall write a note to tell him you will be there on ... shall we say ... Monday ... about six o'clock? *Très bien. Au revoir, Mademoiselle.* It has been a pleasure. Please come back any time. I would like to see your work one day."

How easy it had been! My feet danced inches above the pavement and headed in a direction away from home, knowing intuitively where Brancusi lived. Brancusi — the greatest sculptor of them all. I was no longer timid. Madame Scheyer had told him to expect me. Why should I wait?

The elderly man, gentle, of small stature, and with a neat grey beard, welcomed me cordially. I was suddenly surrounded by soothing shapes and lines. Sculpture was everywhere — large pieces and small. None of it intruded — it belonged there — part of the environment, part of the old man, an extension of himself, unperturbed, invulnerable.

We sat on an ivory-colored divan with yellow cushions facing the large fireplace of white stone. I knew he had cut the face of it himself — that he had been carving wood and stone ever since he was a poor shepherd boy in Romania.

When I commented on it he said, "Oh, yes, I've made most of my furniture, and many of my tools, as well. I find carving, working with wood, keeps me close to not only the earth, but the universe, also. All things — even the inanimate — have a consciousness ...."

That was the essence of our *tête-à-tête*. He talked easily with a minimum of prodding. Eventually I got him on the subject of the conflict between his "Bird in Space" and the U.S. customs officials.

He laughed and shook his head in despair. "They absolutely refused to believe it was a sculpture! Even accused me of trying to smuggle in a component for some industrial setup. We were in the courts for two years but finally, in 1928, I won. As you can imagine, it was excellent publicity." The elderly man beamed like a boy. "Since then I have exhibited and sold very much in the States, so I am no longer angry."

"And now the public is accepting your simplification of physical features."

"They are beginning, at least. It is most evident in the mannequins one now sees in the shop windows. What got me started in that direction was that when people saw a sculpture of a person, someone would inevitably say, 'How wonderful! Look at the expression on the face. Isn't it beautiful?' They see only the visage and ignore the whole. So I thought — if I remove the face, then they will be obliged to consider the entire sculpture — the basic substance of it. Most people are still living in the Romantic Age, when they were fed pretty pictures and stories with happy endings."

I asked if he ever took pupils.

"No. I tried, but teaching disturbs me. Sometimes I take on young sculptors to do odds and ends of carving that requires no genius. In a short while I may need another. Come back, Mademoiselle, from time to time. Perhaps I can use your help before long."

Chapter Forty

It would be difficult to find two artists more dissimilar than Constantin Brancusi and Alberto Giacometti. Though he was only thirty-one, Giacometti's face seemed old — weary and deeply lined. His wild hair was of a nondescript color, and the hand that clasped mine was calloused and strong.

"*Bienvenue, Mademoiselle.* Welcome. I am happy you have come. Jeanne Bucher wrote well of you." His mellow voice was cordial. "I'll show you my work, then we'll have coffee so I can hear about yours."

Tranquility and neatness were missing. The floor had obviously not been swept or, rather, shovelled out for years. In the corners were mounds of cigarette butts, plaster scrapings and debris of all sorts. The workbench in the center was cluttered with tools, folios, and work in progress. To one side against the wall was a couch where he apparently slept, and a small table — incongruous in the setting — covered by a pure-white linen cloth, two porcelain cups and saucers, and a polished silver dish with pastries.

"My sculpture's nothing special," he said. "I'm not earning a living from it, and there isn't much here to show you. But I'm flattered you came."

"However that may be, you are recognized. That's important. In the last issue of *Transition* I saw photos of two of your pieces — in wood, I think."

"*Mais oui,* yes. I made them a couple of years ago ... still have one .... I call it 'Suspended Ball' ... from my Surrealist time. Erotic, some say."

From a shelf behind a stack of books, he lifted the piece out and brushed off some of the dust with his sleeve. The object consisted of a small wooden sphere suspended from a bar by a thread over a fixed block in which was a curved groove. Giacometti pushed aside some tools, placed the piece on the workbench and, with a gentle touch, set the dangling ball in motion. Back and forth it swung directly over the groove, not quite touching it.

I gaped for a moment. A year before, I'd have blushed. What could I say? "Suggestive," I murmured, "and interesting."

Giacometti changed the subject. "Do you like working in wood?"

"Yes ... better than in stone. I'm on my second piece now. It's the act of carving I like. Clay requires a completely different approach. I've started something I might have cast in bronze — 'Fish in Water.'"

"It's good to keep changing — investigating new media and techniques."

Talking was easy. I felt we'd known each other for years. Over coffee the conversation turned to Italy, and we exchanged anecdotes from our travels there.

"Aren't you Italian?" I asked.

"My family's been Swiss for generations, but I believe my soul is Etruscan. Ever since I saw their sculpture — especially those thin, elongated bodies — I've felt a powerful bond with them. Weird. I'd been experimenting with that style even before I found it in museums." He leaned back in his chair, ran his fingers through his unkempt hair, and went on. "I'm going back to figurative ... but want to transcend reality. That's not easy to do ... in any medium." He threw his hands out in the air, grinned, and looked years younger. "All I can do is *try* to portray Intrinsic Man."

"I know what you mean," I said. "I've a problem, too, attempting to make water for my fish in bronze. It's not easy."

"I was going to ask how you solved that. When can I come and see it?"

We agreed on the following Saturday. "By then it should be nearly completed — in clay, that is. What about early afternoon?"

"I never wake up till after three. You see, I work all night. Let's say six o'clock on Saturday."

It was partly perverse habit that made me tidy the apartment on Saturday afternoon. The main reason, I convinced myself, was that I had a good half hour to spare before Giacometti arrived, and I couldn't think of anything else to do with the time.

"You have a lovely apartment and a splendid view," Giacometti said. "Don't you find it distracting?"

"Sometimes. But I'm used to it now. I've done a lot of work this week. Besides completing the fish, I've another piece to show you."

Cautiously, Giacometti helped me remove the damp cloths from my prime exhibit. I didn't have to wait for his reaction. It was evident in his face.

"A skillful solution," he said, "and satisfying the way you suggest the movement of water with that wavy strip at the side and the larger band encircling the fish as though it's swimming through a wave. *Très bien, Mademoiselle.* It will look well in bronze. First, I suppose you know, they'll reproduce it in wax and bring it back to you to correct any flaws. Then they'll make the final cast from the wax."

"That's the procedure called "lost wax," isn't it? They make a mold around it, melt away the wax and pour in the molten bronze where the wax was."

"That's right. And this other piece? Tell me about it."

"I'd rather you tell me what you see in it."

"*Alors* ... most people might say it's merely a column a foot high with a dent in it. But to me, it's not just any dent. I see a significant concavity with a slight bulge below it, and the shaft narrowing toward the base. Hmm ... might be 'Genesis' or 'Pride.'"

"*Voilà!* I've thought of calling it 'Creativity.' I want to carve it in stone, about a meter high, and polish it."

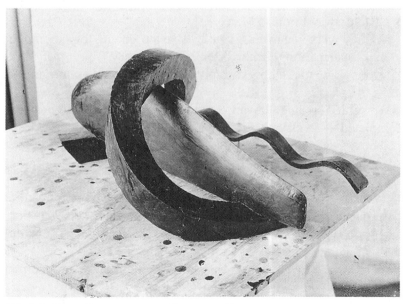

"Fish In Water"; wax version. Private collection.
Photo by Andreas Feininger.

"Creativity"; Whereabouts unkown.
Photo by Andreas Feininger.

"And these are the first two pieces you've done on your own ... in just a couple of weeks? I'd say you're on your way. What will you be doing in a couple of months?"

"I'm leaving in March. Going to Spain and then England."

"Eh, *bien* .... When you come back."

"No. After that I'm going to Moscow — to stay."

"To Russia?" He took two steps backwards, put his hands on his hips, half closed his eyes and whispered, "Mademoiselle, are you crazy?"

"But I have no money to stay here. And there's a war coming. What have you against Russia?"

"Not a damn thing! Scratch me and you'll probably find a Marxist. It's not that. What they need are engineers and scientists. Sure, I know, they honor artists, but so do we. They can do without you. They want socialist realism, not abstract phallic symbols of creativity." He sighed wearily and raked his fingers through his hair. "No money, you say. How many of us foreigners have come here with less than you? We shelved our vanity and did menial jobs so we could eat and go on working."

Then he shrugged, "Sorry, Mademoiselle. I shouldn't talk like that. You know what you're doing. You have your reasons." He looked at me under his bushy brows. "It isn't money, is it?"

"Only partly. There are lots of reasons. I don't want to lock myself in ... to be limited. The world is full of different ways of looking at things. I'm inquisitive. Frontiers and passports are uncivilized impediments. An artist is an artist, whether he sculpts sophisticated symbols in Paris or spiritual emblems in Africa. Diversity attracts me ... the unknown. I believe I could make it here ... if I tried ... if I wanted to. Then what?"

"Eh, *bien*. You don't want to give up your privacy. Neither do I. I've tried being antisocial, being incompatible, but some people call it eccentricity and even charming. Imagine that! *Alors*, Mademoiselle, I feel better about your going. It does make some sort of distorted sense. And now ... I must go ... home to work."

"Won't you have supper with us? My friend will be here soon. I'd like you to meet him."

"*Merci bien.* Some other time. I had breakfast just before coming here."

We said good-bye. At the door he turned with a grin and commented, "I do admire your guts."

Chapter Forty-One

71 rue Cardinale Lemoine
February 28, 1933

Darlings,

I'm getting ready to leave the City of Light — the city that has enlightened me, given me lessons on growing up, on using my mind and my talents.

I said "au revoir" to Zadkine when I finished the teakwood head. It was a sad good-bye. He called on me one day to see what I'd been doing at home, and said (as others have) that I am ready to work on my own.

The fish I was making is at the bronze caster's. A friend, Andreas, took pictures of several sculptures of mine. I showed them to Madame Bucher, who has an art gallery. She wants me to leave the fish with her. I don't know whether to cry or sing or dance. I've put a price on it of $250. That's high, but I don't want to sell it. Of course I'm honored my sculpture will be in Madame's gallery.

I went back to Brancusi's the other day and stayed a couple of hours watching him work. He's so gentle and unassuming, and seemed to like talking to me. If I were staying in Paris I'm sure that sooner or later, I could work for him.

I've told you, haven't I, Gordon has invited several of us to his home near Liverpool for a month or two? The boys will be working on a town planning competition for Antwerp. I'll see Spain first. There's a package deal from Paris to England, too tempting to turn down: all through Spain, with trains, some hotels, food, and an N.Y.K. liner from Gibraltar to Southampton — twenty days for only $52. Not bad.

I'm collecting information on Russia from people who have been there recently, and directly from the Soviet embassy. The official word is that I can go there as a tourist, tell the authorities I want to stay and work, and they'll give me permission. It sounds easy enough, but will it be?

I'll leave my stone and wood possessions here in storage for 80 cents a month — with a reliable company that will pack and ship, too, when necessary. Why, oh why didn't I become a writer instead of a sculptor? Then my heaviest tools would be a typewriter and a fountain pen, and I could carry my profession in one hand.

Eve and Edward arrived here yesterday. I showed off my sculpture, and they told me about Italy. Eve is lovely and I like her immensely, but I wouldn't want to be in her alligator pumps for anything. In spite of all her money, I think I'm richer than she. They go from one city to another doing the same thing: staying at the best hotels, drinking at fashionable bars, buying clothes and speaking only English. They're off to Brussels in a few days with a hired car and chauffeur, and will go to London in April.

Vance writes that John's father expects to be there then. What a reunion that should be!

I haven't mentioned Mary Knight for a long time. She lived at Reid Hall and is a correspondent for United Press. According to her, there's gossip that the U.S. is going off the gold standard soon.

I'm having dinner with Harry next week — in fact, the day Roosevelt is sworn in. I wonder if Harry will confirm the rumor. He's always been candid with me.

With love and all that,
Sisi

"I know how much you like Italian food," Harry said, "so when I heard of this new Florentine restaurant, I thought we'd try it together."

"A nice kind of salute to our futures." I said, "You're on your way to bigger responsibilities at the bank. Doesn't your trip to New York in April mean a promotion?"

"No, I don't think so. It's a private visit."

"But you do have a lot of inside information."

"Such as ....?"

"Oh ... as ... the U.S. going off the gold standard. Is it?"

Harry raised his eyebrows and cleared his throat. "I cannot tell a lie — at least not to you. I've heard talk of it. You'll know tomorrow. American banks have been closing at an alarming rate, and depositors are withdrawing their gold. Who can blame them? In his inaugural address today, Roosevelt borrowed a phrase from Thoreau — something about the only thing we have to fear is fear. Well, tomorrow he's going to declare a 'moratorium,' effective for four days, to stop the run on the banks. All dollar transactions will cease, and there'll be no export of gold, silver or currency."

"But that's tomorrow, and I'm leaving for Spain in two days! I have three hundred dollars in the bank! What'll I do, Harry?"

"You're okay, my dear. Your money is in French francs. Don't you remember — I had you change it all a couple of months ago?"

"You knew this was coming, didn't you?"

"More or less."

"Why do we have depressions, Harry? I was brought up to believe Capitalism had the answer to every economic problem — that it was nearly perfect."

"It is — for some — for the one or two percent that owns most of the world's riches. It's they who are running the show. It's this concentration of wealth that builds up and builds up into a speculative bubble. One day the bubble bursts and, *voilà,* we have a depression. Big money controls even what it doesn't own directly — newspapers, textbooks, advertising, armies. You think our country is a democracy? Capitalism is not democracy. We don't have free enterprise. We have monopolies. We don't have free speech. If you go home and criticize our treatment of the Negroes or Jews, or the Indians or Catholics, or say a good word about Russia or try to form a union, you'll be called a troublemaker and a Red, and be fired — if you have a job."

"Harry! How can you talk like that? You're working for the very people in control."

"Ha! I wouldn't be if they could hear me now."

"What could they do?"

"Well, for starters, they could make me look like an embezzler, or get me eliminated — 'accidently.'"

"How do you know they're not on to you?"

"I don't. Here — have some more wine. It's Chianti. So — you'll be in Spain in a couple of days. They have good wine, too — different, but very good."

"It's peaceful there, I hear, since they got rid of the king."

"I wonder for how long."

"What do you mean?"

"It's common knowledge that the Duke of Alba can travel from the north of Spain down to the south without setting foot off his land."

"So what? He's rich."

"The liberal parties and peasants — some are terribly poor — are talking about agrarian reform. So you think the great landowners will ever let that happen?"

"How can they stop it?"

"They'll find an unscrupulous man with ambition who will start by declaring solidarity with the reformers. Then, as soon as he's in, backed by the industrialists, he'll show his colors, and the poor be damned."

"Sounds like what happened in Germany and Italy."

"That's exactly what happened."

"Gosh. Roosevelt claims to be a friend of the dispossessed. Do you think he'll turn out that way? Is he bluffing?"

"It's too early to tell. He's been in office only a day."

"Harry ... are you a Red?"

"Heavens, no! I don't think Communism is the solution. I'm an ambitious, incurable Capitalist. That's why I can see it for what it is."

"Why are you telling me all this stuff?"

"Partly, my dear, to ease my conscience, and because you're going away. I can't tell Sonya or my other friends. They'd misunderstand. Besides, I wanted to contribute to your education. You shouldn't go off to Moscow ignorant of what you'll be comparing Communism with."

"I'll drink to that," I said as we clinked glasses.

With a wily grin, Harry went on, "And when you read derogatory reports in our papers about the Soviets, take them with a grain of salt. A lot of what our press tells us is distorted or simply invented. I'm going to miss our casual dinners, Agnes. You'll keep me posted, won't you?"

Chapter Forty-Two

At two a.m. I awoke and stood at the open window of the train. We were rolling through a flat landscape, naked except for the umbrella pines with their long, bare trunks topped by a cluster of evergreen branches.

Ahead, in the distance, the foothills of the Pyrenees grew larger. We'd soon stop at Narbonne, not far from the Spanish border. The warm night air smelled clean and new. Between the train and the silhouette of the mountains was a lake with the full moon floating on its surface.

I lay down again, stretched out on my padded bench with a sweater for a pillow. François was sound asleep across the aisle.

I shut my eyes and let thoughts wander through my mind. A new chapter in my life was beginning. How would it read in six months? Why did I seem to gravitate to the unknown, and turn my back on the comparatively secure? Because I was Peer Gynt's daughter, running away from the Button-Moulder?

John would have a fit if he knew I'd left Paris, abandoning all I might have accomplished there, among people who could have helped me over the bumps — the Arps, Brancusi, Giacometti, Bucher ....

And Madame Scheyer would be back in April ... only a month away. She'd have a fit, too, probably. Was I letting John and her down?

But she always said people should do what they, not others, feel is right. Okay. So François and I were on our way to Moscow — with a detour through Spain, England, Holland, Germany and Czechoslovakia. That's what I wanted to do.

François stirred, stretched, and sat up. I went back to the window. "The train is slowing," I said. "The border can't be far away. We'll be in Barcelona in an hour or so."

Barcelona, Spain
March 9, 1933

Darlings,

I wish I could describe every moment and every step in this Latin land, but I'm afraid I'll have time to send you only brief notes now and then.

A colleague of François', who works with Corbu and also has his own studio here, drove us about in his tiny car and gave us helpful suggestions for our itineraries. He is José Sert, one of the best city planners in Europe, though he's only about thirty.

We walked through the old quarter, and had lunch in a plebeian restaurant near the docks: fish soup with white wine, a large dish of lobster, shrimps, snails, squid, clams, with rice and red wine. Dessert was a gigantic orange. The bill was 30 cents a piece.

In the evening, José took us to a famous music hall where the customers were professional men and laborers. I was the only female, but obviously a foreigner with proper escort, so Sert assured us it was okay. Entertainment consisted of buxom women on the stage, scantily dressed, high-kicking, and singing ribald songs. It's easy to tell when humor is off-color by the kind of laughter it evokes. The custom is that, if one of the audience takes a fancy to a dancer, he sends an usher to her with a note. If she agrees, they retire upstairs.

Valencia
March 11

I've never met such courtesy, dignity, hospitality and animation. I'm captivated. Spain is a mixture of races. Blonds are not rare. Even the Vikings invaded a thousand years ago. Just now in the street below our hotel windows, a Gypsy girl is dancing to the rhythm of a drum beat. The Moors developed an elaborate canal system that still brings water from the mountains to irrigate the plains of this region to produce rice, and oranges so plentiful they literally roll in the gutters and cost almost nothing.

Last night at an eating house, we had wine, a small loaf of bread and fresh sardines fried in olive oil. Three fishermen at our table used their fingers, ate heads and all, wiped their hands and chins with chunks of bread and then consumed the bread. When they saw us doing the same, they insisted on treating us to a carafe of wine to show their pleasure.

Madrid
March 14

Madrid has elegant Baroque buildings and broad boulevards crowded till late at night with noisy people, and music broadcast into the out-of-doors. At first we thought they were having a holiday, but now know it happens every evening.

We missed seeing a bull fight the other day because it rained. But we've been to all the important museums which have a lot of Goya, El Greco, Velasquez.

Public transportation is by streetcar, and very efficient. A mailbox is attached to the outside of every car, and when it comes to the central post office, the letters are unloaded. Inside the cars are conspicuous signs that read, "Please do not spit on the floor or on the walls."

Every tourist tries to visit El Escorial, tucked in the mountains about 25 miles away. It's an immense, austere monastery built about 400 years ago with harmonious lines and proportions, 1,100 windows, the private chambers of Phillip II, a church, a burial vault for Spanish kings, and a library of rare books and manuscripts.

Toledo
March 15

This was already a city in 193 B.C. when the Romans conquered it because of its steel armaments. Weapons are still made here. Marzipan, too.

I'll never forget Toledo, but not for those things or for its fabulous position on high, bathed on three sides by a river. Nor for its architecture in Arab, Jewish and Christian traditions. I'll remember three small boys we made friends with while rambling through the crooked streets. They wanted to practice French, so became our guides, pointing out El Greco's house, a Catholic church built as a synagogue centuries ago, and other interesting places.

The next morning, they found us again. Before saying adios *we lamented not having seen a bull fight. A signal passed among*

217

them and suddenly, right there on the boulevard, the biggest boy became a toro, snorting and roughing up the ground with his hoof; another boy was a torero, provoking the bull with his imaginary cloak, while the littlest was transformed into the collective audience, cheering the celebrated hero with impassioned whoops and roars. I'm sure the real spectacle would not have thrilled us more.

I'm writing this sitting at the station waiting for the train, which is an hour late. We'll get to Cordoba in time for breakfast so will sleep on the train and save a hotel bill.

Cordoba
March 16

Here we can see a mixture of at least five cultures: Roman, Visigoth, Moor, Jewish, and Christian. Sometimes they blended, or lent each other skills, or stood distinctly alone.

Once upon a time, Cordoba must have been glorious. I can imagine people strolling the cobbled streets long ago, wearing robes of exquisite silk brocade hand-woven right here, and jewelry and leather fashioned by local artisans; the buildings are embellished with designs in marble and gold mosaics, the peasants make or grow what they need, and there are no paupers.

Then comes the Industrial Revolution. Craftsmen are replaced by machines and mass indigence begins. The Dukes of Elba own most of the land.

Today, in 1933, beggars are everywhere. The poverty and lack of sanitation is appalling. Every third person seems to have some illness. Little ragged children with sores follow us constantly, and old people stand silent, with cheerless expressions and palms held out.

It's time for another sweeping change to clean up what the kings left. Will they elect a man who promises to make reforms but is really a puppet of big corporations?

Granada
Sunday, March 19

We've moved eastward, to within 50 miles of the Mediterranean Sea. Granada is famous for two things: the Gypsies living in comparative luxury in caves dug into the rocky hillside, and the Alhambra, a Moorish palace and fortress built 700 years ago. Washington Irving, who lived there when he was our ambassador to Spain, described it in a book.

Algeciras
March 20

A locomotive, hardly bigger than a toy, brought our train here. In our third-class compartment, we met a German missionary couple who've lived 29 years in Spain. Besides giving us a lot of local history, they advised us where best to eat fish in Algeciras for only 11 cents.

The sun was setting as we arrived. We headed straight for the docks to watch the late fishing boats tie up.

Algeciras is the most southerly point of the Iberian Peninsula and faces Gibraltar across the bay. From the pier where we stood, the Rock rested dark against the dusky sky. One by one, lights came on, then a string of them and another string, all reflected in the still water of the bay.

I have now seen Fairyland — for real.

This morning we crossed to the British Colony of Gibraltar and booked tickets for Southampton on an N.Y.K. liner, leaving April 5. That's a couple of weeks away, and we've decided to spend them in Africa. So we're off to another continent, only 90 minutes from here by regular ferry.

Adios, au revoir, good-bye and aloha!

With love,
Sisi

Chapter Forty-Three

Our crowded ferry steamed southward across the Strait of Gibraltar toward Africa. François and I leaned against the rail to watch the frothy wake trailing at the stern.

"My first time out of Europe." François' expression was smug. "But, I assure you, not my last. The Rock back there ... not bad, with those morning clouds for a crown. Ulysses may have seen it just like that. Our odyssey will take us much farther afield than the Pillars of Hercules. We'll see the Urals and Caucasus and Fujiyama and ..." he put an arm around my waist, "and I'm taking Circe along with me."

"Come on," I said, gripping his hand and pulling him away, "let's go to the prow and discover that other continent."

What we saw from up front resembled an abstract painting. In the distance, Spanish Morocco emerged on the tip of Africa. The infinite blue sky was separated from the bluer sea by a thin, uneven white strip: the low buildings of the town of Ceuta.

We were intruders in another world. Men stood about the narrow streets talking quietly in groups or walking solemnly, minding their business. Some were swathed in white woolen robes, others in colored trousers, short to the knees and baggy at the back for easy squatting, or in colored jackets and turbans. We saw no women.

"I feel out of place," I whispered to François.

"So do I. Let's head on to French Morocco."

A bumpy bus took us from Ceuta to Tetuan, to Rio Martin, to Xauen and, after a short way on horseback, to Alcazarquivir. By another bus, we saw Larache on the Atlantic, and Tangier before returning to Algiciras by ferry.

We watched Arabs making leather slippers, weaving fabrics, and fishing with long nets as our Hawaiians do. We sketched, and painted watercolors, and gaped in awe at the scenery. Hills of brilliant green vegetation showed patches of bare earth, the color of red lead, cut by winding, unpaved roads of the same red; seascapes of wave-beaten crags, towns and hamlets of simple blue or white houses, hardly touched by our so-called "progress" — all of it under that enormous vault of sapphire sky. For two weeks, the only other Europeans we talked to were a retired English general and his wife at a *pension* in Xauen.

Back at the steamship office in Gibraltar, the young clerk had our tickets ready: two third-class bunks on the Dutch motorship *Dempo*, bound for Southampton.

That evening we devoted to reading English newspapers. For two weeks, we had ignored the world: Hitler proclaimed a totalitarian state and his official goal to eliminate all Jews from Germany .... A devastating earthquake struck Long Beach .... The end of Prohibition prompted frenzied rejoicing across the United States ....

Aboard MS Dempo
April 9, 1933
Bay of Biscay

Dearest All of You,

Tomorrow we'll disembark at Southampton and take a bus to London Town, where Vance will meet us.

The "Dempo" is gorgeous. Even in third class, we eat extremely well. I like the Dutch. I'm sharing a stateroom in a cabin below the water line at the stern with two women. The engine isn't very noisy, but its rhythmic reverberations function as a soothing lullaby.

Last night we were awakened at midnight when the engine stopped. Up on deck, we witnessed the sinking of a freighter that had suffered an explosion. An amazing sight, as several ships gathered and shone lights on the disaster. The crew and some passengers, about a dozen in all, were unhurt and came aboard our ship. As they climbed up the rope ladder from their lifeboat, each carrying a small suitcase of personal treasures, one women's valise opened, and all of its contents fell into the Bay of Biscay.

In first class is a retired English general and his wife, whom we met in Morocco. We've had some nice chats. This evening, in bidding our good-byes, she said to me, "It's been a pleasure

knowing you and your friend, François. My husband and I have
traveled a great deal in all parts of the world — even far beyond
the Empire." She hesitated before going on. " ... I understand you
two are not married." I nodded. "My dear, I want you to have our
address .... If you are ever in trouble, please, please count on me
to help you."
A big lump formed in my throat. I could hardly thank her.

Love to everyone,
Sis

Chapter Forty-Four

From Southampton, we proceeded to London. Vance lived in a
boarding house in Bloomsbury, within haunting distance of the spirits of that exclusive group of liberated intellectuals — Virginia Woolf,
E.M. Forster, Lytton Strachey, Bertrand Russell, Aldous Huxley, T.S.
Elliott, and others — who, since 1907, had challenged every accepted
idea.

"Don't be fooled by the apparent modesty," Vance said as he unlocked the door of 77 Guilford Street. "Only pompous sages live
here."

"I know, I know," I said. "Quality of life — not standard of living.
Is that why you're wearing a bowler hat and affecting a cane?"

Vance laughed. "All right. I knew you'd confront me with that sooner
or later. I *had* to acquire this camouflage, I mean — dress as my
friends, so I wouldn't be conspicuous. Well, comrades, here's your
room right across the hall from mine. You two make yourselves comfortable and then we'll go over to Soho and have lunch."

We walked the few blocks to Soho, past delicatessen shops and
restaurants that exuded aromas not characteristically English.

"You've got the entire world right here!" François said. "Hindu,
Chinese, Jewish, Nigerian ...."

"Which will it be?" Vance asked.

We settled for Italian, filled our glasses with Chianti, our plates
with pasta and our curiosities with news of all our close friends.

"A year ago, Vance, you were poor. Do you want to tell me where
you found the means to come to London for a year? Are you a Rhodes
Scholar?"

"Even better! I'm a rogue scholar. An anonymous benefactor made it possible." He laughed aloud. "John's father is in town now ... at the Savoy. We're going there this evening. Eddie and Eve were here, but went to Scotland till tomorrow."

"She's beautiful," I said, "especially in her high-fashion clothes. But still ... enigmatic. Don't you think so?"

"Hmm, rather. If I had to describe her in a book, I'd say, 'She tore off the days of her life as though they were worthless pages of a calendar and tossed them carelessly away ....'"

"Eloquent, my dear Vance, but a bit strong."

"No, it's not. She's unhappy. We had a long talk one night last week when I took her dancing. She wished she could toot around the world with a man she adored, thumbing her nose at conventions, as you do."

"Well, what's stopping her?"

"I asked her that, and she said she lacked self-confidence. You know, they hired a car and chauffeur to drive from Paris to Belgium, spent the entire trip drinking and had, literally, to be poured into their suite in Brussels. She'd be better off without all that money, but I can't imagine her sleeping on a third-class train to save a hotel bill."

"We didn't do it for fun," François said. "For us, it was either that way or not at all. I'd never turn down a hotel suite or limousine."

"For me to live as Eve does," I said, "that would take real courage. I'd get drunk, too. Now tell me about Pop Embree. He's more interesting."

"He's here on business, so he brought his secretary along and ... and Grace, as well."

"But didn't Grace remarry recently?"

"Yes. But the Embrees are pretty fond of her and thought she'd like a trip."

"Gosh ... I feel a little weak," I said. "Maybe I'll just go on to Liverpool with François this afternoon."

"No you won't," François said quietly. "You'll stay here a week as we planned, see your old friends, and meet Grace."

"He's right," Vance said. "You've nothing to worry about. She told me yesterday *she* was concerned about meeting *you*. I know you both well, I think. She's an intelligent young woman and happily married now. In fact, she and Mumford are planning a large family. Now she looks back dispassionately on her episode as John's wife, although you can imagine how it hurt at the time."

In the elevator at the Savoy, I whispered to Vance, "The qualms in my stomach won't go away."

He squeezed my arm and looked down at me with assurance. "It's going to be all right."

And it was. As soon as we entered Mr. Embree's rooms, my uneasiness seemed absurd. A half a dozen people sat in comfortable chairs drinking highballs and laughing at someone's humorous remark.

Pop Embree clasped my shoulders. "You look wonderful, Agnes," he said convincingly. "Come and meet Grace, and my secretary, and our English friends."

How painless it was. The warmth I had known two summers before at High Cliff glowed again inside of me. Grace took my hand with a firm grip. We didn't speak, but her eyes told me what I wanted to know. There was no time or place in her life for rancor.

Much of the evening's discourse was about Mr. Embree's two books. The latest, a series of philosophical conversations among people close to him, wasn't selling well. The first, *Brown America*, dealing with the plight of Negroes in the United States, was still in demand. Mr. Embree's job was head of the Rosenwald Fund, established for the education and advancement of American Negroes.

"It's ironic," Vance said, "that the people who gave jazz to world culture should be treated with an almost total lack of respect."

"Right you are," said one of the Englishmen. "Jazz is the first of the two new art forms you Yankees have given us."

"The other," Mr. Embree said, "being the development of the movies. The Jews, for the most part, did that. And yet, we Anglo-Saxons look down on both communities."

"And he who consorts with them," added Grace, "is looked at with contempt and suspicion, as being disloyal to his breed."

"Unless ..." Mr. Embree threw in with a chuckle, "... unless he's wealthy — in which case he can do no wrong."

While they talked on about the late Julius Rosenwald, curiosity made me stare at Grace whenever I could do so unnoticed. Her feelings varied, and showed clearly in her well-proportioned face: humor, doubt, opposition, accord.

Such a head, that didn't need or use makeup, would make a fine sculpture in bronze.

Chapter Forty-Five

29 Salisbury Ave.
West Kirby, Cheshire
Friday, April 28, 1933

Dearest Everyone,

We're a block from the water, a few miles west of Liverpool, where the River Dee meets the Irish Sea. The Stephensons have a two-story house, much like all the others on Salisbury Avenue, with tidy gardens in the front and rear. Bill and Alex are bunking there, but François and I are across the street at Gordon's cousin's.

I thought of telling you only I was staying there but, since the British are so tolerant and civilized, and think nothing of François and me sharing a room, I don't see why I should mislead you. Evidently, all the Old World Puritans have moved to America.

Every morning, François and I are awakened by Flossie, the maid, bringing us each a cup of tea. Then we go down to breakfast with Roland, Jean and little Roger, aged three. I spend the day helping the boys with some drawings, or Mrs. Stephenson with the housework. If no one needs me, I take my bag of tools and walk way down the shore, along the cliff. The cliff is of red sandstone and rather bare of vegetation and of people, too.

The other day I found a chunk of the red stone about fourteen inches long and eight inches thick that was sort of the shape of a weird head, and I couldn't resist chiselling. I came back several days in a row to carve. No one saw me working, and I didn't tell anyone. When I finished it, I left it there on the cliff — on a whim.

Before supper, I usually run with the boys along the beach, or bowl on the green, then listen to the news on the radio and discuss the latest political events. War seems inevitable. Till then, living is wonderful!

The bus ride from London took nine hours, over gentle, emerald hills, through towns where inns have names like Boar's Head and The Rose and Thistle, past old timbered structures, and cottages with thatched roofs.

Roland has a speedy touring car and tomorrow is driving us into Wales to have tea at one of those storybook inns.

Sunday, May 14

The boys are on their final drawings for the Antwerp competition. We're all satisfied with their solutions for the new city. The commercial, civic and cultural centers are placed so the heavy traffic of the future will flow easily. All living quarters are in tall buildings, exposed to the sun for a part of each day, and have recreation grounds close at hand.

The plans must be in Antwerp by May 31, so in about three weeks, we'll all be going our separate ways. François and I will head for Czechoslovakia to visit his family in Pilsen, traveling by way of Amsterdam and Berlin.

Hitler's speeches are intoxicating the Germans. He repeats that the Jews are the cause of unemployment, and prosperity will return when they are eliminated. He sent Dr. Rosenberg to London to enlist friends in Britain. Instead, he took an awful razzing last week. The wreath he placed on the tomb of the Unknown Soldier was thrown into the Thames by a good citizen who said Rosenberg's gesture was hypocritical.

Rosenberg then held a press conference and was asked so many awkward questions about the treatment of German Jews and Socialists that he walked out, past a group of anti-Nazis with banners saying, "Rosenberg, go home!" "Down with Hitler, the Hun," and so on. The tragedy is that he has friends in England, and some are in high places, as, for example, the Prince of Wales.

Thursday, May 25

We're awfully tired, working our heads off all day and much of the night till 2:00 a.m and less than a week to go. There are a number of drawings — charts and perspectives — the largest of which is three meters by three. My job is to sketch in people and vehicles to scale on the streets.

Mrs. Stephenson runs in and out with bowls of stew, pots of tea and apple pies. Except for the kitchen and bathrooms, every part of the house has been converted into a studio. Going from one room to another requires stepping over jars of paint and ink, piles of scrap paper and eraser crumbs, and hurdling drafting boards, T-squares, tea cups and bodies of pooped-out architects.

Bill and Gordon will carry everything to Antwerp and personally set up the exhibit. So far, 250 people have applied for the rules of the competition — fifty of them from the U.S.S.R. The winners will be announced in August. First prize is $2,500. There will be two second prizes and four third.

Saturday, June 3

At noon on the last day we were still finishing various charts and dodging the photographer who had come to record the documents.

Since the plans departed, none of us has done a serious thing. We've been swimming and, when the tide is out, walking to a little island to dig cockle shells. Some of us play golf or bowl or just run about the countryside.

Now we're rested, packed, ready and unwilling to leave. Next stop: Amsterdam.

François' sister, Milca, has written that I'll be very welcome at her home in Pilsen.

Much love,
Sisi

The day we arrived at our boarding house in Amsterdam, Mama and Papa Wehr and their son-in-law were present. Mama let the two men fix the charge for our five-day stopover. We found the rate reasonable and gave Mama our passports to be registered with the police, as was customary in all of Europe.

We were getting ready for dinner when Mama knocked at our door. She was a handsome woman, about fifty, and modestly dressed in discerning taste.

"I am returning your passports," she said with a subdued voice." Forgive me for mentioning it, but I noticed you are not husband and wife. Please ... I don't wish to embarrass you, only .... We'll not tell the rest of the family. It's possible they would not approve." She waited for us to agree and then added with a finger to her lips, "And the price of your lodging ... it will be ten percent less. All right? Dinner is in twenty minutes."

We were in the bosom of the family — ten of us around the long dining table, with Papa at the head and Mama at the other end. Each of the regulars who came in paused beside Papa and fawningly wished him a good appetite before taking his or her place. Papa acknowledged the tributes with a formal smile and nod of his head.

On his right sat a longtime boarder from Delft, a medical student at the university. Then there was Papa's brother — short, chubby and oily — who liked to puff on a cigar and never failed to end each meal with a fatuous joke.

Beside him sat the family's younger daughter — a sweet, shy, girl in her teens, who had stopped studying to learn the art of housekeeping from her mother.

The chair between her and Mama was occupied by the son-in-law, a stuffed shirt of about thirty-five, already balding and developing a "paunch of prosperity." He liked to discourse at length on foreign currencies and trade, and wanted us to be aware that he knew how to live. Had he not traveled to *Amerika* a few years ago?

His wife, the elder daughter, sat on the other side of Mama, aloof and indifferent. Even the enthusiasm of the young composer on her right didn't infect her. Because he had studied music in Prague, the composer and François kept up an active conversation in Czech.

My place was between François and Papa, who was so sure only he knew everything worth knowing. I felt it wiser to observe than participate.

Evenings presented a different tableau. Around nine-thirty, most of the household reassembled at the large table for tea. Papa and ceremony were missing. The son-in-law, apparently aiming to be worthy of Papa's chair one day, expounded his theories on various philosophies of life while his wife, unmoved, drank her tea. The medical student read a biography of Marie Curie, and the younger sister crocheted a cushion cover.

Silently, in slippered feet, Grandmama would appear. She crossed the dining room to a corner where she sat in a rocker and turned the radio on low enough for only her to hear.

Breakfast was total informality. The dining room table overflowed with food and beverages. People came when they pleased and helped themselves to as little or as much as they wished of breads, sausages, eggs, cheeses, smoked fish, jams, and coffee, tea, cocoa and milk.

I had never seen anything like it.

Germany
June 14, 1933

Darling Everyone,

We're on the move once more — en route due east to Berlin. Holland was full of touristy things to do — a bicycle ride out to Hilversum to see some modern architecture, and a boat ride to Volendam and the Island of Marken in the Zuider Zee. In those two towns the people still wear native costumes every day, as you'll see on the post cards I'm sending.

Our boarding house in Amsterdam was inexpensive and comfortable. I've never seen anything like it. The family —

I put my letter away and stood at the window looking out at the summer landscape, though seeing nothing. François glanced up from his paper.

"It's hard to write, isn't it, when the train jostles so?"

"That's not it." I sat on the bench facing him. "I can't get the Wehr household out of my mind. You know, two years in Europe and that's the first time I've watched an average family in action without disguise. Tourists never see that inner side of a country. Maybe one day I'll write a story about them ... get into the ego of each personality, understand how and why they interact the way they do."

"Aha! A drama! Who would be the central figure? Papa?"

"No, no. Mama. She's the power behind the throne. In her inconspicuous way, she keeps them all together. She listens, never contradicts, then does everything her way, always giving credit to someone else — never to herself. Only because she's so strong, and knows her strength, is she able to pull it off so well."

"Old Grandmama survived," said François, "with her autonomy intact. And the two daughters will, too, I'll bet. Don't forget to describe the fringed lamp shades and plush upholstery."

"You're right. Then I can give it a title with a double meaning: *Dutch Interior.*"

229

Chapter Forty-Six

23 Uhland Strasse
Berlin, Germany
Wed., June 21, 1933

Darling Everyone,

*I have applied for a visa at the Soviet embassy. Here's how it works:
I must go in as a tourist because I don't already have a job there.
To get a tourist visa, I have to determine my itinerary and length
of stay, and pay in advance for everything, including meals and
return fare.*

*I filled out several forms, supplied two photos, paid for five days
in Moscow, a guide, interpreter and city transportation. Third class
costs $45. A month and a half in Spain and Morocco cost less!
The visa is valid for one month but may be extended.*

*François is fluent in German and saw me through the visa business
before he left for Czechoslovakia yesterday. I'll be able to defend
myself with the help of a dictionary and the few phrases I use to
death. Many Germans speak English, but few know, or admit to
knowing, French.*

Sat., June 24

*I'm still in Berlin, in a café, isolated from the wind and rain. I
planned to spend the day on the shore of a nearby lake, but the
weather sent me to the American Institute to see what I could see.
The affable host was the director, Dr. Bertling, sporting a scar on
his cheek — similar to many of his generation — a memento of his
fencing days in college. He introduced a young architect from
"Amerika" who was about to show a documentary he'd made on
the building of Rockefeller Center in N.Y.*

*The architect, Mr. Killam, started filming at the earliest planning
of the project and continued through its completion. To the usual
question, "Why did they do it?" he said Rockefeller had already
leased three blocks from Columbia University. It would cost three
million a year to keep, so he hoped to get some returns from it.*

After the show, Dr. and Frau Bertling took several guests, including Killam and me (the only non-Nazis) to an open-air café in the Tiergarten. It was like living a documentary. Uniformed officers strutted through the park, saluting each other and clicking their heels. The swastika fluttered everywhere. The conversation focused on the mutual benefits of good relations between the U.S. and the Third Reich.

Killam left that evening for the Black Forest to spend a week walking through the woods in solitude, playing his flute. He said that might blow out the bitter taste of Nazism.

I got a beautiful letter from you today, Mom, approving my decision to go to Moscow with François. As you say, if you were in my shoes, you'd claim the right to make your own choice. You did, too, when you left Norway at eighteen for the "wilds" of South Africa. I'm glad I have your blessing. And I'm going to thank Vance for writing you the letter that got rid of your apprehensions.

Before François left, I talked him into cutting my hair. I'm sorry, but long tresses are too much trouble while I'm a nomad.

I've asked the Soviet embassy to forward my visa to Prague because François wants me to be there on July 1. He and four friends are organizing a canoe trip down the Moldau River. We'll take the train to Budjovice — what we call Budweiser — near the source of the river, close to Austria. From there, we'll paddle downstream about 200 kilometers (130 miles), cook our own meals and pitch tents at night.

auf Wiedersehen,
Sisi

During the decades since that distant summer of 1933, I can relive our two weeks meandering down the Moldau whenever I hear a certain piece of music. It's one of a series of symphonic poems written by Bedrich Smetana, a Czech patriot and composer. Before the Great War, when Bohemia was part of the Austrian Empire, Smetana's music inspired the people in their struggle for independence. The opus he called *The Moldau* describes closely the adventures the six of us experienced in our pair of canoes.

The music begins with two mountain springs gurgling over crags, and trickling downward.

We put our boats into the river where the bubbling streams merged in the shade of mountain woods. Then we navigated, or drifted with the current whose gentle rhythms obeyed the baton of Smetana. The composer must have known every movement of the flow, every surge and billow, each ripple and eddy. He put them all in the *pastorale* ... even the village festival on our second day, with folk dances and rustic flirtations — those fugues of summer fairs that keep the countryside lively. We mingled well, taking part in the diversions as though we belonged.

Smetana played for us at night, as well, around our campfires. His melodic zephyrs fanned the trees and stalks of grain, evoked elusive calls of forest creatures, and blended the scents of wildflowers with the fragrance of new-plowed earth in the fields.

Near the end, as we thrilled to maneuver the rapids, Smetana increased the tempo and volume to a resounding *finale*.

We were children again, for the last time, squealing and whooping as though all were right with the world, mindless of the ugly forces beyond the horizon preparing disaster for Bohemia and many other lands.

Long, long after we're all gone, *The Moldau* will still play, and flow on.

Too soon, we were back in the man-made world of laws and strife. My visa came and the Soviet consul stamped it in my passport. The next, and final, event before leaving was to meet François' family in Pilsen.

"I'd better get there a day before you," François explained to me, "because my father needs to be put in tune. He's not exactly an advocate of our way of living. I'll be staying at his house, and you'll be at my sister's. Her two boys are little rascals, but you'll get on well. They're all eager to meet you."

"What if your father doesn't like me?"

"Not *like* you? He probably won't. You just wait and see. He's more apt to *love* you. Now, I'd suggest you get the ten o'clock train, and I'll meet you at the station."

But I misunderstood. I later learned he meant for me to leave Prague at ten o'clock, and I thought I was to arrive in Pilsen at that time. Consequently, I saw no one I knew when I got there. I walked the few blocks to Milca's, No. 55 on Otakarovy Sady.

I found the apartment one flight up with no difficulty, pressed the doorbell, heard it buzz somewhere within, and waited — but not for long. A small dog barked. Noisy shouts and footsteps, like a platoon of hussars, approached. The door opened wide, and two small boys with flaxen hair and huge blue eyes stood there, expressions frozen, in a mixture of confusion and disbelief.

The older one — that was Otto, aged five — whispered, "Agnes?"

I had hardly nodded when he clasped one of my arms, while his brother — Kamil, three — took the other. I let them steer me, galloping into the living room and over to the davenport where we rolled onto the seat. A uniformed maid appeared in a doorway as we tumbled and wrestled playfully. To stifle a laugh, she raised her hand to her face, turned abruptly and left the room without interrupting our affectionate fracas.

Their little dog yapped, trying in vain to join us, as the door opened again, and a tall young man strode in.

"That's enough now, boys! Let's see who you've captured this time."

The rough and tumble stopped, and Otto introduced me. The man gave me a hand and pulled me to my feet.

"I needn't tell you how welcome you are, need I? They have just initiated you into the family. I am François' brother, Joseph."

We were all still laughing when Milca came in, tossed her coat and hat onto a chair and embraced me.

"My dear," she said in French, "I am so happy you have come." She kissed both my cheeks. The scent of lavender surrounded me. "For a long time, we have been looking forward to meeting you." Milca was tall and blonde and beautiful.

Otto tugged at his mother's sleeve. She listened to what he had to say, then laughed and told me, "We explained to the boys that you don't speak Czech. To them, there are only two languages: Czech and Moravian. You see, every summer we spend our holidays in the province of Moravia. Now he wants to know what gibberish I am speaking to you."

François arrived soon afterwards with Milca's husband, and the hours sped by. At suppertime, I was ready to meet Grandfather Sammer, a formal occasion, not without warmth or humor. No one disapproved of me! François' young half-brother, Jan, broke the ice, commenting that he had expected me, coming from Hawaii, to have long black hair and dark skin and eyes.

"You sound disappointed," I teased.

233

"No .... Yes .... Well, it would have been an event if I could tell my schoolmates I know a real, native Hawaiian."

His mother, Mamminka, confessed they had all tried to imagine how I looked. "I'm sure I speak for all of us," she said, "when I say how delighted you're just as you are."

We turned to the elderly Mr. Sammer. He smiled, perhaps in spite of himself, through his dignified façade.

On the train
July 18, 1933

Dearest Family,

You'll be glad my visit to Pilsen was a success. François' sister, Milca (pronounced "Milcha"), made me feel like a princess. I slept in a four-poster bed with fluffy down pillows, a quilt, and lace-bordered linen sheets.

I bought some winter underwear and a pair of gorgeous ski shoes, handmade to measure, supple and strong.

You'll be interested in how some of the Old World does its laundry. Here, it's an annual event. Their supply of linens is evidently inexhaustible.

Milca was preparing to do hers. Every summer, she and the maid pack up the children and all the soiled pieces in a wagon that takes them out to a cottage in a meadow near a stream. At dawn, the soaped-up articles are spread out flat on the fields. All day long, the sun beats down and bleaches them. Then, one by one, each piece is rinsed in the stream and spread again to dry in the next day's sun. Milca says it's always been done that way.

We've just entered Poland. In Warsaw, we'll change trains and in two days, we'll be in Moscow. That's all we talk about — wondering what we'll find. We don't expect Utopia. There will be difficulties and new customs. We must try not to judge them by our standards.

In two years, I've seen thirteen countries and will soon reach the fourteenth. At this rate, in fifty years, I'll have traveled to 375 countries. I don't think there are that many on this planet, so I guess I'll have to take off into space some day.

With love from Warsaw,
Sisi

❖*Part Three*❖

Chapter One

At six o'clock in the morning, we reached Warsaw. We had to change trains hurriedly — barely enough time to transfer our luggage, grab a quick breakfast and buy some fruit and bread for lunch.

Not until we settled in our compartment, with the train underway, did we count our suitcases piled on the racks above the seats.

"Oh, no François! One of my suitcases is missing!"

"Are you sure? Let's count them again."

"I'm positive! It's the metal one with some tools and most of my winter clothes. It's not here!"

We explained our problem to the conductor, who said he would notify the Warsaw station and, if the suitcase was found, it would be forwarded on the next train.

"Remember," he warned, "there's only one train a day, and it goes only as far as the Polish-Soviet border."

François and I stared at each other, both with the same thought, which the conductor voiced.

"One of you will have to be there to claim it."

"It's *my* suitcase," I said weakly.

"But you'll be there overnight. You can't speak Polish. Don't worry, my dear, I'll stay with you."

The conductor left François and me to talk it over. I was obstinate. "No harm will come to me, and I need practice in self-reliance. You can be helpful by surveying the Moscow scene."

He agreed reluctantly. That afternoon, we said good-bye at the Stolpce station, the last stop before the Russian frontier.

Our friendly conductor explained my predicament to the two clerks at the tiny station. Through improvised sign language, I learned that the town of Stolpce was some distance from the station. The wagon parked outside would take me there.

My luggage was loaded onto the rustic conveyance, and I climbed up and sat beside the driver. The horse, who obviously knew the route well, avoided the bumps and depressions in the winding dirt road while the wagoner and I conversed the entire way. I explained I was *Amerikanka* and a sculptor. He asked if I was from New York. I said yes because if I said Honolulu, he might have thought I was making fun of him.

A church, a few simple wooden dwellings and a boarding house — that was Stolpce. Its one street was unpaved, and everyone I saw was dressed in working clothes. Farming, apparently, was the principal occupation.

At the boarding house, the driver introduced me to the landlord and his wife, explained why I was there and gave them an elaborate account of my life.

The room they assigned me was on the upper floor and utterly charming in its unpretentiousness. Everything in it was authentic 1850s or earlier, unadulterated by any modern convenience. A basin and large jug, and embroidered linen towels rested on a stand beside the marble-topped dresser. A hand-crocheted spread covered the large four-poster bed. In case I needed light during the few hours of darkness — a kerosene lamp and candles. The toilet, without running water, was down the hall.

No other guests appeared at supper. I ate lightly and went to bed early. In the morning, I took a sketch pad and walked past the tiny church to the river, where several small boys sported in the water. They saw me drawing them but continued cavorting, uninhibited and unconfined by clothes. It was a scene one might have found anywhere in the world, in any century.

Dinner at one o'clock began with borshch, topped with sour cream. Next came fried potatoes and trout covered with thick, fresh sour cream, and a green salad crowned with sour cream. For dessert, I had a large bowl of wild strawberries — of course, with sour cream — topping a meal I would never forget.

Well before three, back at the train station, I heard the bad news: My suitcase had not been found. There was nothing to do but accept the fact and go on without it.

When we crossed the Soviet border, the train halted briefly, as though in salute, before proceeding on "Red Soil." Shortly afterwards, we stopped for customs and to transfer to a train on tracks with a wider gauge. A large red flag fluttered from the roof of the little station house, and comrades in uniform stood at attention. My body tingled. I had made it.

The customs functionaries carefully inspected each of my suitcases and made a list of items of any value, including my money — no more than eight dollars — explaining that I could take out only what I brought in.

The second train offered more space for my luggage. A porter was tucking away my last bag when a man came in, smiled, and said, "*Zdrastvitye*. Hello."

"Hello," I replied.

"Ah, you speak English? I'm from New York ... a doctor ... unemployed. Gonna look for a job in Leningrad. I was born there, you see. My parents emigrated when I was a kid, before the war."

Another man appeared in the doorway. "*Français?*" he asked. "English?" It turned out he was a Russian who had been in Paris since 1916, playing in a jazz orchestra. He wanted to settle back in the Motherland. The two men chatted awhile in Russian, then switched to English. I sat on the bench opposite them. Having nothing to say, I just looked from one to the other, back and forth, as they went on.

"— But," the doctor sounded a bit smug, "how the hell can you claim labor is more important than capital? It doesn't make sense. Without financial backing, labor wouldn't have a chance. Capital is indispensable!"

The musician threw his head back with a laugh and rubbed his hands together. "You think so? I'll make a deal with you. Let's say the two of us go to a desert island. *You* bring a million dollars, and I'll have no more than two capable hands and my know-how. *Va bien?* You take that side of the island, and I'll take this. What do you think our situations will be in a year?"

The doctor scratched his head. "I see what you mean. I can't eat money, can I? But I still think you wouldn't mind having some of my dollars."

"*Bien sur.* I'll gladly *sell* you my labor. You won't get far without it. Of course ... I've oversimplified the question. But you'll never convince me that, from the economic point of view, Capitalism is good for the working man."

"All right." The doctor raised his hands. "I surrender on that count, only because I don't know enough to argue intelligently. But ... there's another issue that bothers me."

"Fire away, Comrade."

"It's this thing about ... about welfare. What do the Russians have to aim for if the government takes care of them from birth to death? Education is free, everyone has a job, a roof over his head at a ridiculously low rent, and health care is paid for by the government. They don't have to struggle."

The musician shook his head and heaved a tolerant sigh. "So you think security is bad for productivity, huh?"

The doctor nodded. "Takes away ambition."

"Well, first of all, it isn't welfare. Those benefits are not handouts. The government doesn't pay for them — the *workers* do. With their labor, they *earn* every damn bit of it. The government administers it — perhaps not perfectly — but just compare the poorest Soviet citizen with the poorest American and see who comes out ahead."

"That's why I'm here," the doctor said. "Tell me more."

"Yes. About security taking away ambition. May I remind you, Comrade, that Tolstoy was a wealthy aristocrat, that Tchaikovsky had a patron who supported him, that your new president was born with a silver spoon in his mouth, that old Rockefeller's sons are not deadbeats? They and many other great ones didn't lack security, yet they were productive."

The doctor stood up. "Thanks. You've reinforced my confidence, Now let's eat. May I share my smoked fish and cucumbers with you two?"

"I got some bread and a big sausage in Stolpce," I replied.

"That's called *kolbassá*," the musician informed us. He brought forth some caviar. "And this is *ikrá.*"

Before we could begin our picnic, the train stopped at a small town. Minutes later a young soldier paused at the door of our compartment.

The musician said, *"Dobro poshalovatye! Welcome!"*

The soldier, who was going home on leave, joined us, adding his ration of black bread, fatback and a bottle of vodka to our provisions. We made the meal a festive one — a promising prelude to my encounter with whatever awaited me in the Soviet capital.

Chapter Two

Moscow!

I first saw her crowded streets from the back seat of a Lincoln touring car, top down. No one told me that third class would include luxurious transportation. But there I was, the only passenger, being chauffeured from the station to the hotel like a celebrity. Automobiles were scarce, and people turned to stare at me. I wanted to stand up, blow kisses to everyone and shout, "Here I am!"

How long before I'd become a part of those crowds, hurrying to or from some important engagement, maybe stopping to chat with someone in fluent Russian? Would it take weeks? Months?

At the Hotel Moskva, two doormen took my bags for me. The clerk at the reception desk welcomed me, with good English, while I gaped at the elaborate crystal chandeliers hanging from the high, ornate ceilings.

My spacious room looked over the Moscow River and a bridge spanning it. On the opposite bank, the route led up a slope, past St. Basil's Basilica, to Red Square. The Kremlin wall extended along the embankment, behind which were the white government buildings and a church with a gilded cupola.

An urgent knock at the door made me turn from the window. François!

"Thank Heavens you're all right," he whispered as we held each other close.

Down in the dining room, we paid little attention to our surroundings, even the menu. A day's separation had given us much to catch up on. François had a job already! With a letter of introduction from Le Corbusier, he called on an architect named Colli. The good news was that there was no end of construction, and Colli wanted François to work on a huge stadium going up at the edge of the city.

"Now all I have to do is get my work permit and a place for us to live. Apartments are scarcer than water-holes in a desert."

I couldn't resist making light of it. "Leave it to me. I've brought along a bit of gall and a dash of guile. First thing in the morning, I'll start reconnoitering."

"But where will you begin? You have no letter of introduction and the language is ... is Greek to you."

I looked at him sideways. "Don't underestimate me, my love. I survived in Stolpce, didn't I?"

After breakfast the following morning, François returned to see Colli, and I went to the hotel desk where the clerk greeted me cheerfully.

"*Dobry utro*, Madame. Good morning. Will you be joining the tour of the city? The bus leaves in fifteen minutes."

"Maybe tomorrow," I said. "Today I'd like to meet some artists in their studios. I'm a sculptor, you see, and have heard Soviet artists are doing excellent work. Do you happen to know where some of them live?"

The clerk raised his eyebrows and looked at me over the rim of his glasses. "Well, now ... let's see .... There are a number of places. The newest one is out at Maslovka ... that's a suburb .... You can get there by tram in half an hour or so."

He wrote something on a piece of paper and gave it to me.

"You take tram number eleven, I think. Cross the river, and you'll find it on the other side of Red Square. Show this note to the conductor. It says, 'Please let this comrade off at the artists' cooperative at Maslovka.'"

I thanked the clerk and hurried out. Halfway over the bridge, I stopped to look around but had to move on with the multitude. Already, in less than twenty-four hours, I was a part of the crowd, with private business to attend to. An auspicious beginning.

At St. Basil's, I paused briefly in its shadow to admire at close range the carved and colored "onions." And then I was on cobblestones crossing Red Square. How enormous it was!

Tram number eleven was easy to find. The conductor read my smiled, nodded, and held out her hand. I stared from her palm to her face and back. She shoved her hand at me, this time saying something — I had no idea what. I understood only one word — kopeks — and looked around for help. A voice nearby explained, "You must pay the fare."

What? Did he say *fare?* I had misunderstood! Transportation *wasn't* free. Oh, well. From my pocket, I took a fistful of change and let the conductor pick out the right amount.

The old suburb of Maslovka consisted of small houses, many of them of logs and with decorative window frames, and grass growing on the roofs. The artists' cooperative, by comparison, was outstanding — a large, modern structure on a compound. I went through the open gate, up to the front door and knocked. No one answered.

I figured everyone was working, so tried out back on the sunny side of the building. Three men sat on the steps engaged in animated conversation. I turned on a virtuous smile as I approached.

"Dobry utro. Parlez-vous Français? Or English?"

One of the men jumped up and answered in German, *"Ja! Ich kan Deutch sprechen."*

They all appeared eager to help, so I ad-libbed in French, "I'm looking for a painter named Lisitsky." I had seen his name in a magazine.

Their faces lit up and, to my astonishment, the man who spoke German said, "He's in Leningrad now, but I can give you the address of his friend, Malkin, who's head of a publishing house. My name is Bogorodski."

We shook hands all around, and I told them my name and that I had just come from Paris where I studied sculpture.

Bogorodski was agog. *"Von Paree? Kommen Sie!* You must see my paintings!"

The four of us went to his studio, adjoining his two-room apartment. His wife, Vera, who spoke French, made us welcome. She told me her husband had fought in the revolution as a sailor, then worked with a circus, was a boxer for awhile and, for the past ten years, had been painting.

The subjects of his canvases were mostly sea battles and circus life, done from memory. What they lacked in technical finesse was made up for with rhythm of line and color.

We talked for the rest of the morning, during which time another painter, Misha, joined us. He, too, spoke French. I explained my purpose for being in Moscow and learned some of what might lie ahead for me. Getting a studio of my own would not be easy. All of them at Maslovka had waited years but, as things improved, there were fewer delays and more advantages for artists, such as *trusts,* offices that found employment in various fields.

They invited me to have lunch at their cafeteria, where I met several more colleagues. By then, thanks to Bogorodski, my predicament was well-known.

"This is Comrade Agnessa," he informed those who had not yet heard. "She is a sculptor who has come from *Paree* to be one of us. Her friend is an architect, working with Colli on our new stadium. They have to leave the hotel in a few days and find somewhere to live till they get a place of their own."

When I finally took my leave, Misha insisted on accompanying me back to the hotel.

"We don't want to lose you, Comrade Agnessa. It's not every day foreign artists drop onto our doorstep."

I answered his many questions about Paris and had a few queries of my own. "Is Bogorodski a distinguished painter?"

"In a way. He's well-known. A congenial fellow, as you've seen. We jokingly say that, among sailors, he's the best painter and among painters, he's the best sailor."

The crowning gratification of that day's achievements was revelling in the incredulity on François' face as I recounted, detail for detail, my adventures since breakfast.

Finally, he said, "Well, my little Circe, what sort of enchantment will you perform tomorrow?"

I affected an arrogant pose. "First, I'll call on Malkin. He's the friend of Lisitsky — the man I pretended to know — and show him photos of my work. After that ... well ... I'll report to you, Ulysses, tomorrow night."

Chapter Three

I found Comrade Malkin's office on the second floor of a large building on a busy street. Though I had no appointment, he agreed to see me and, in fact, treated me with the cordiality an important person might have expected.

After I told him a little about myself and showed the pictures of my work, he leaned back in his chair and clasped his hands behind his head. "Tell me, Comrade, why is it you wish to live in our country and not in your own? Is it because there is no work there, and there is here?"

"Of course, that's part of it! But it's also because I believe the arts have no frontiers. They're indispensable to the cultural survival of any society. If I'm not allowed to do what I do best in my own country, not only am I wasted but, who knows, culture may be the loser. And besides, I'd like to see your new society succeed."

Malkin's smile told me all I wanted to know. He dipped his pen in the well of purple ink and wrote a few lines on a piece of note paper.

"Here ... take this to Comrade Stukov. He's in charge of the artists' *trust*. Show the photos of your work to him. You'll find his office with no difficulty. Good-bye, Comrade. It has been a pleasure."

In Stukov's outer office, I was one of a dozen women and men waiting to see him. For an hour or more I sat, with nothing to do but study the setting and the people.

The furniture was commonplace. Except for three framed pictures on the partition behind the secretary's desk — photos of Marx, Lenin and Stalin — the whitewashed walls were unembellished. A single, unshaded light bulb at the end of a short electric cord hung from the center of the ceiling.

I looked around at my fellow creatures. Whatever it was that motivated their unalloyed expressions, the sculptor in me studied the play of light and shadow on their features. Yes, I wanted to work on portraits, I wanted to capture feelings and thoughts in clay, I wanted —

The secretary spoke, interrupting my thoughts. "Comrade Stukov will see you now."

The tall, middle-aged man greeted me in good English though with a strong accent. He studied my photos carefully while I sat on the edge of my chair and held my breath till he nodded.

"I like your work," he said bluntly. "You understand the material and your technique is competent. Zadkine is a good teacher, yes? We have his sculpture in our museum of modern art."

He smiled broadly, and went on, "I must consult with my colleague, Comrade Grabar, who will return from his holiday on the 25th. There is much work to do in our country. When Grabar gives his consent, I will write you a contract which you will take to another office that will grant you permission to stay here. And then you can get a room to live in."

I thanked him and danced on air all the way to the hotel. François wasn't there, so after lunch I went back to Maslovka and told Bogorodski of my progress.

"The bureaucracy is never in a hurry," was the gist of what he said. "You'll need a place to sleep after your time at the hotel is up. When is that?"

"On the 26th."

"Well, that's only three days away. Wait here, I'll be right back."

He soon returned with several comrades I met the day before.

Misha, the one who spoke French, said, "We've put our heads together and are happy to tell you there's a studio in this building you and your friend may use. It's Marina's .... You met her at lunch yesterday. She's leaving tomorrow to spend a few weeks in the country."

"But how do you know it's all right with her?" I asked.

"Because last evening we were talking about you. We expected you might be in this pickle and she ... a number of us, in fact ... want to help you."

"That's very kind," I said, the emotion swelling inside me. "What will the rent be?"

Misha laughed. "Rent? Oh, no! You will be guests."

By eliminating Sunday from the calendar, the Soviets had reduced the week to six days, the last of which was their *vihodnoi*, or going-out day. That week it fell, propitiously, on the 24th. At last François and I could spend some idle hours together.

After a late and leisurely breakfast, we went to the museum of modern art. Most of the works had been collected by a private connoisseur who donated them to the State after the Revolution. There were some fine examples of Cezanne, Van Gogh, Gaugain, Picasso, Matisse, and even Zadkine and Archipenko, along with others.

In the afternoon, we explored the downtown streets. Because of the holiday, they were more crowded than usual. Were the people shopping? But the store windows were almost empty of merchandise and, whatever was displayed didn't attract either of us.

"Don't forget the shortages," François reminded me. "They're probably glad to be able to buy anything at all."

"Let's go in one of the stores and look around," I said.

We approached one, but at the entrance, the doorman asked to see our passes. He and François talked a while — an exchange of Russian and Czech — and as we moved away, François explained. "There are ration books for practically everything — clothing and food. Each district has stores to provide for its local residents. We won't get ours till we have an address as well as a job."

"Golly ... that may not be for weeks ... if we're lucky. What are we going to do till then?"

"Actually ...." He squeezed my arm, "The fellow knew we weren't Russian. He told me there's a store especially for foreign workers. It's called INSNAB — that's an acronym for something or other. It's up on Gorky Street, and it has better choices than the others. I'm getting hungry. Come on, it's time to eat."

We didn't hurry over dinner. After a frenetic week, we wanted to savor each leisurely moment.

"The world we left seems so far behind us," I remarked.

François' face was grave, but his blue eyes laughed. "Do you think we were a bit crazy to come to Russia?"

"Certainly! Who in his right mind would jump off a cliff without a parachute, not knowing where he might land?"

"I'm glad, Agnessa, you feel as I do ... the exhilaration of the unknown. Those who must have everything planned beforehand miss most of the fun."

"We're going to have to learn to do without some material comforts and not to expect any luxuries."

"You're right," François replied, pretending to be serious, "Necessities such as caviar and smoked salmon and cheap opera tickets are good enough for us common folk."

Only a few diners lingered over their coffee and liqueurs. I recognized several people I'd seen coming and going during the past days. One woman in particular, a couple of tables away, attracted me. She was about fifty, with graying hair and a face that expressed understanding and benevolence. She and the man opposite her appeared to be in deep conversation.

François saw me watching her and said, "It would be nice to have her for a friend, wouldn't it?"

I nodded, and just then, she looked toward us. As though reading our thoughts, her eyes caught mine and sent a smile with a message. My mother used to look at me that way when she wanted me to know she loved me and approved of what I was doing.

Unprepared, my bravado fell apart. I wanted to cry.

François understood and took my hand. "Come ... let's go for a walk along the river."

Beside the embankment, François gave me his handkerchief. "Go ahead. You're thinking of your mother, aren't you? The disturbing news you received from home?"

I sobbed against his shoulder.

Around us strolled groups with children, couples courting, or laughing teenagers. A horse and buggy announced its approach with the clip-clop of hooves. We joined the throng when I had dried my eyes. The warm, clear night was at eleven; darkness had not yet reached the 56th parallel.

From The Desk Of
Mrs. George F. Larsen

June 1933,

Sis, darling,

I am glad I got your letter yesterday — I mean the private note. I trust you, Sis. You have to live your life your way, but don't get hurt, dear. Give my love to François. Tell him I love him as long as he is good to you, and God bless you both. I know that you both will succeed. Just plug along and be determined, then, when you are older, you will be able to look back and say ... I did what I thought was right, and what I wanted to do.

Joan is going to Maui this afternoon to stay with Astrid, and I to the hospital to have an operation for gallstones tomorrow morning. I have been terribly bothered lately with the most awful pains, and the doctor thinks that I can't stand any more suffering. They will wait for the money.

Stan is on Hawaii, so it's only Pa and Dick home. I won't worry about a thing, only to get well again so I will be fit to continue the rest of my life. Don't worry about me. You know I have courage. Only people that are afraid need to be felt sorry for.

George and Jessie got married Wednesday. They are over at Kahana now for a few days. Jessie is a very nice girl. We all like her, and she likes it here, too. They are going to live down at the beach.

Don't expect any more letters from me for awhile. I will ask Dick to write — he's a darling.

Loads of love to you,
Mama

Chapter Four

Darling All,

After only two weeks in Moscow, I'm working! The route has been through a bureaucratic labyrinth and I'm not yet in the clear. Residence permits and ration books are harder to get than jobs.

We are temporarily living in a friend's apartment at an artists' cooperative in a suburb called Maslovka. Our arrival was spectacular.

Since we were entitled to be chauffeured to the train station from the hotel as part of our tour, no one objected when we asked to be taken here. I phoned to say we were on our way, and when the chauffeur drove into the courtyard, just about all the residents of the building, some of whom I'd never seen before, welcomed us. Even the driver took part in what was a gala occasion. We danced and sang while someone played the balalaika, and shared a bottle of vodka.

After getting installed, several of us went to a painter's studio for tea. One of our party, a ceramist, told me he'll be going away and that when we leave here, we can use his house.

When I said my visa will expire on August 20th and that I may not be able to stay on, he said, "Don't worry about that. In a city of three million people, who will know the difference if one or two more comrades are squeezed in?"

Anyway, the next day, a helpful painter named Bogorodski took me to meet the president of an artists' cooperative, who sent me to another office and then to another. Result: As of today, I am assistant to a venerable sculptor named Mercouroff. He does those bigger-than-life statues of Lenin and Stalin that are in the main squares of all the Soviet republics.

Before the war, he studied in Paris under Bourdelle then came back to fight in the Revolution on the side of the Bolsheviks. Now he lives on three acres at the edge of town in an old, rambling house with his extended family. Attached to the house are his huge studio and a garden where they grow all the vegetables they need.

For thirteen years, they've lived there. The first two winters were bitter, with no glass panes in the windows, no electricity or running water, and not much food. Most of the country was in the same condition after the devastation caused by the fighting.

August 5

Whoopie!

I have my first contract! It's with an artists' cooperative. My assignment is to model an elephant about six inches high, for which I'll get 550 rubles.

Let me try to explain the value of that in dollars: There are 100 kopeks in a ruble. A ride on a streetcar costs 10 kopeks; a pack of cigarettes costs 1.50; the rent of an apartment is five percent of whatever one's salary is, no matter how many rooms there are. So, you see, I wouldn't be at all poor. A good restaurant dinner is about 2.50. François is earning much more than I will be.

Well ... of course, I hurried out to the zoo. It's in a lovely park with a lake and trees, walks and benches. I saw all sorts of birds, bears boxing, tigers and lions, but no elephants. As I was leaving, I stopped at the gatekeeper's to ask, in my best Russian, "Gdye elephant? Where is the elephant?"

The gatekeeper smiled knowingly, nodded, and pointed to her right. I looked where she indicated and saw only a telephone booth. Then the absurd truth hit me! Their word for the animal must be very different. But "telephone" and "elephant" do sound much alike.

Today, before going back to the zoo to make sketches, I learned that the word I wanted was "slon." Meanwhile, the gatekeeper had also done her homework. When she saw me coming, her face lit up and, enunciating slowly, she said, "E-le-phant."

It was my turn to show off. "Slon," I announced, and we laughed. Then, gesticulating, she added in intelligible Russian, "Go to the far end of that walkway and turn right and then left."

I found not one but two slons, made a dozen sketches and, when I left, gave one to the gatekeeper. I think she's now a lifelong friend.

The next hurdle will come on August 20 when our visas expire.

249

They can be extended another month or so for $12 each in foreign currency. Neither of us has that much.

Please, Mama, don't worry — I'm eating well. As non-members of the Maslovka collective, we're not authorized to have all our meals here. But that's no problem. A couple of blocks up the street is an open market where we can buy all sorts of fresh foods. Farmers sell the produce they've grown in excess of the quota they supply to the State. Prices are higher than in government stores but not at all expensive.

We cook on our primus, a little pump-up camp stove. No one seems to use electric or gas. The only two kinds of stoves I've seen are the primus, as ours, and a cylindrical one-burner kerosene type called a kerosinka. Our homemade meals are one-dish events — soup or stew.

François' boss, Comrade Colli, and his wife invited us to dinner last night. They speak French, and their twelve-year-old son is studying English in school.

During the week, I have my midday meal with the Mercouroff family.

I'm going to make my elephant in his studio and use his equipment. In exchange, I'll do any hackwork I'm able to. He has two full-time assistants — Dimitri and Fyodor — nice young apprentices who'll soon be on their own.

Do svidania
(That means au revoir.)

Maslovka
August 17, 1933

Dearest Family,

As of today, I have my food coupons, even before François has received his. And there's more. I can stay on with impunity although my visa will expire, thanks to our new friend, Comrade Gourov. He is Secretary of the International Bureau of Revolutionary Artists, and knows the ropes.

He sent me to an office called Narkomtrud, where they endorsed my being here and working, and gave me permission to apply for a permanent visa at another office, called Mosksoviet.

Mercouroff insisted on going with me to the first office, where he did all the talking and helped me fill out a questionnaire. The woman in charge said I should bring an official letter, serious and convincing, declaring that I was a specialist in my field and essential to the organization I worked for, and to the State.

The next day, Gourov accompanied me to the artists' cooperative that had ordered the elephant. The director and another man produced the required letter in a short time — signed and properly rubber-stamped. Back at Narkomtrud, the woman said I'd hear the result in due course. In the meantime, I don't have to worry about my August 20th deadline because the reply is pending.

If you think it's tiresome reading about this bureaucracy, imagine how frustrating it is living through it.

Tomorrow is "going-out" day ... a welcome change.

Goodnight to all,
Sisi

P.S. We didn't win the Antwerp competition.

Chapter Five

"Oh, what a busy week this has been!" François tossed his hat onto a chair and kicked off his shoes. "Thank goodness tomorrow's *vihodnoi*. How would you like to spend it at a *dacha,* my love?"

"Don't tell me you've bought a house in the country already."

François chortled. "No, Chérie, not yet. But I can offer you the next best thing. A fellow in the office has rented one and invited us to spend tomorrow out there with his family."

"Wow! I hope you accepted."

"I sure did! He — that's Victor — will meet us at the train station with his two brothers and their wives. We'll go to a place called Galitzina, about seventy kilometers away, and then walk through the woods and farm country."

By the time we had been a half hour on the train, no one would have guessed the seven of us had not been friends for years. Not surprising — every Russian we'd met, from the humblest farmer at the market to the most influential, treated us with unaffected warmth.

251

Door after door had opened, and not because anyone would gain by it. We were not famous and obviously not rich.

Inwardly I giggled as I thought, "Look at them! With the finest qualities all God-fearing Christians strive for, and yet, they're not religious. Who needs religion to be good?"

The train rolled past factories, a radio broadcasting station, farms and woods. Our talk was lighthearted — some in faltering English and French, and always vivacious. When we got off at Galitzina, Victor explained that part of our walk would skirt the edge of a *kolkhoz.*

"What's the difference," I asked, "between a *kolkhoz* and a *sovkhoz?* They're both collective farms, aren't they?"

"Oh, yes. Under a *kolkhoz,* farmers own a lot of land in common, plant their grain and vegetables, and harvest and thresh collectively. Of what they produce, the State guarantees to buy a large percentage, and the rest is theirs to sell on the free market."

"And the other?"

"Under the *sovkhoz* system, all the produce belongs to the State, and the farmers are paid a salary."

"Don't forget," someone said, "there's a third kind — the *kulak,* the individualist who works by and for himself, and sells his produce for whatever price he can get."

"They're at a disadvantage, aren't they?" François asked.

"Of course. They can't afford the mechanical equipment that would cut their costs and, naturally, their prices are higher. Every year there are fewer of those."

"Look over there," said one of the brothers, pointing toward a cluster of machines on the flat horizon. "It's threshing time."

"They tell us we'll have a good harvest this year, and that means we'll have more bread and other things."

"But a shortage of kerosene, because they use so much of it to run the machines, and the factory workers who lend a hand with the harvest get added rations of fuel as a bonus."

"How do you account for the cigarette shortage? Surely, that's not due to a lack of kerosene?"

"No. That's because three factories have been closed for reorganization."

"Wouldn't you think they'd close one at a time? Oh, well, at least there's plenty of milk and sour cream. And the butter ration's better."

We tramped over meadows, through woods and across brooks. Late in the morning, we reached a dirt road that led us up to the little log cabin. Victor's wife, Lydia, waved to us from across the large yard, and his two youngsters ran up to welcome us.

Victor hugged the boys and announced, "We're starved! Is breakfast ready yet?"

There was plenty of elbow room for the ten of us at the table under the evergreens. The rustic planks were laden with platters of salt herring, black bread, salad and fruit. Most of the conversation was of family matters, so when I wasn't eating, I took in the bucolic ambience, trying to recall the scenes of country life from old Russian novels. Except for the birches, the pines, and the untrimmed garden, this was nothing like them. There would be no place for these people in Chekhov's pages of futile tragi-comedy or in Gorky's stories of peasant life. Young pre-revolutionaries would not have made that clearing over there with the volleyball net, or gone, as we did after eating, into the woods to gather mushrooms for the fun of it.

The children handed each of us a basket and led us to an area they had staked out for that day. We separated, and I was on my own. The first shouts of success came from the young boys, followed closely by cheers from the others — but my basket was still almost empty.

I caught up with François. "How do you tell the difference between a stone or a fallen leaf and a mushroom? I've found only three."

François picked them out of my basket and threw them away. "Sorry, but those are poisonous." He showed me one of his. "Take only this kind and you'll be safe."

But I lost interest. The filtered sunlight, the bracing fragrance of moss and regenerating matter was enough for me. Then ... the music! Victor started it with an old folk song ... softly. From a distance, one of his brothers joined him in falsetto, and soon, all three were in harmony, gradually increasing the tempo and volume with each verse and chorus, until it seemed that every tree and all of me reverberated. As they finished, the cadence slowly waned till the notes faded one by one into the wind.

We remained silent — to speak would have been sacrilegious. The mushroom hunters filled their baskets with muted gestures of success.

Eventually, on our way back to the cabin, François asked if they sang professionally.

"No," Victor told us with a laugh. "That would never occur to us. We get too much pleasure from being impulsive."

One of the brothers explained that they grew up surrounded by music. "All our relatives sang, and Father played the balalaika. I guess it's just part of us now, as it's part of most Russians."

The youngsters ran ahead to get a fire started. Lydia and her sisters-in-law took off behind them and called back, "We've got to clean the mushrooms and begin dinner."

When we arrived, there were appetizers waiting on the table with a bottle of vodka and goblets. I was more interested in following the fate of the mushrooms. In a large pot over burning coals, a mass of buckwheat bubbled.

"Here ...." Lydia offered me a spoonful. "We call it *kasha*. Like it?"

I murmured my praise.

"Wait till I add the mushrooms," she went on. "In our opinion, it rates as a gourmet dish."

It did in my opinion, as well. I would put it high on a list of ten best meals from any country.

At eight o'clock, we started home. Daylight still lingered when we reached Maslovka.

"There ...." I said. "I'm going to make some tea. I've just finished another letter — bringing my family up to date on our adventures in wonderland. You know, François, I can't get over how friendly these Russians are. They treat us as if we belong here."

"Agnessa .... " François looked up from his book. "Have you thought of writing some articles about what you are doing here? I should think an American audience would be interested in a description of life in Moscow — from the point of view of an ordinary observer. Like today out at the *dacha* .... And then, Gourov told us you're the only American free-lance artist here."

"I've thought of it. But I'm afraid they'd want the articles slanted in a certain way."

"How do you mean ... slanted?"

"Americans have been taught to be afraid of Communism."

"I know all that. But ... but they're always bragging about their free speech. Doesn't that mean hearing *all* sides of a question?"

"You'd think so. But it comes to a struggle for survival between the two systems. Americans are just as alarmed about the positives of Communism as the Soviets are about the merits of Capitalism."

"Hmm .... I guess so. But, tell me, how would you have to change the articles to make them acceptable?"

"Well ... in describing the three types of farms, I'd dwell on how badly the poor *kulaks* are treated because they work for private profit. About the two-room cabin, I'd emphasize the lack of running water, and the untidy yard, without describing the wild flowers. I might ignore the brothers' singing, but tell how they liked to play volleyball, an American game. And I'd end by writing, 'There is so little food, the guests have to help scrounge for edibles in the woods ....'"

Chapter Six

Maslovka
September 9, 1933

Darling All of You,

I've turned in my elephant, cast in plaster, and it has been accepted. In a few days, I'll receive another contract — this time to design an ashtray. It doesn't sound spell-binding, I know, for an aspiring sculptor whose aim is to conceive a great opus. But look at it this way: It could be an objet d'art rather than a mere object of small merit. Besides, I'm glad I'm here designing an ashtray and not unemployed in Honolulu.

On the last vihodnoi, the amber light of autumn turned to silvery September drizzles. What better way to spend a rainy day than visit a library and destroy another myth?

All those rumors about Soviet citizens not being allowed to get any news from abroad is just propaganda. True, we can't buy foreign magazines or papers on the newsstands, but the Foreign Library has the latest periodicals and books published abroad in all the languages you can think of.

I was most interested in what Roosevelt has been doing, so I grabbed "The New York Times" first, and then read the London

255

"Times" and a French paper. Actually, I'm going to be better informed on world affairs sitting here than I would be reading the "Honolulu Advertiser," isolated in the middle of the Pacific Ocean.

Hitler says he'll abolish unemployment. We know how — by setting up concentration camps where, eventually, he'll send all the anti-Nazis, gypsies, Jews, and homosexuals. And he's suppressing labor unions and modern art. Thousands of German painters, actors, authors and musicians are emigrating to other countries.

By contrast, Roosevelt's New Deal sounds promising. He has set up a National Labor Board that gives organized labor the right to bargain collectively and to strike. They want to shorten the work week to 40 hours and boycott German-made goods. Roosevelt has appointed a <u>woman</u> as Secretary of Labor — the first female cabinet member! Hooray for our side! And there's talk that the U.S. will soon resume diplomatic relations with the U.S.S.R. They were suspended in 1919.

A U. S. court ruling has finally allowed James Joyce's "Ulysses" into the States. It's been banned in the land of "free speech" since it was written, in 1922.

Speaking earlier of rain, I believe there are six umbrellas in all of Moscow, including mine. Half are bent or broken. On the other hand, (or should I say foot?) everyone has rubbers but me.

During the long walk to Mercouroff's from the streetcar line, I must skip and hop from one dryish spot to another to avoid getting mired up to my ankles. Every day the edges of the road get soggier from being trampled by boots seeking solid earth, and foot traffic has to circle ever beyond. I imagine it's worse in the spring thaw.

François and I have seen our first opera at the Bolshoi Theatre: "Eugene Onegin." It's a poetic romance by Pushkin, with music by Tchaikovsky. From every point of view, it was a new experience for me. Each role required acting as well as singing; the sets were carefully executed and never overdone. For instance, the simplicity of the winter scene for the duel suggested tragedy to come. On the vast snow-covered plain, we saw only one leafless tree and part of a fence in the icy dawn.

For people here, laborers and intelligentsia alike, opera is not a one or two-time event, and they don't take it lightly. Every generation claims certain operas as its personal property. "Eugene Onegin" is obviously a favorite. It gives us a grand ball, romance, tragedy, and passion. Communication between cast and audience was intense and electric. I felt powerful vibrations of empathy for the protagonists, or praise for a singer's rendering of a cherished aria. The audience was intimate with every note and, at the final curtain, let go of its emotions. Everyone stood, clapped, cheered, roared, and shouted, "Bravo!" "Bis! Bis!" and would gladly have sat through a repeat performance immediately.

Their ecstasy was contagious and exhausted me.

Goodnight, with love,
Agnessa

Maslovka
Sept. 13, 1933

Dearest Everyone,

New constructions are going up all over the city. Out here at Maslovka, close to us, they're building another artists' cooperative — twelve stories. It should be completed in January. How I'd love to get a few square meters to call my own, on the top floor facing the morning sun. Sculptors, however, must take studios on the ground floor because of the heavy equipment and materials, and because pounding on stone or wood, common in our work, can be noisy.

But I may not be here in January. My request for a permanent visa has been refused on the grounds that I came as a tourist. I'm going to apply again and, as long as an answer is pending, I can stay with impunity.

I know a lot of Russian words now and can almost make sentences, but I still need to use gestures as well as my voice.

This afternoon I went shopping again with my ration tickets. Here's what I got:

1/2 kilo dried peas	*23 kopeks*
1 dozen large dill pickles	*40 kopeks*
5 salted herrings	*28 kopeks*
1 packet of tea	*15 kopeks*

That's my month's allowance for those products. Men and women who work harder get more of everything. On different days I receive other things, such as sugar, potatoes, vegetables and meat.

Our daily ration of fresh bread is about one pound for 40 kopeks. We never eat even half of it, so I've learned to barter it at the free market. For a pound of bread I get a quart of fresh milk.

In a recent New York paper I read an article about life in Moscow. It said people buy and sell what they need or don't need at the "secret" market. That makes it sound illegal when it isn't. Those markets are open and free, and vendors don't even need a license to deal there. See how the Western press distorts things?

We'll be moving from Maslovka on the 26th. Our ceramist friend, Frih-har, who said we could live in his house, told us this morning his sister-in-law needs it, but that we're welcome to use his studio which is near the center of town. We haven't seen it but, of course, accepted with gratitude.

In two days, I'll be 23 years old. To celebrate, we're going to another opera: "Queen of Spades," also by Pushkin and Tchaikovsky. Admission costs so little we could go every evening if we had the time — time to stand in line to buy tickets and time out of our busy days and nights. Mercouroff has gone to Siberia for a couple of weeks to supervise some sculpture he's doing for a new theatre. I still go out to his studio every day to work. Dimitri and Fyodor, his assistants, are there and always gallantly help me with the slightest thing — my ashtray, for example, which hardly deserves such chivalry.

Comrade Gourov is having a dinner party next week, inviting several foreigners he wants us to meet. That will be our first evening party here and my first acquaintance with fellow Americans.

With love to all,
Sis

Comrade Gourov's plump wife, Gourova, opened the door and drew us into the noisy, crowded room. We told her our names.

"You're so welcome!" she said. "My husband speaks often of you, and warmly. Come and meet some of your compatriots."

An improvised table left little space for guests to circulate, a fact that intimidated no one. Laughter and bilingual chatter filled the small room.

"This is Carol," said Gourova, "from New York, and her husband, Eliot. He's an economist."

We shook hands with a striking young woman and her handsome spouse. The classic beauty of Carol's face was framed with blonde hair done in a knot at the back.

"And these two," Gourova went on, "have been here already three years — Ethel and Fred Ellis. He's a political cartoonist and used to work for the *Daily Worker.* Now he draws for our labor paper, *Trud.*"

Fred's gray hair didn't match the bronzed, youthful face that grinned at me. "So — you're going to stay in Moscow?" he asked.

"My first application was refused, but Gourov has helped me try again."

Ethel gave me a look of encouragement. "There'll be a way ... hope so, anyway."

Our hostess moved away, saying she would bring us some vodka, and asked Ethel to complete the introductions. Three people we hadn't yet met — a young Russian couple, Romass and his wife, and an Austrian artist.

Gourova returned with a bottle of vodka. "We must toast to your victory over the bureaucracy," she said to François and me while filling everyone's glass. "Your success will be ours! *Zdarovaia,* your health!"

"Bottom's up!" someone shouted.

The door opened just then, and Gourov came in with a large bowl of salad. "All right, everyone! Find your places at the table."

"I must go and bring in the other platters," said Gourova. "Sit down please, comrades."

Chapter Seven

Some time after my first helping of meatballs and gravy, I lost count of the number of toasts and of who made them and to whom or for what purpose.

Gourov had just wished us all good health again when he said to me, "Agnessa, I see you have not yet learned the art of drinking vodka."

"I don't understand," I replied. "Haven't I been drinking?"

Gourov swayed a bit and sat down.

"He means," Fred explained, "that there's a tradition — a way of tossing off a whole glass of the stuff in one gulp, without flinching."

"Then I'm guilty, too." François said. "Can you teach us both in one easy lesson?"

Several volunteers stood, but the proud Romass cleared his throat and took charge. "It gives me great pleasure, comrades, to demonstrate the age-old and esteemed technique. In your left hand you will have a piece of black bread — black, not white — and in your right, a full glass of vodka. You are ready? Good. Now you will exhale and, without breathing, you will drink till the glass is empty. Then, with your mouth closed, you will put the chunk of aromatic bread under your nostrils ... so ... and inhale deeply. That's all there is to it. Shall we try together?"

Carol and Eliot raised their glasses and chunks of bread with François and me, and while the others cheered, we passed the test. As the liquor slipped down my throat almost unnoticed (as far as taste was concerned, that is), Romass broke into song — one of those fast-moving folk tunes.

"Away with the table," Gourov ordered. "We'll stack the boards against that wall and turn on the gramophone."

Carol and I helped Gourova carry the dishes out to the kitchen. Fred had already looked through the pile of records and chosen one. Ethel wound up the player. A Charleston rhythm put us all in motion, with or without partners.

No one looked at a watch as the hours passed. There was no lack of wit or animation until the third hour of the morning. Ethel was the first to give in to fatigue, and we all agreed it was time to go home.

"We'll have to walk," Fred reminded us. "The streetcars stopped running at one o'clock."

"Marvelous!" said Carol. "A few blocks in the fresh air will be good for all of us."

Gourova looked anxiously at François and me. "But you two can't go all the way out to Maslovka on foot. It would take hours! No, no! You will sleep here on the sofa till daylight, then you can ride back on the streetcar. Don't you have to move today? You can't do that without a little rest."

Eight o'clock in the morning found us at Maslovka somewhat refreshed. An hour later, we completed our final packing and were ready to take our possessions to Frih-har's downtown studio.

With a shake of his head, François surveyed the heap of suitcases. "No limousine this time. We'll need at least two trips by streetcar,

I'm afraid. Let's take what's necessary now and the rest this afternoon or tomorrow."

Even so, it wasn't easy. The streetcar was no less crowded than on a workday, and once in town, we had to walk almost two blocks.

The studio was a large corner room on the ground floor of an old two-story building scheduled for demolition in a year or so to make room for a modern structure. Its entrance, double doors secured with a padlock, opened off the sidewalk. François removed the lock and pushed the doors wide open. For a long time, we stood at the entrance, staring in disbelief. Occupying the center space was the model of a ceramic fountain on a stand five feet across. Turntables, tubs of clay and plaster, old boards and other materials cluttered three of the room's corners. The fourth corner was crudely partitioned to serve as what might be called, comparatively speaking, the "cozy corner." Between there and the entrance, the floor was strewn with shards, tools, boxes, scraps of all sorts, and thick dust.

François and I stared at each other, tongue-tied. Then he lifted me in his arms, transported me across the jumble and litter to the oasis, and set me down on a stool.

"*Voilà*, my princess, I've protected your dainty feet from the debris, and carried you over the threshold, into your new palace."

"Oh, Prince Charming, I didn't expect all of this! You have given me more than I deserve."

There was nothing to do but laugh. We laughed as we cleared a path to the door and as we set up two saw horses and planks covered with excelsior and wrapping paper to serve as a bed. Even lugging buckets to and from the club across the street to fetch water became an adventure of much amusement.

"I've just realized," François observed during a pause, "there's only one key to the padlock. We come home at different times so we'll have to look for somewhere to hide it."

The foyer of the apartment building next door was the logical place. We could see the portal was never locked, and above the transom ran a ledge wide enough to hold the key safely.

All went well — to begin with. Our work kept us busy, and our meals were good, if irregular.

One evening in early October, François came home with more than usual cheer in his hello. "Remember Romass, the fellow we met at

Gourov's party?"

"Sure."

"Well, he came to see me at the office today. Did you know he was designer in charge of decorations for Red Square? He's getting ready for October Day — the anniversary of the Revolution."

"When is that?" I asked.

"On November Seventh."

"Oh, of course. The old calendar has been brought up to date .... So what did Romass have to say?"

"He has a lot of work for all the artists in town, designing and constructing temporary plywood statues, floats for the parade, posters and things. It'll be evening work and will pay very well. For you, too, if you're interested. I told him you were, and he asked if we could drop in on him and his wife this evening."

The Romasses lived only a few minutes' walk away in a building that had not only a concierge, but an elevator as well. Up on the top floor, their apartment was everything I would have dreamed of having: two rooms and a studio, a private bath and kitchen, all furnished with modest but elegant taste, and with a view over the river and the Kremlin.

We talked about Paris and Spain and all the other countries we had been to, then got down to the reason for our visit. Before we left, François agreed to drop in after the office every day to work on plans for the festivities, and I said I'd gladly submit a small sketch of a soldier in clay.

"It'll be one of many enlarged into a twelve-meter statue," Romass said. "There'll be a number of contenders, but even if yours isn't selected, it'll be good practice for you, and besides, you'll be paid for your effort, regardless — two hundred rubles."

That's when François and I started our long hours. I turned in my clay sketch in mid-October. As November approached, François worked later and later. The temperature dropped steadily, and the daylight hours shortened.

One chilly evening I came home at half-past ten to find the key to our padlock missing from its hiding place. I searched every square centimeter of the floor, the sidewalk and the gutter, but found no key.

Could François have inadvertently taken it with him? Oh, well, he usually arrived around eleven.

I strolled down to the river a block away and rambled along the embankment. Hardly anyone else was there to see the full moon reflected on the gilded minarets within the Kremlin wall. I'd gladly have lingered for hours enjoying the placid beauty of the scenery on both sides of the river, but it was November and my winter coat was lost somewhere in Warsaw.

I shivered and headed home. François was not yet there. Gritting my chattering teeth, I resolved to wait no longer and go straight over to the Romass' apartment. With long strides, I was soon at their building ringing the concierge's bell. I waited. No one came. I rang again and waited. Still, no one appeared. I crossed the street and looked up to the top floor. Two windows of the Romass' apartment were bright with light. The men within were warm and working and had had a good supper. The concierge was off duty and probably asleep. I was hungry and cold. Should I go to Gourov's? The streetcars had stopped running. Instead, I returned home and huddled in the foyer next door, emerging once in a while to see if François had come.

A uniformed patrolman passed occasionally on his rounds, each time eyeing me with curiosity. At last he came over and asked if he could be of any help.

With my usual mime when words failed, I was able to explain my plight.

"But, Comrade, you should not be out in this cold. I'm going off duty in a few minutes. When my replacement comes, I'll advise him of your situation so he'll watch for your friend and tell him what's happened. I'm going to take you to district headquarters for shelter and perhaps some sleep."

The police station wasn't far. Its warmth was so welcome I paid no attention to the noise and confusion common to such places. Someone found me a chair, and an angel put a glass of hot tea in my frozen hands. I remember thinking, "If Heaven is half as blissful as this, I'll be glad to die."

Then an officer took me gently by the elbow and said, "We have no cot to offer you, Comrade, but over here we've put several chairs together. You might stretch out on them for a few hours. We'll cover you with a couple of overcoats."

If I'd had the energy, I'd have cried with joy. It was then after

263

three-thirty. For the next four hours, I was insensible to the world. Then, with more hot tea in me and with the good wishes of the station, I hurried home. Our door was still secured with the padlock, and no patrolman was in sight.

I ran all the way to the Romasses, who listened to my tale with compassion, fed me a good breakfast, and sent me home restored. The door was unlocked, and François stood in front of the wall mirror calmly shaving.

Without looking at me, he said, "Oh, there you are. I hear the cops picked you up for vagrancy."

"You beast!" I bawled, and burst into tears.

In a flash, his arms were around me, and his soapy cheeks against mine. "Oh, *ma chére, mon amour* .... Forgive me. I know what really happened. The patrolman told me all about it."

Between sobs I asked, "Did you have the key with you?"

"No. Somehow it got lost. I went to the district station, but you had already left. The police suggested I go to the market and buy another padlock. Fortunately, there are stalls nearby. I bought a lock with two keys and ... guess what, *Chérie?*" He lifted my chin and grinned. "The darned keys of the new one fit the old one perfectly!"

Chapter Eight

Moscow
November 2, 1933

Darling All,

There's good news among the no-news. Two months ago, I applied for permission to shop at INSNAB, the special store for foreign workers, and this morning I got my little grey booklet full of ration tickets. Don't ask me how that was possible when I'm here illegally, without a visa.

Anyway, I dropped everything and rushed over to see their clothing department. I'm allowed to buy one winter coat a year, one suit and one pair of shoes — more than I'll ever wear out in twelve months. They have some beautiful furs. A tailoring department is part of the deal, too, so I'm having a coat made to measure from a fur called "Siberian cat."

The food section has all sorts of good things and is never out of stock. I'm teasing François because he hasn't his INSNAB book yet. He says it's only because I'm prettier than he.

Did I tell you my ashtray turned out well? Yesterday, I began a new piece of sculpture — a bust of Karl Marx, about eight inches high — for a competition. Portraits are easy for me because I like doing them. I try to probe the inner person.

We've been working extra for the celebrations on November 7, the anniversary of the Russian Revolution. I was asked to submit a sketch for a large statue of a soldier for one of the squares. It didn't win, but they paid me well, anyway — half the price of my fur coat.

We've adjusted to living in the studio without the comforts one is used to. It's a lot better than being out on the street these cold nights, believe me.

And we've seen another opera — but not at the Bolshoi. The gypsies have their own theatre to present plays and operas in the tradition evolved by them over the centuries. The opera we saw was "Carmen." Imagine the role of Carmen interpreted by a <u>real</u> gypsy! The audience, too, was mostly of gypsies. The way they interacted with the performers — it was nearly like living those days in Spain.

Last week in a second-hand store, we bought a complete set of Vasari's "Lives of the Painters," in ten volumes. This edition is in French, over 100 years old, and cost 125 rubles. Vasari was a painter and architect born near Florence in 1511, in the heyday of the Renaissance.

November 4

So much has happened I don't know where to start. François got his INSNAB book <u>and</u> his visa.

Meanwhile, we were at a party at Fred and Ethel's. Eliot was there without Carol. They have separated, and Eliot had nowhere to sleep so, naturally, we invited him to our ceramic palace.

He had a list of rooms for rent. For two days we checked them out, found one we all liked, and moved in together yesterday. It's in a huge five-story building constructed just before the revolution for families of good income. The apartments are all spacious, with big double-glazed windows and are centrally heated.

After the overthrow of the Czar, these apartments, and hundreds like them, were divided up to house the multitudes who lacked adequate living space. The new tenants were given one or two rooms per family, and the use of the bathroom and kitchen in common.

Our room is one of two allotted to Olga and Constantin. She's a dentist, and he's a lawyer. We'll pay them 100 rubles a month. For that she'll also do our cleaning and shopping at INSNAB. She can have the things from our books that we don't need, such as white bread, half our meat, flour and sugar. Rations for foreigners are generous.

Three families (four, with us) share the kitchen and bathroom. Each of us has a corner of the kitchen with a table and shelves.

More later — François just came home.

With love,
Sis

"How's my favorite concubine?" François looked about the room. "Oh, good. Eliot's not here yet."

"He's out and won't be back till late," I said.

"Oh, *mon amour.* So, there really is a Santa Claus."

I wiggled out of his arms. "What are you talking about?"

"About us ... about your visa. I've been thinking about it all day. Just because they refused to give it to you doesn't mean you have to leave. I have *my* visa. That'll serve for both of us if ... if ...."

"Yes, I know. If we get married. *I've* been thinking about it all day. But we agreed back in Paris not to get married. We made a pact, remember?"

"That was months ago. So much has happened since then. Let's cancel the pact. I wasn't as much in love with you then. I want to be a family now — we belong together."

"Of course we do. But a pact is a contract! I'm talking about a *principle*, François, not only for me, but for all women, even for those who aren't aware what marriage has done to them over the centuries because they've been *taught* to believe it's the natural condition of women.

"Without integrity, that principle is worthless. Look, for example, at the fetish some societies have made of virginity. Virginity for *women only!* Do you realize that it is our virginity that created the profession of prostitution?"

François turned away and sat at the table with his chin cradled in his hands. I perched on a chair on the other side of the room. The only sound was the ticking of the alarm clock on our bedside table. I remembered how John used to fervently declare: "*I marriage disparage!*" Then how he later pleaded with me to marry him and got angry when I refused. I'd have to be on guard. I wondered how François would react.

Whether moments or minutes later — I didn't know — François, in a gentle voice, said, "One of the many reasons I love you, Agnessa, is your loyalty to what you believe in — your constancy. You wouldn't be in Moscow now if you were otherwise. You've told me how your sister's singing career was crushed by her husband when she married, and your mother's, too. And because of that, your mother encouraged you to go off to Paris. As you know, I grew up in a conventional environment."

He looked across at me before going on. "You know what? Women's autonomy means more freedom for men, as well. So why would I be against it?"

"I know you're not against it, François."

"But, Agnessa, what alternative is there for you?"

"Oh ... I could become a Soviet citizen."

"Sure, and risk not being able to leave the country?"

"Or ... I could find some Russian who'd marry me as a favor."

"What the hell's the difference if you marry some Russian or me? You'd still be married."

"The difference is ... my emotions wouldn't be involved, and you and I could still live in sin."

"Very funny! Be serious. Here in the Soviet Union, a woman can keep her maiden name. Actually, no one knows, or even cares, whether or not a couple is married. Come on, you'll still be a free spirit. I promise not to let you change."

"Well ... maybe. But only on one condition."

"Anything. Name it."

"That when one day we leave the country, we'll get divorced ... just as a matter of principle."

François threw his head back and laughed aloud. "All right. I'll risk it. Whatever you want. Now, what do you say we celebrate with a drink of that wine I bought yesterday?"

"And we'll christen those antique goblets we got at the second-hand store."

François offered the first toast. "May your future husband make you as happy as you deserve."

I raised my drink. "And may I deserve the happiness the kindest man in the world will give me."

I put down my glass, took one of François' hands in both of mine, and went on, "I must tell you what happened at Mercouroff's this morning. I explained that my second application for a visa had been turned down and that I was determined to stay here anyway. Mercouroff and his two assistants were sympathetic and Fyodor, who's about thirty-five, was especially consoling."

"Did he have a solution?"

"Indeed he did. He stood up straight and said, 'Comrade Agnessa, please don't think me impudent. We don't want you to leave. I am not married and willingly offer you matrimony if that would make it possible for you to remain — in friendship, you understand.' I didn't know what to say. Fortunately, Mercouroff came to the rescue. 'If your young architect doesn't want you, you won't be without chivalrous hopefuls, will you?'"

François refilled our glasses. "He's not a serious rival then?"

"What do *you* think, my love? Put your arms around me and hold me tight. I know what you meant about Santa Claus. The giving of ourselves to each other."

Bolshaia Communisticheskaia Ulitsa,
Moscow
November 5, 1933

Dearest Family,

I'll mail this letter tomorrow, and before it reaches you, I'll be married.

Yes — married!

François and I are changing our civil status painlessly on November 11th at the Office of Marriage and Divorce.

The clerk behind the desk brings out the appropriate book, and we register the event by merely signing our names and paying a charge of three rubles.

There will be no rings, no futile promises, and no witnesses.

Divorce is just as easy. The couples simply sign out. The name we enter is the one we'll officially be known by. We can take our spouse's, keep our own or choose a brand new one. We're keeping our own.

Please note our new address.

With love to all,
Sisi

Chapter Nine

The three of us awoke early on November 7th, before the sun was up. For days, Eliot, François and I had talked about the coming celebrations and were determined to see as much of them as possible firsthand.

I didn't know where my artists' group was to assemble, and François decided not to join his architects. Eliot wanted to take a chance with us and, with a little luck, get close enough to watch the parade from the sidelines.

"We won't have to worry about the weather, at least," François commented. "It looks like yesterday's snow has melted. I suggest we have a good breakfast. Who knows when we'll be able to eat again."

"Yeah," Eliot observed. "I doubt we'll find any Capitalistic hot dog or popcorn stands."

The sky was still dark when we left the building. Many of our neighbors — whole families with grandparents and small children — were already out. By the time we reached downtown, daylight caught up with us, and the streets flowed with waves of citizens commemorating the sixteenth anniversary of the Bolshevik Revolution.

"I've never seen a Fourth of July at home this crowded," Eliot said.

"Your liberation day was a century and a half ago," François reminded him. "Maybe a hundred and fifty years from now the Soviets will be less fired up about it."

Eliot snickered. "If, that is, the system lasts that long. I give it another twenty years at most."

"I don't agree," François replied, "but we'll see."

The crowds became denser as we neared the center of town.

"It might be difficult to stay together," François warned. "If we can't, let's say we meet later at the Ellis'. They'll be expecting us any time from four o'clock on."

Soon after that, a sudden wave of parade-goers separated us, sweeping me along toward the parade route. I looked back and waved to François and Eliot. A moment later, they were out of sight.

Long before reaching the opera house, we came to the first cordon manned by several uniformed guards. I knew how to get through that barrier. I took out my passport and, in undiluted English, fibbed, "Look, Comrades, I have to go to the Hotel National .... It's over there. See — I'm an American tourist."

Two of the officers, one old, the other young, examined my document, then looked at each other questioningly, nodded, and let me pass. I hurried on, weaving my way through the confusion till I reached the inner cordon. There the guards were skeptical of my stratagem. One of them lowered his bushy eyebrows, studied the passport, looked me slowly up and down, and insisted on accompanying me to the entrance of the hotel.

The parade was just beginning so I stayed near the doorway to watch. Marchers streamed right past the hotel. For more than an hour they tramped — soldiers on foot and horseback, trucks, tanks, machine guns, heavy artillery and other things I didn't know how to name, heading toward Red Square a block or two away.

Well before noon, the military part was over and workers' organizations followed, carrying signs and standards identifying themselves and proclaiming they had overfulfilled their quotas and would do even better next year. On they filed — railway employees, bricklayers, actors of the Vaktangov Theatre, teachers of such-and-such a school, nurses .... A good supply of accordion players were among them. Singers raised their voices in chorus after chorus of folk ballads and revolutionary songs.

I grew impatient. How long should I wait for my group to come by? What if it approached by another route? An impulse sent me across the sidewalk to fall in alongside a row of singing young women, whose banner declared them to be textile workers. While they sang, all was well, but then the women near me in line asked who I was and suggested I didn't belong with them. Without waiting to be expelled, I left their company and, still walking, dropped back a few paces.

A burly patrolman raised his voice, addressing me, "Comrade, keep the sidewalks clear! Get back into line!"

I rejoined the textile workers only to be shooed out again. Another patrolman eyed me. I slipped in with the next group — the boiler-makers. To my surprise and delight, they welcomed me, even though they soon learned I was a foreigner.

By then, we were about to enter Red Square. Several approaching streams of marchers merged and I was swept along with the masses.

Music came from every side. Red flags fluttered on the tops of all the buildings. On the right, against the Kremlin wall, bleachers had been erected on either side of Lenin's tomb, and on top of the tomb — there they were, a dozen of them — the most important communists of all. I recognized Voroshilov and Molotov, and Stalin in the middle.

As the boiler-makers' band started playing, the young woman next to me smiled and firmly grasped my arm. Around us everyone sang lustily. At the top of my voice I joined in. The louder I sang, the more I felt a great release of emotions, a riddance of the stresses I had carried about for several months.

Out there in the middle of Red Square no one knew me. I was one of thousands, unburdening myself in a way I never would among those I lived and worked with. A ballad ended, a mazurka began, and then a march. I made up words to familiar tunes, sharing my euphoria noisily with infinite space.

I kept up with the boiler-makers till we reached the far side of the square and were past the basilica down by the river. The crowds of marchers, no longer in formation, disbanded alongside the bank. Some wanted to get away, while others lingered to share a few dances and an occasional swig of vodka from a pocket flask. Unable to resist the strains of an accordion, I gladly let someone twirl me around among other couples, while onlookers clapped to punctuate the rhythm and increase the volume. The tunes varied, faster and slower, folk and jazz, and we changed partners again and again.

A few of the men may have had too much to drink but, alcohol or not, everyone's spirits were high. A bell in a tower of the Kremlin struck three, brusquely reminding me that time didn't loiter. The sky would soon be dark. I moved with the flow of those who were leaving.

My objective was Ethel and Fred's apartment on the other side of the Square.

To avoid going the long way around, I once again let my passport deliver me, with an escort, to a hotel — this time, the Metropole. The Ellis' house was not far from there. François and Eliot, among a score or more guests, were already toasting one thing or another.

> *Bolshaia Communisticheskaia Ulitsa*
> *Kvartir 1*
> *November 12, 1933*

Darling All of You,

The great holiday — two days long — is over. The second day was for recuperating. I was in the parade, though not with my artists' group. I marched and sang and danced and had a wonderful time. It was almost like Christmas or New Year's. People exchanged gifts, cleaned and decorated their homes, and gave children's parties and grand dinners.

Yesterday was our wedding day. The U.S. embassy will open for business here on November 16, so I'll have them record the nuptial tie in my passport.

Our ambassador is William Bullitt. In 1919, President Wilson sent him to Moscow to look the Bolsheviks over. He recommended to Wilson that the U.S. recognize the Soviets, but Wilson refused. That caused Bullitt to resign and stay out of the diplomatic service till now. He's only forty-two.

Note my new address above. The name means "Street of the Grand Communistic." Please send my mail here from now on instead of c/o Intourist.

> *November 15*

The temperature has dropped to about 20 degrees. I got my fur coat just in time.

The other day, François came home with a pair of skis for each of us and gave me my first lesson right here in our room. I learned the Kristiania, how to turn and stop by pressing on one heel, then another technique where I push my knees together, keeping the skiis apart, and put my weight on the outside. The plains around Moscow are fine for beginners and for what is called cross-country.

Eliot has gone to London. He's a bright young man, interested in economics, a protégé of Bernard Baruch.

Carol, however, is staying. She got her visa because she's employed as a secretary to one of the foreign correspondents. She gave a party the other evening. Most of the guests were American and Russian reporters from the "Moscow Daily News," an English-language paper started by Anna Louise Strong, the revolutionary daughter of a Seattle minister.

I met Milly Mitchell at the party. Milly lived six years in Honolulu long ago and many years in China with Anna Louise and Sun Yat Sen.

Clifford Gessler, art editor of the "Star-Bulletin," wrote her to look me up. He wrote me, too, a month ago, and sent an article he'd written for the paper about my life in Paris. Wasn't that nice of him?

Anyway, at midnight when the party was over, we came out to a wonder-world of drifting white. At that hour, with few people about, there were hardly any tracks in the powdery snow. The only conveyances were horse-drawn sleighs, and the only sound the jingling of their bells. It would have been romantic to ride one, but we didn't have the sixty rubles it would have cost to take us to Taganka (our district), so we walked. The exercise kept my feet warm, but my high heels slowed our pace and gave us more time to delight in the sights transformed to a bewitching diorama of snow-covered shapes that used to be roof tops, church spires and trees.

With tons of love,
Agnessa

P.S. I just got a message from Comrade Stukov, one of those who finds work for artists. He wants me to drop by his office one day soon. That might mean another job.

Chapter Ten

Comrade Stukov greeted me with more than usual cordiality. "Well, well .... I hear you now have your permit to stay in our country."

"Yes. I'm very glad that has been settled at last."

"Good. And you have turned in your bust of Karl Marx. You should be hearing the result in a week or so. In the meantime, I want to congratulate you, Comrade Larsen."

"Yes? What for?"

"You have been accepted as an *aspirant.*"

Because of his impeccable English, the way he pronounced the word surprised me. Did it have a meaning I was unfamiliar with?

"An *aspirant* for what?" I asked.

Stukov scratched his balding head and smiled indulgently. "You may have forgotten that months ago, when you were filling out forms for all sorts of things, you applied for this, as well. Let me explain. For all the arts we have, well, there are 'academies' where those who have reached a certain level of maturity of technique, and demonstrated skill and style of articulation, may work without the cares and anxieties sometimes caused by the need to earn a living."

He waited for me to comment but, seeing I still didn't grasp the significance of what he was telling me, went on, "Come, Comrade, I will show you. My car is downstairs. I'll explain on the way."

As the chauffeur drove through town, out beyond Maslovka and past open fields, I learned what being an *aspirant* involved.

"A committee has reviewed your qualifications," Stukov began. "They studied the photos of the work you did in Paris, and considered your originality and your technical competence. This undertaking for *aspirants* in general was started soon after the revolution. For sculptors, however, it's only a few years old. The buildings are new, but temporary. One day, they'll be replaced by large, more adequate studios."

"Tell me about the students, Comrade Stukov. Why are they called *aspirants?*"

"Because they aspire, they strive for improvement, and we help them. It operates much like one of those academies in Paris, only here, we furnish the necessary equipment, materials and models, and give *aspirants* 250 rubles a month, besides. Can you manage that amount?"

"Oh, yes, indeed. My rent is fifty rubles. I don't need any clothes and, with my INSNAB book, food is cheap. I'll have rubles left over."

"Well, you know, you'll still be able to take outside jobs, as you have been, and execute them here."

"Gee!" was all I could think of saying.

The driver turned off the dirt road, parked beside one of the many barrack-like structures, hopped out and opened the back door for us.

Stukov glanced at his wristwatch. "We've arrived at a good time. The class will be reassembling after lunch. The canteen is in that building over there. No gourmet meals, mind you, but they're adequate and inexpensive."

I was still tongue-tied when Stukov let us into the vast, well-lighted studio. At least fifteen people in three groups were standing at turntables, working in clay from three models. No one noticed us. Stukov put a finger to his lips. The silence was almost complete except for an occasional rasping sound as someone rotated his sculpture.

Then one of the men said, "Break time!" and there was a sudden buzzing of voices.

Stukov took my elbow, and we moved forward. "Good afternoon, Comrades," he said.

Men and women of a wide range of ages — mid-twenties to something over fifty — grouped around us as Stukov went on, "I have brought Comrade Agnessa to join your class. She is *Amerikanka* and has been studying sculpture in Paris for two years."

The murmur of voices grew louder. A young man near me shook my hand and, with a broad smile, said, "I am Anatole Gregoriev. You are very welcome."

As I went around the room, each student and the models shook my hand and told me his or her name. Somehow, I found the appropriate Russian words to express my eagerness to begin working with them.

That evening I couldn't wait to tell François about my becoming an *aspirant*. With most of the afternoon free, I stopped in at the INSNAB and came home with arms full of special things for dinner. He arrived later and more tired than usual.

"What a day! Oh, it's good to hold you." He ruffled my hair. "We're starting to work on the new underground, and I'm going to have a hand in it. Our office has been assigned the Kirovsky station.

He held me away at arms' length. "You're as excited as I am! Hey! Look at that table ... and with vino! How come?"

By the time we were well into the meal, I had told him almost every detail of the great event in *my* day.

"If anyone deserves it, you do, Agnessa. When do you start?"

"Tomorrow ... at nine o'clock. In the morning till twelve, we work on our own compositions in separate studios in the same building. Then we have an hour for lunch, nearby, at a cafeteria. After that, we work from models in the big room, and the last hour, from three to four, we sketch with pencil or charcoal from the models who change poses often ... as it was at the Grande Chaumière in Paris."

"You're going to like it, I can see, and making Russian friends .... What do you say we go dancing at the end of the week — just you and I — at the Metropole, to celebrate?"

In reply, I just grinned and clapped my hands. François continued. "And they'll play a waltz — they always do sooner or later .... Remember that first night we all went to that *boîte de nuit* .... ? And our first dance was a waltz, and I knew then I was going to fall in love with you."

"I knew, too. But you didn't say anything."

"No. I was afraid you'd turn me down."

"And you wanted to keep your options open, didn't you?"

"Well, maybe. I guess so. But then you went off to Italy and were gone for six weeks. It seemed like six years. I'll never forget the day you came back. I was alone in Corbu's office. I looked up and there you were — standing in the doorway at the far end of the *atelier* with sunshine all around you. Every time I hear a waltz I remember ...."

Moscow
Dec. 15, 1933

Darlings,

The morning sky doesn't begin to pale till after nine o'clock and, oh boy, is it cold! 25 below zero, centigrade. That's the same as 17 degrees Fahrenheit. But our room is always warm, and so am I

276

with my new felt boots that cover my legs up to the knees. I'm beginning to look Russian.

In the mornings, we judge the outdoor temperature by looking to see how the people are walking in the street. If they saunter, with arms swinging, it's comparatively warm. When they tramp, bent over, hugging themselves, it's cold and windy, as today is.

Did I tell you my bust of Karl Marx was chosen, the only one out of several? They gave me 600 rubles for it, and I'll get a royalty of five percent of the sales, besides, as with the elephant and ashtray.

The academy I told you about is stimulating. In the mornings, I'm doing a portrait, and after lunch, I work with the others from a model — anatomical studies.

During breaks, we sit around the wood stove and talk. One day I showed them the calendar you sent me with all the gorgeous tourist photos of palm trees and sunny beaches. They can't understand why I would ever leave Honolulu by choice. I try to tell them, but the language stumps me.

They're teaching me Russian. It's an eloquent tongue — made for poetry. I've already learned to recite a piece by Pushkin and started reading their classical literature in French translation — Dostoyevski, Gogol, Tolstoy, Gorky — to begin with. One of the young men, Anatole, has read more of our classics than I have. He likes to declaim Walt Whitman in Russian.

I've read somewhere that the English language has four times as many words as either French or Russian.

December 19

Two days ago, François had to be hospitalized — nothing serious, but painful. They removed an inch-long stone from his saliva gland. The second day I wanted to see him but wasn't allowed into his ward because there's an epidemic of grippe in town. I sat downstairs with a lot of other visitors, and he and I sent notes back and forth by messenger.

There is no charge whatever for doctors' visits or hospitalization, and no insurance premiums to pay, either. Whoever needs medical care gets it — anywhere in the Soviet Union. Most medicines are free, too. Is there another country that does that for its people? And we're not even citizens.

I'll be thinking of you over Christmas. On New Year's Eve we're going to a party at Ethel and Fred's. We've been meeting many Americans and have a lot of Russian friends, as well.

François' colleagues are planning a weekend skiing in the country. We'll stay at a rest house that belongs to the architects' cooperative.

With hugs and kisses,
Sisi

Chapter Eleven

Moscow
February 19, 1934

Dearest Everyone,

We've had a visitor from Paree: Charlotte Perriand. You may recall, she's Le Corbusier's interior designer and was a colleague of François'.

After a week at a hotel, she spent several days with us. One night we took her to a performance of "Twelfth Night." I saw it last summer in London at the Old Vic Theatre. Here, I wasn't able to judge the poetic translation, but the humor of this interpretation came through. Malvolio's Russian obtuseness was more emphatic than in the London version. The audience loved it. Charlotte, who doesn't know a word of Russian, understood the wit from the acting.

She went back to Paris a few days ago, by way of Vienna, on the day we heard of the Austrian Civil War. We don't know yet if she got through.

Before leaving, she gave me an elegant wool dress. It fit perfectly, but when I looked in the mirror, I saw a country bumpkin who couldn't stand properly. I slouch, and move like a gawky peasant. That comes from not having the time or inclination to put the finishing touches on my toilette. I'll have to reeducate myself to do the dress justice. A little vanity never hurt anyone.

Because clothes are so hard to come by, Moscow women have little choice of style of color. They are without fashion; their dresses are, for the most part, purely functional.

One day Vera, a sculptor friend at the academy, bought a piece of lightweight fabric and asked me to go with her to have it made up. The seamstress is self-employed and works in her home, a single room. On the coffee table were several foreign fashion magazines, all well-worn and dog-eared, and no newer than three years old. The long waists and short skirts of 1928 seem silly now that hems are mid-calf and belts at the natural waistline. Vera had a hard time choosing. Eventually she decided on a party frock with a full skirt of uneven lengths. It was too far out of date to please my taste, but Vera liked it so much I hadn't the heart to deflate her.

All the women will probably turn out on the First of May happy and beautiful, in brand new finery. Like most of us, I'm afraid I've been conditioned to obey the laws of the rulers of the fashion industry, whether they improve my looks or not. In the ideal world, we'll wear only what accentuates our best features.

May 1st, or May Day, is International Labor Day — in every country except the U.S. and Canada. (Ironically, it was an American, I believe, who first proposed that May 1st should honor working people.)

Work is going well, and there's lots of it. Yesterday, I went to François' office because his boss, Colli, wanted to see me. They showed me the plans of a new elementary school under construction. In an open area there'll be a fountain, and in a wall behind it will be a niche. Colli wants me to make a sculpture for it, and be free to do as I please. In a few days, he'll drive me out to see the school. Almost everyone at the academy has outside work.

With love to all,
Sisi

Moscow
April 18, 1934

Darling Everybody,

My recent letters haven't been very interesting. We're busier than ever and nothing unusual has been happening — till now, that is. The latest excitement is a genuine Cornflakes factory in Moscow. Some enterprising American talked a venturesome Russian entity into experimenting. The cereal is sold in large, plain cartons about two feet by one. To me, it tastes as good as ours, but François says it's like eating air. He prefers rolled oats. I wonder how it will catch on with the general public.

For the rest of the month, I'll be tied up, working till late at night with a group from the academy making papier mâché masks for the May Day parade. The masks are huge caricatures; we do them from drawings. First, we cover light wooden frames with chicken wire, which we then fashion roughly into the desired shapes. Over the wire we place paper dipped into large buckets of glue, and mold them onto the final contours of the features. After that, we use broad brushes and poster paint to finish them.

I'm having lots of fun. Everyone is enthusiastic and full of buffoonery. Not only are we paid well — 90 rubles a day — but they supply us with refreshments and good meals, and I've met many new people, besides.

Different organizations in the parade will carry the masks, along with banners that tell of their accomplishments so far this year. François and I haven't decided yet whether we'll march. We might try to get tickets in the bleachers on Red Square.

I know why God planned the year in seasons. Summer is for playing. If there were not winter, I wonder how I'd spend my time. Looking back, I can see I worked hard partly to obliterate those dark, cold days. On May 1st, the masses will tell what they have done. As for me, I've learned another foreign language, and some of the customs that go with it. I have created several pieces of sculpture — tangible contributions to anthropology, if not to the improvement of humankind.

I'm going to buy a piece of cotton material and make a summer dress just in case the weather turns hot. That little chain-stitch sewing machine I've had for so long still works. It clamps on to the table and is a lot faster, and stronger than sewing by hand.

With hugs and kisses,
Sisi

P.S. François sends his love, too. He's just returned, says all tickets for the bleachers are sold out. He's reserved a table at the eighth-floor restaurant of the New Moscow Hotel. That's where we stayed when we first arrived. From there, we'll have a splendid view of the marchers as they leave the square.

My plan for the First of May was to wake up early, put on my new dress and get myself all prettied up to surprise my spouse. But I had stayed up so late finishing it, I overslept. When I opened my eyes, I saw François holding the dress by the shoulders, examining it. For awhile, I lay quietly, trying to think of a facetious remark. François beat me to it. Without turning his head, he pretended to talk to himself.

"Wow! If I ever saw a young woman wearing this, I'd fall in love with her on the spot and never let her go."

Then he came over and sat on the bed beside me. "Did you really make it? Where did you find the material? I like the blue and white pattern."

"INSNAB got a bolt of it last week — just in from one of the republics. It sold out immediately."

Getting dressed that spring morning — I have never forgotten. We opened the windows wide, letting in the warm air. Outside, others, too, had put the winter behind them.

"You might change your mind," I said, "when you see all the pretty girls out there."

"For me," François whispered, "you'll always be the prettiest of them all."

I walked to the New Moscow Hotel on François' arm believing every word he said. At the restaurant, I felt the head waiter agreed with him. The man gave me a flattering smile, bowed slightly, checked our names on his list of reservations and motioned us to follow him.

Never — before or since — have I felt so special. Was it my imagination, or did heads turn as we passed? Generations later I knew the experience was a boon of that particular spring of 1934.

Our table, next to an open window, could not have been better placed. Down below, we saw it all — the river, the old stone bridge, St. Basil's, the walled-in Kremlin beyond, and the streams of noisy paraders. Part of me was with them, down there singing, wanting to dance.

The dining room filled up and hummed with the sounds of a dozen foreign tongues. I paid attention only to the view outside, and barely heard François order drinks.

At last came the thrill of seeing the first of the masks my friends and I had made.

I clasped François' arm. "Look! Here come the floats! Gee, I'm excited. Isn't it beautiful? What fun they're all having. This parade is even better than in November."

The waiter brought us our drinks, nodded and left. We turned back to the window.

"Yeah! Look at that!" François said. "It's like Carnival time — all the color and excitement and abandon .... Only at Carnival, they celebrate before *fasting* and here, they're celebrating before *feasting*. Looks like *everyone* has worked like the devil all winter. Good thing, too, tomorrow is a holiday."

I raised my glass and, with an exaggerated flourish said, "Workers of the world unite!"

"Yes, a good slogan, but I can think of another one."

"Like what?"

"Well ... we workers are lucky — we have jobs. Think of the rest of the planet. How about this: *Unemployed* of the world, unite!"

Chapter Twelve

Moscow
May 3, 1934

Darlings,

More visitors from the West. This time it was Luis Sert, the Spanish architect who was so nice to us in Barcelona last year. He was here with some friends for a few days, staying at the Metropole. François saw them every day, but I joined them only on the their last evening.

They asked a lot of questions about my being an aspirant at the Academy and about the sculpture I'm going to do for the elementary school. My pencil sketches for it are progressing. It will probably be two children — one, a girl, sitting on the floor of the niche, with a foot extended so the fountain splashes on it; and the other, a boy, leaning forward behind her, with an arm stretched toward the water. We don't know yet whether it will be in stone or bronze. Fired clay won't hold up long under that steady cascade.

That generated a debate on the role of the arts in the changing world. The gist was that poets and politicians alike use words to spread their views. Political systems alter with the needs of society, and are replaceable. The arts evolve with us but leave a permanent record, a tangible one of our passage from one form of government to another.

Discussions of that sort take place all the time. No one expects to win. They're mostly brain exercises to keep our wits alert.

Now, let me entertain you with a couple of anecdotes to show my progress in the language department:

The other day, I was at home, in our collective kitchen, trying to boil water for tea. The primus stove, which works faster, wouldn't light up, so I had to use the kerosinka. The woman who comes in to clean the floors and the windows was there and helped me. We chatted about this and that, getting on well, I thought. After awhile, she put her soapy hands on her hips, shook her head and said, "My goodness, Comrade, you speak lousy Russian!"

Imagine that! In less than a year, I can speak lousy Russian! It took me longer than that to put a whole sentence together in French.

The very next day, I made a joke at the Academy. During lunch break, three or four comrades were telling me about the czar, Peter the Great — what a remarkable man he was, physically as well as intellectually. He brought Russia out of the Dark Ages and into the 18th century. I learned that in Russian, he's called "Peotr Primus," which means, "Peter the First." Then they told me about Catherine the Great, that she was not the first Catherine.

That's when I made my pun! I said, "Well, if the great czar was "Peotr Primus," she must have been "Katerina Kerosinka!"

For several weeks, François and I have noticed we seemed to be the only ones using the tub in our bathroom. Eventually, I found the audacity to mention it to Olga. I needn't have fretted.

She chuckled when she realized what I must have been thinking. "But, everyone goes to the banya!" she said, meaning the public baths. She made it sound so attractive, François and I are going this evening. Every district has one. Ours is close by in a two-story brick building constructed ages ago.

With love and kisses,
Sisi

At the top of the broad steps, François turned left and entered the door marked for men, and I went into the women's section on the right. "See you in an hour," he said.

I gave the young woman in the ticket booth a few kopeks, received a large linen towel, then followed two women into the anteroom. There I lingered and watched the others to learn the routine. Trying to appear nonchalant, I undressed, hung my clothes on a peg and proceeded through the swinging doors into a large, warm area shrouded in steam. Vague shapes moved about, and voices spoke. Another world surrounded me, a microcosm of bare limbs and torsos, fat and skinny, old and young. I sat down on a wooden stool and, taking in the scene, began to soap myself as I saw the others do. On a bench next to me, two teenagers talked earnestly.

"... And after that," said the dark-haired one, "I just didn't want to see him again."

"But he loves *you*," insisted the blonde one. "He told me so."

"Sure — me and how many others?"

I moved to another part of the room. Two women, the older one having a massage and the younger one a pedicure, were exchanging confidences.

"... It's my mother-in-law," said the young one. "I'm grateful she takes care of the children, but she won't accept the fact that my husband is no longer one of her kids."

An attendant in a white dress and apron approached them with two glasses on a tray.

"Your beer, Comrades," she said. After taking payment, she left.

Disguised by nudity, I felt invisible, and walked about the misty space eavesdropping, imagining I was an anthropologist or a psychiatrist collecting data on the nature and behavior of a segment of the human race.

Cleansing the physical body was only one function of the *banya*. For me, it was as good as a movie — a slice of life. No wonder the bathtub at home was not used. I wondered .... As modern apartments replaced the old, and cramped quarters disappeared, would the *banya* become extinct?

The hour was suddenly drawing to a close. Reluctantly, I stepped under a hot shower to rinse off the soap, and immersed my body in the pool. François would be waiting for me. I had to hurry. Next time, I'd stay longer.

Moscow
May 25, 1934

Darling All of You,

Our days off have become oases of calm and restoration. On the last one, we took an early boat ride up the twisting Moscow River to a place forty-five minutes away. One bank stretched out flat and green, covered with grass and grazing cattle. We stayed there to swim and look across to a wood of sprouting birches spread over low hills. During the morning other people came — families with children and grandparents.

Sooner or later, everyone went swimming but me. I'm not used to such cold water. One of the women wore trunks, but all the others, including us, were stark naked. Russians have never thought of their bodies as something to be hidden as we Puritans do.

Some young men tied a net between two trees and organized a volleyball game. François joined them, but I took a sunbath. We stayed till the sun had nearly set and then got a river boat to town — with our clothes back on, of course.

I'll continue this tomorrow. I'm tired and don't feel well.

François left for work earlier than usual in the morning. I was taking the breakfast dishes to the kitchen when suddenly, there was such a pain somewhere in my lower torso, I nearly dropped the tray. Fortunately, Olga was there to help me. I couldn't stand, and the pain worsened.

"Oh, Agnessa! Sit here on this chair. I'll run and find a taxi. You must see a doctor."

I didn't have to wait long. When we reached the hospital, only a couple of blocks away, I had to be carried in on a stretcher.

By afternoon, I was in a maternity ward. Four doctors had examined me. One of them spoke English well.

"The trouble is in one of your fallopian tubes, between the uterus and an ovary. There might be a pregnancy in the oviduct. If so, we'll have to remove the tube and the ovary. Tomorrow we'll see how you are. Till then, rest as much as you can. Call the nurse if there is more pain."

When he left, I tried to sleep, but couldn't — it was feeding time. As an attendant wheeled babies into the ward to be nursed, curiosity replaced my anxiety. I spoke in Russian to one young mother.

"Hello. May I see your baby?"

A dozen heads turned in my direction. The young mother came closer, timidly.

"You speak Russian? But they told us you were *Amerikanka*."

"I am."

Her eyes grew large and round. "Honestly?"

I nodded.

"Gee!" She stood beside me and looked down, searching my face. "I've never seen a real, live *Amerikanka* before. You look just like one of us. What's your name?"

"Agnessa. What's yours?"

"Liuba."

"May I see your baby, Liuba? Is it a boy or girl?"

The young mother held the child so I could see its face.

"Her name is Valentina. Are you going to have a baby, Agnessa?"

I shook my head. "I'm afraid not .... There are complications ...."

By then, five or six women surrounded my bed. The nurse was among them.

"All right, now, comrades," she said, "the *Amerikanka* needs rest just as we do. You can talk to her when she feels better."

They went away, and I soon fell asleep — a long sleep without pain.

When I awoke, it was nighttime, and François sat beside my bed. We talked quietly. One of the doctors had briefed him on my condition. He stroked my forehead and kissed me.

"The most important thing is that *you're* well, my dear. Perhaps tomorrow they'll have a prognosis. I'll be back .... Goodnight for now. Visiting time is over; they're shooing us out."

Two days later, there was good news. The doctors could find no pregnancy, but they would keep me at least another week to see if the problem would correct itself.

On the fourth day, I was able to sit up and chat with my fellow patients. How good it was to be alive — it was May, going on June. Through the open windows came the potpourri of spring.

On the fifth day, I walked unaided to the bathroom. And finally, after ten days, François took me home in a horse and carriage.

June 6, 1934

Hello again,

I can now end the letter I left unfinished on May 25. I've been in the hospital. Nothing serious — female stuff. I'm fine now, but the doctors don't want me to return to work for another two weeks. I'll still get my stipend in spite of being absent.

There were no private rooms in the hospital. I was glad to have company in the ward. Several of the women had never seen an American up close before. They asked a lot of questions:

Is it true that everyone in America is rich? Are there really buildings of more than one hundred floors? Some people say all the streets are paved with gold. Are they?

One woman said she'd heard there was so much poverty in the U.S. that a lot of people lived on the streets and ate out of garbage cans, that Negroes couldn't eat or travel with white people, or go to the same schools, that only rich people were elected to Congress.

Another asked, "And what if you're sick and can't afford a doctor or medicine?" I'll let you guess how I replied.

One day we got to talking of folk remedies. A young patient told us what she'd heard about garlic from her grandmother. I wrote some of them down.

To dissolve kidney stones and relieve arteriosclerosis: Fill 1/3 of a glass jar with garlic. Add vodka to the top and cover. Keep in a warm place for two weeks and strain. Drink a glass of warm water with a drop of garlic brew each day for 25 days, then decrease drops for another 25 days. Repeat after a pause of two weeks.

For angina pectoris, senility, and loss of energy: 1/3 garlic; 1/2 onion ; 2 tablespoons vinegar. Let stand 24 hours in a warm place. Add hot honey. Mature for one week, strain. One t. 4 times a day.

Garlic is also good for epilepsy, ringworm, acne, hemorrhoids, and as an aphrodisiac. For a cold, rub cloves on the soles of your feet before going to bed, or hold a cut clove in your mouth between teeth and cheek.

I thought you'd be interested in this information because of the Norwegians' abhorrence of the magic bulb. Imagine what you've been missing all these years.

With hugs and kisses,
Agnessa

Chapter Thirteen

We were having dinner on the Second of June, discussing our options for the summer, when the bad news came.

"What about going to Samarkand?" François had just suggested. Think of all the history we can trace. It was already old in the 4th century B.C. Or we could visit Tiflis in the Caucasus Mountains, then relax on a beach on the Black Sea."

I was about to propose spending most of the time where we could swim, when there came a knock at the door. Olga entered.

"Comrade Agnessa, this has just come for you." She handed me a telegram.

I thanked her and tore the telegram open: *"Mom dying of cancer. Can you come? George."*

The message was not a surprise; a part of me had been expecting it, but the reality shook me, nevertheless.

A week later, I had completed the many steps required for getting an exit and a reentry visa.

"They will be ready on June 29, Comrade," a bureaucrat informed me from behind a desk. "You may pick them up then."

What could I do in the next several weeks but agonize over my helplessness? Working at sculpture was impossible. My mother was only forty-nine years old. Three of her six children were still minors; Joan wasn't even eight. I was grown up, but who would give me the emotional and moral support I had always counted on from her? François, yes, but he was my husband, not my mother.

François knew how I felt. His mother had died when he was a small boy. The woman his father then married was a poor substitute, although she tried hard.

My anxiety made waiting difficult. No one knew how much time Mama had left. Under the circumstances, every day was precious. I gave up the idea of completing the sculpture for the school and told Colli so.

"Don't be in a hurry," he said. "We can wait. If you're not back by October, we'll see."

Then I withdrew from the Academy. Some of my colleagues gave a party for me, and I asked them to think of what I should bring back for them.

Early in July, Gordon came from England to spend his summer vacation with us. Originally, he was going to join us on a tour of the smaller Soviet republics, but because of my leaving, our plans had to be revised.

The three of us went to Leningrad for a few days, especially to see the treasures of the Hermitage, but also to experience the grandeur of the city itself.

Back in Moscow, we attended some concert or play almost every night. There was a new Shostakovich opera that stimulated no small amount of controversy over the plot as well as the music. For a long time, Shostakovich had been accused of imitating modern European culture. Opinions were divided. The West was degenerate, some said, while others insisted we couldn't stay glued to the past. Evolution meant change. Progress required change!

Gordon and François offered their views on the subject.

"Change, sure," Gordon said, "but what kind? I think it's far too early to determine where Soviet arts are going. They're still too close to the upheavals of the revolution for us to expect a concerted trend."

"Do you think," I asked, "Shostakovich's music is degenerate?"

"That depends," François said. "He composed that music specifically for the story of *Ekaterina Ismailova.* Her tragedy could happen solely in the rotten society before the revolution, where her only escape was to murder and commit suicide."

"So you're saying that the music for it could not be in the traditional harmonious style?"

"Yes. Some people call it atonal, but I found the unconventional phonetics more appropriate than 'approved' sounds would have been. I'll bet in time, the public will come around to accepting him. Remember — Beethoven was booed more than once. And the public thought so little of Mozart, no one knows where he's buried."

Moscow
August 2, 1934

Dearest All,

Oh, bureaucracy! It's been two months since I applied for an exit visa. It was to have been ready on July 29, but some dope mistakenly made it out for the western border instead of the eastern. So there's been a delay. Now I'm definitely set to leave Moscow on August 8. I've sent you a telegram to that effect.

From Vladivostok to Japan, there's a boat every ten days. I should reach Yokohama on August 24. I'll send a wire to tell you what ship I'll be on. Under a month en route. Not bad. Hooray for modern transportation!

A week after I leave, François and Gordon are taking off for Odessa, Constantinople and Greece for a few weeks.

I'm bringing you some lovely presents that I've found in antique shops. When homes of the wealthy were disbanded during and after the revolution, many old families broke up. Some went abroad, and others moved to smaller quarters. What they couldn't take with them — jewelry, books, paintings, furniture, and objets d'art — they sold for whatever they could get. To browse in any one of those shops is as captivating as a visit to a museum, only the articles are for sale and affordable.

I'll have a few of them with me: a large leather-bound folio of world maps printed in the 16th century, several pieces of Wedgwood and Meissen porcelain, a great ancient cashmere shawl, some handmade peasant dolls, and lots of other things, as well as a kilo of caviar in a tin.

With love and an extra hug for Mama,
Sisi

The eighth of August dawned warm and sunny — the kind of day made for lovers to slip away to the woods or to an isolated beach.

In the middle of the morning, however, François and I were loading my suitcases into a taxi. The young driver busied himself with the job of putting the top down.

"You don't mind, comrades, if we get all the sun we can?"

"On the contrary," François told him. "It's wonderful."

"Looks like you two are on your honeymoon," the driver observed.

We laughed to avoid answering, and the taxi headed for the train station through streets almost bare of traffic. We said little, for fear of betraying our feelings. François grasped my hands in his — gripping them so tight, it hurt. Without looking at me, he whispered, "I'm going to miss you, damn it!"

Finally, on the platform, we made a feeble attempt at humor just before the train left.

"Well, it's too late now," François said with a hollow chuckle and a raised eyebrow.

"Too late for what?"

"Don't you remember? To get divorced. We agreed our marriage would last only while we were in Russia."

"Hey, you're right! Oh, but that's only when we both leave. You'll just have to remember we're still married. I have every intention of coming back."

With his eyes glued to mine, and his arms locked around me, he said with measured words, "If you don't, I'll come and kidnap you."

"Is that a promise?"

Chapter Fourteen

When one is twenty-three, the world doesn't stop spinning when catastrophe crosses one's path. I would be separated for months from François, and my mother was dying, but the trans-Siberian train rolled me on to distracting happenings.

The thousands of kilometers ahead meant new personalities, and places with strange names: Kazan, Sverdlovsk, Omsk, Krasnoyarsk, Irkutsk, Khabarovsk, Vladivostok. How different that train ride was from my last one, when I arrived in the Soviet Union the year before. Then I traveled third class, or "hard," as the Russians called it, and I didn't know the language.

This time I was in "soft" class, sharing a sleeping compartment with a congenial woman named Anna. We each had a private wash bowl, enough room so both could dress at the same time without bumping into each other, adequate storage space for all our suitcases, and drawers for the paraphernalia we'd need during the ten-day trip.

Anna worked in Tokyo where she had the post of vice-consul at the Soviet embassy.

"In preparation," she told me, "I've been studying Japanese for two years."

The sound of chimes came from the corridor. Anna glanced at her watch. "At last we can eat," she said. "Let's go. I'm starved."

Two coaches away, we found the dining car filling up rapidly. Anna and I shared a table with two young men, Misha and Yuri. They, too, were going to Japan, but on a trade mission. They had crossed the Soviet continent many times.

"How do you pass the time for ten days without getting bored?" I asked.

"Bored?" Both men laughed, and Misha said, "There's no time for that. When meals are over, the waiters turn the dining car into a parlor. We sit around and read or play chess and talk."

"And then," Anna put in, "every few hours the train stops — sometimes at a small town, sometimes a big one — and we run up and down the platform for exercise, and do a bit of shopping."

They asked me about train travel in America, and I described my trip to Canada three years before. "The Rocky Mountains were majestic, much grander than the Swiss Alps."

"The Alps are older, of course," Yuri said.

"Now I'm looking forward to see the Ural Mountains," I told them. "When will we get there?"

"In a couple of days."

On both sides of the train, as far as we could see, flat fields of grain stretched to the horizon, much like the American prairie, without even a hint of a hill.

During the next two days, I became friendly with several passengers, as well as waiters, who sat and chatted with us when off duty. At work, however, they were professional and formal. One of them explained to me, "This is an international route, you know, and at any moment, some big-shot could come aboard and expect to be served fittingly."

That evening, Misha reminded me we'd start climbing the Urals sometime during the night, leaving Europe and entering Asia.

When I raised the window blind the next morning, I saw nothing but the usual steppe spread out under the bright August sun. Anna had apparently gone off to breakfast. I dressed quickly and hurried to the diner, where she sat with Yuri and Misha.

"You look disturbed, Agnessa," Misha commented. "Anything wrong?"

"Haven't we reached them yet, or have we passed them?" I asked.

"What are you talking about? Passed what?"

"The Ural Mountains, of course!"

Yuri swept an arm outward toward the window. "There you are. We're scaling the western slope of the range now. Not much like the Rockies, is it?"

Trying not to laugh, my three friends waited for my reaction. "You're teasing me. The landscape is the same as it's been for the past three days."

"And it won't change. Seriously, the Urals are so old, they're worn down. It'll take us a couple of days to cross them, and the landscape will be more or less like this the whole way. The rise in elevation is so gradual it's imperceptible to us. Up North, you can find a few high places, but nothing over two thousand meters."

That afternoon, I took a book François had given me and sat in a corner of the transformed dining car, away from the passengers who had more social pursuits. I wanted to read, to feel close to François, and maybe contemplate the venerable Urals.

The book was an anthology of English poetry. As I thumbed through it, a man in a military uniform came in and sat opposite me. We nodded politely to each other but said nothing for several minutes. He opened a newspaper and became absorbed in it. Over the top of my book, I examined his lined face. He seemed to be in his midforties and, therefore, had probably fought in the revolution, where he may have acquired the scar on his forehead.

I beckoned a waiter and ordered a glass of tea. The army officer looked up.

"Bring me one, too," he said to the waiter. Then, turning to me, added, "I am Ivan Ivanovich, a major in the Red Army."

I told him my name, and we shook hands.

"It is a pleasure to make your acquaintance," he said. "I see you're reading poetry .... It is not in Russian."

I handed him the book. He turned the pages slowly and, I thought, reverently.

"Unfortunately, though I have studied your beautiful language, I cannot speak it. I love poetry very much." He paused. "Could I ask you to read something for me .... Some ... Lord Byron, perhaps?"

I was glad he asked me, because I could then hear the sounds aloud instead of only in my head. I chose "She Walks in Beauty," translated the title, and explained it was written in 1814, when Byron was impressed by the grace and charm of a woman in mourning.

> *"She walks in beauty, like the night*
> *Of cloudless climes and starry skies,*
> *And all that's best of dark and bright*
> *Meet in her aspect and her eyes,*
> *Thus mellow'd to that tender light*
> *Which heaven to gaudy day denies."*

Ivan's eyes were closed. I went on, reading the other two stanzas.

"Thank you," he said when I ended. "You are obviously well acquainted with the muse, Calliope."

We talked through dinner and into the night. The major agreed with me that sounds, whether of words or of instruments, or of nature, can be as compelling as any other art form. I told him I was a sculptor.

"Ah," he said, delighted, "you know that the plastic arts are poetry of light and shade playing on forms ... whether the subject be figurative or abstract, the beauty is in the technique, the composition, the proportions ...."

The next morning, when the train stopped at Sverdlovsk, I hurried off. Dodging the crowds leaving and boarding the coaches with their bundles and valises and baskets and children, I managed to run from one end of the platform to the other several times. As I was returning to the train, Ivan Ivanovich wished me a good morning.

"*Dobry utro!* Will you join me in a glass of tea?"

We spent most of the day talking poetry. He told me much about Pushkin.

"In many ways he resembled Byron," Ivan said. "They both loved life and women, wrote in the romantic style and, though born into the aristocracy, were exiled because of their political views."

During a pause, I cleared my throat pretentiously and recited in Russian three lines of Pushkin I recently learned:

"The storm has passed
And the white rose
Wafts me its fragrance."

Ivan flashed me an approving smile. "The simplicity of that poem is oriental. I know it well."

Then he declaimed his favorite, another of Pushkin's, much longer.

"And do you write poetry?" I asked.

"No ... but don't think I haven't tried. To me it's the highest form of art." He was silent for a long time, then said, "My grandfather was illiterate but composed exquisite poems. I wrote many of them down and so did my father. I was fourteen when my grandfather died."

"Tell me about him."

Ivan looked away — far, far away. The subject was obviously a sensitive one. I waited.

The major began softly, as though trying not to disturb the memory. "He used to take me into the woods whenever he had the time ... in all seasons. He taught me to feel the heartbeat of nature, to hear songs in the winds and the rain and the running streams. From him I learned to love our Russian language, the soil, the trees, and the people who toil.

"My *dedushka* was a man of enormous size and physical power. He labored on the docks of Petrograd — a stevedore — and could do the work of three or four normal men. Yet he was as gentle as he was strong.

"In January, 1905, he took part in the abortive demonstration, a peaceful and legal one, with petitions citing their grievances. The police opened fire, killing one hundred of the demonstrators. Many were banished to Siberia, and scores of others, including my grandfather, imprisoned in Petrograd. His miserable cell, crowded, rat-infested, cold, damp, stinking and dark, was not so difficult to endure as was the loss of his freedom.

"High up, near the ceiling, one tiny strip of a window, without glass, let in a meager bit of light and air, and was the prisoners' only means of contact with the world of nature. Deprived of the touches and sounds of the woods, my grandfather suffered more than I can describe to you.

"Though some of his comrades died, he survived the merciless winter. The snows melted, the skies cleared, the trees sprouted new

295

green leaves, but my grandfather saw none of the rebirth. His heart was sad and heavy.

"One day, a bird perched on the sill of the unattainable window. It chirped and ruffled its wings as though to attract the attention of my grandfather. The old man stirred in the filth he lay in, sat up and listened. The bird chirped again and began to sing. My grandfather rose to his feet, swayed on his weakened legs, and stretched up his arms to the bird, whose song rang out through the dungeon. For a few moments, the cell was transformed.

"The other prisoners swore a brilliance and splendor surrounded them all. Then, my grandfather sprang toward the wall beneath the bird, and clawed at the bricks as though he would climb to freedom.

"Futility stayed his impotent hands. His knees buckled and his arms dropped. His heart broke, and the once mighty body fell to the floor, lifeless.

"At that moment, the bird left its perch, circled the cell, still singing, flew out the window, and was gone."

Chapter Fifteen

Siberia. Gradually the scenery changed to a mountainous landscape. The people were different, as well; we had the chance to observe them whenever the train stopped at a station.

Not far to the south was Mongolia, where farmers and their wives traveled from nearby regions to sell their produce, dressed in traditional garb. I was surprised to find many of the men wore their hair in long queues down their backs. To me, everything was new and enchanting. The other passengers, however, didn't interrupt their reading or games of chess. One of the waiters joined me in looking out the window.

"We have less than three days to Vladivostok," he said. "We're coming up to Lake Baikal now — it's quite a sight in any season. I never get tired of it. We'll skirt the southern end. May I bring you a glass of tea? I'm going to have one."

"Thank you."

By the time he returned, I had my first glimpse of the lake, as the train started along the edge of a cliff, high above the water. I forgot about the tea.

"It's the deepest lake in the world," the waiter told me. "About 1,800 meters. And more than three hundred rivers and streams flow into it."

"I imagine it's a good place to spend a vacation," I said.

"It sure is. The fishing's wonderful. I know a man who caught a sturgeon almost two feet long."

After dinner, Ivan Ivanovich asked me to have a farewell drink with him.

"We'll get to Kharbarovsk at dawn," he said. "I probably won't have a chance to say good-bye to you then."

"You've made my trip very interesting," I said. I was about to tell him just how interesting, but a sixth sense judiciously warned me to change the subject. I got him to talk about Leningrad and, in particular, the Hermitage museum.

"I was there in June," I said, "but only saw a small part of it."

"We are fortunate to have such collections. You know ... governments will come, and governments will go, but with such treasures, the essence of civilization will survive."

Inevitably, we moved once more to the subject of poetry, and then it was time to say goodnight and good-bye. As we shook hands, Ivan said, "Agnessa, would you give me your volume of poetry?"

How could I reply? He knew it was a gift from François.

Seeing my confusion, he went on, "I know what it means to you. For that reason I ask you for it." His hand pressed mine.

I felt myself blushing, and said, "I can't."

"Please, Agnessa?"

I couldn't meet his eyes, so turned away and shook my head.

He released my hand. "I shall remember you, nevertheless. Good-bye."

Ivan left the dining car without looking back. To myself I said, "And I'll never forget you, Ivan."

Sometimes the ache
And the pain in the heart,
Rather than joy and laughter,
Bids the soul awake
The part of my heart
That conceals the poem I'm after.

Chapter Sixteen

The Honolulu I returned to in September, 1934, was not the one I left three years earlier, nor was I the same. My eyes saw different things, and what they saw, my mind interpreted in ways inconceivable before I went away.

Our household had shrunk. My older sister, Astrid, had moved to Maui with her family, George had married, Stan was at Schofield preparing to go to West Point, and my father was seldom home. Dick, little Joan, and I were the only steady residents.

Mama had been in the hospital for several weeks; I was happy to see she had a private room. My father could not afford it — he was much too in debt. Fortunately, a benevolent organization maintained a few rooms at Queen's Hospital for indigent patients who needed privacy. My mother qualified. Still, doctors' and medication bills needed to be paid.

The cancer had invaded her stomach, her spine, and uterus. Mama had not been told the name of her illness, but I was sure she knew, and suspected it was terminal. The doctors said it was for her psychological good that she not know. I complied, but didn't agree.

She needed attention around-the-clock. Astrid, who came over from Maui, and I were each with her eight hours. We had to hire a nurse for the third shift. Every week, we rotated schedules.

Mama's body had wasted to a frail entity of flesh-covered limbs and torso. Her once-luxurious chestnut hair had been cropped short and was now reduced to wisps of grey. Weakness made speaking difficult for her. When I asked if she'd like to take Joan for a visit with her sister in California as soon as she was better, Mama's eyes became bluer and larger — she told me with mute eloquence how joyful would be the deliverance from her diseased body.

I wanted to crumble, to cry out, to beg her not to die. Instead, I read to her from a book about Norway, *Growth of the Soil,* by Knut Hamsun. With eyes closed, she listened to descriptions of her native land that must have stirred memories of beloved places and people she hadn't seen for twenty-eight years. A tear escaped, running down the side of her white face, so I put the book away and clasped one of her bony hands. Its fingers pressed mine and whispered, "Thank you, Sisi, dear .... I'm going to sleep now ...."

3808 Paki Ave.
Honolulu, Hawaii
October 4, 1934

Mon cher François,

Today I received three letters from you, written several days apart. How I wish you were here. There's so much to do, I have difficulty distributing my time. Joan is a sweet child and no trouble, but I still have to see that she has clean clothes, eats properly, does her homework, has play time, and gets enough sleep.

Dick is cooperative, and, at seventeen, pretty independent.

I make time to see my old friends. A few former classmates, Lorraine and Alice, especially, are as close as ever. Both have progressive and open minds. And Eve — remember, you met her and her brother in London — is married now.

Charlotte's views of the world have remained narrow and limited. We've been close friends since the fourth grade and, as we grew up, often discussed what we hoped to find at the end of the rainbow. There was always a rich, handsome husband with whom we'd have two children, a large house with servants and, most important, an enviable position in society. What a bore!

I called on her the other day. She hasn't changed course. After an hour I was ready to leave. When I suggested she and I visit Eve, she didn't hide her disapproval: "But," she sputtered, "but ... she's Jewish!"

Most of the people I talk to are curious to hear what Russia is "really" like. They seem to think I can answer all their questions. My goodness! I'm not an historian, a politician, or a mining or agricultural expert.

If you were posed such questions about the U.S.A. after being here a year, no one would expect you to know all the answers.

Katy McLean — she's the director of the Academy of Arts — has asked me to give a lecture on Russia next month. I'll have to do a lot of research, and where will I find the time? She also wants me to teach a sculpture class at the academy. So — I'll be earning some money. Somehow, I'll make time.

Yesterday, when I was with Mama, an old friend, Miss Mellum, called. She's about sixty, rather dotty in the opinion of most, but harmless. While she was there, Mama's doctor, Nils Larson, dropped in for a few minutes, as he often does. Miss Mellum took him aside, and I heard her say, "Doctor, I know a cure for cancer."

"That's interesting," he said, clasping her elbow and piloting her down the corridor. "Come into my office and tell me about it."

This morning I asked him how, as busy as he was, he could give a batty old crone so much of his valuable time.

He placed his hands firmly on my shoulders and looked at me with compassion. "My dear, have you a cure for cancer?"

I shook my head.

"Well, neither have I. We cannot afford to overlook anything that might give us a clue. Maybe Miss Mellum, with her disordered mind, might inadvertently put us onto something that could lead us in the right direction."

I'll write again in a few days, my love.

Agnessa

The house at Kahana was still a treasured sanctuary. Even if I wasn't the only one there, I could isolate myself. I could walk down the beach to a secluded crag under a *kamani* tree, or retire to a corner of the living room, where I'd become imperceptible in the enormous space, and contemplate the whys and whynots of the world.

My mother would always be part of the house. She designed the floor plan, the details, and chose the furniture. There were times when I could evoke the fragrance of her freshly baked bread and her voice singing romantic ballads from the days of gaslights and corsets, or arias from *Peer Gynt*.

Good old Peer Gynt. I hadn't thought of him and his escapades for a long time. And the Button-Moulder who followed him everywhere, trying to trap the elusive Peer and make him conform to the circumscribed mores of times even more restrictive than the '30s.

I used to fantasize that the Button-Moulder was after me, too, and that I'd never let him overtake me. I'd imagine catching a glimpse of him gaining speed. Then I'd make faces at him and deliberately rush off to do something outlandish. I wondered if he was the reason for my moving to Russia. He was certainly the cause of my heading for Europe ... he and Mama and John.

Remembrances of John were inevitable at Kahana, too. There was his voice telling me about the world beyond our insular orbit. Almost five years had passed since that day on the beach, when he declared passionately, *"I marriage disparage!"* and I swore nothing would stop me from going to Paris.

And what had happened? I went to Paris, and even farther away. And John? He was on his second marriage! Oh, the irony! Was it fate or karma? "Karma" was still a new word to me then. I had heard it for the first time on the train crossing Japan, from an English couple who used the term. They had been in India studying Eastern philosophy and were on their way to Kyoto to learn more about Buddhism.

Literally, meaning "cause and effect," karma taught that what we harvested in this life was the result of the seeds we had sown in a former one. Eastern sages said we were all instruments, criss-crossing one another's paths, somehow influencing and being influenced by everyone and everything we touched.

François would say it made better sense than the dogma he was brought up with. I wondered what John would have thought. Maybe some day I'd go to India and talk to one of those sages.

Right then John would have been useful. I needed someone to help me put material together for that talk at the Academy. It was a big job and out of my line. Perhaps I should call it off?

Chapter Seventeen

I had little patience with those who baited me with vacuous questions about Russia. And why did my mother have to die so young, so good, while my indifferent father lived in good health? And there were the little things that irritated me, like the fact that I couldn't afford a new dress for the party that night. But why be angry? Well ... why not? As long as I didn't react angrily, it might make me feel better.

I said good-bye to Dick and Joan, told them not to stay up late, and drove off. Sitting behind the wheel of my mother's car always gave me a lift. Even after six years, the Buick's sporty lines had class. The motor purred, and as I sped along Kalakaua Avenue headed for Manoa Valley, my acerbity vanished. By the time my hosts greeted me, I looked forward to having a good time.

Only a few faces were familiar. In rapid succession, the hostess introduced me to a dozen guests. A tall, tan young man handed me a Tom Collins and said, "Katy McLean tells me you're going to give a talk at the Academy."

"Yes ... and I'm scared. I'm no public speaker."

"Well now, I teach English at the University. I wonder if you'd like to practice by talking to one of my classes some morning. Everybody's curious about Russia these days, you know. My students will be eager to ask questions."

"Good idea. Yes, I'll do it. And maybe I can ask you to help me put the lecture together?"

"Sure. I intended to offer you a hand — for purely selfish motives, you understand." He laughed. "By the way, my name's Blake."

We shook hands and mingled with a group on the lanai where a gramophone played a hula. A young woman wearing a *muumuu* kicked off her shoes. With her arms rhythmically simulating the movement of undulating water, she moved in time to the music, toward the center of the floor. Most of the guests, highball in hand, gathered around to watch and encourage her. I didn't notice the young man moving close to me until he said, "Hello, I'm Brad ...."

It was obvious his interest was not in hula dancing because he went on, "Shall we go refill our glasses?"

A note in his voice impelled me to follow him into the dining room. Though no one else was around, he lowered his voice when he said, "I want to warn you to be very careful what you say in public. There are ears and eyes everywhere."

Had I heard correctly? Stupefied, I asked, "What on Earth are you talking about?"

"Evidently, you haven't noticed you're being followed."

"Followed!" I had to laugh. All I could think of was that some swain was too timid to speak for himself. Brad's serious expression, however, told me there was another reason.

He continued, "Now listen carefully. No one, not even my friend, Rita, knows that I work for the F.B.I. Everyday a report on your activities crosses my desk."

If he had slapped my face I'd have been less stunned. How could that be? This was a free country! I had broken no law. Everything I said or did was aboveboard. I had no subversive motives. The reason I went to Russia was that my own country had more unemployed than it could handle. Maybe Brad (not his real name) was trying to frighten me so I'd stop telling people how much I liked living in the Soviet Union.

"You don't believe me," he observed.

I shrugged.

"All right. Tomorrow after work, I'm going to stop by your house with a folder of papers. I want you to read them. Okay? Come on, I'll introduce you to Rita."

Sure enough, the following evening he brought me the papers. He had not deceived me. There it was. On October 2, 1934, at 7:30 p.m., for example, I departed my home at 3808 Paki Avenue at the wheel of a tan Buick with orange trim, and drove to the Punahou district, where I stopped at such-and-such an address on Kewalo Street. I joined a party of a dozen people, left at 11:00 p.m., and returned home alone.

There were several pages of the same sort of insidious triviality. I was furious. Did they seek to prove I was guilty of treason, to catch me in the act of planning to overthrow my government? For a long time I sat reflecting, wondering what I should do. I couldn't tell anyone about it, or Brad would be in trouble.

After awhile, I began to see another side of the scene — the humorous one. Was I really dangerous? Little Sisi a threat to her country? How funny! Was the great U.S.A. so insecure? Whatever happened to free speech? My civil rights were being violated, and I could do nothing to prevent it. So ... I might as well exploit it and feel important .... It would be good for my ego.

The pains in my mother's legs had been so severe in spite of opiates, the doctors decided to sever the nerves in her lower limbs. She seemed to accept the half-truths they told her, namely, that the surgeon wanted to "adjust" the nerves so she wouldn't suffer. After the procedure, she was unable to move her legs, but it mattered little as she couldn't even turn her torso to either side without help.

On November 23, she turned fifty years old. That day, Dr. Larson was somber. "Your mother has endured more than one woman's share of purgatory," he told me. "Her heart is so strong, she could go on indefinitely."

Shortly before the nurse came to relieve me for the night, Stan arrived on one of his infrequent leaves from Schofield. I gave him an account of the events of recent weeks and of Mama's deterioration.

"She seems to be comatose," I said. "We don't know how much she's aware of, as she doesn't react to stimuli. I think it's all the painkillers they give her."

Stan stood beside the bed for a long time, looking down at the motionless figure. Her eyes remained closed, and her breathing was imperceptible.

Then he stroked her forehead, clasped one of her hands, bent down, kissed her cheek, and whispered, "It's Stan, Mom. Happy birthday."

Suddenly the worn-out body convulsed and trembled. A spontaneous moan and a feeble cry escaped her lips.

She knew! She knew! Her soul was alive and vigorous, but hopelessly restrained in that withered sheath.

Chapter Eighteen

I attended a gathering that turned out to be more of a political probe than a social occasion. The usual drinks and buffet food covered a large table but, instead of circulating, the dozen or so hand-picked guests grouped themselves in a semicircle — with me as the focal point. All were friends or acquaintances whom I had met just a few weeks before. Among them were Brad and Rita, and a young woman who took everything down, verbatim, in shorthand.

It surprised me that only a few of my "interrogators" were skeptics. None showed hostility, most were sympathetic, and one, named Ellis, apparently anti-capitalist. Was he a plant by the F.B.I. to provoke me to "expose" myself as a Communist? Had the party been arranged to ensnare me? I decided not to worry.

The woman taking notes later sent me a complete transcript — twenty-three pages — little of which I thought noteworthy.

Q: Were you invited to Moscow by the Soviet government?
A: No! They had never heard of me.

Q: Then why did you go?

A: Because I had to earn my living, and no other country, certainly not the U.S., had work for a beginning sculptor. I had been studying in Paris so was already in Europe.

Q: Do you plan to return to Russia ... and when?

A: I came here for family reasons and can't say when I'll go back.

Q: Do you like living there?

A: Yes, indeed.

Q: Are you a Communist?

A: No. But let me add, Sir, that in our present American political climate, the question is impertinent.

Q: Would you like to spend the rest of your life there?

A: No. Maybe another two or three years, but not all my life.

Q: Why not?

A: The world is a big place. I want to go to India and maybe back to Paris.

Q: Because of material comforts?

A: The basic comforts in Moscow are adequate. I like Paris. The world goes there to experiment in art forms. For me the emphasis is rather in that field than in building a nation politically or economically. In France beauty and aesthetic taste extend beyond the commercial level to skills in intersocial relations.

Q: Do you think Moscow's shops will equal the French one day?

A: Probably not. Russian talents lie in other directions.

Q: Such as ....?

A: Oh ... music, poetry, the theatre ....

Q: What are the roots of Russian architecture and painting?

A: Byzantine.

Q: What's the aspect of Moscow today? Is it industrial?

A: No. It's sort of an overgrown village, a charming one. I suppose you could call it commercial. There are not many buildings higher than six or seven stories.

Q: And they're used, I suppose, for offices, apartments, stores, etc.

A: Yes. Industrial centers are placed away from commercial cities, and develop around factories.

Q: Well, with their system they can plan how and where centers grow. What's the population of Moscow? Four million?

A: I'm not sure. I've heard it's doubled since the revolution, but I believe it's still under two million.

Q: This business of not manufacturing for private profit ... no mass competition or advertising for the benefit of the goddamn parasites we have here in America ... we could cut down the business sections of our cities considerably.

A: I suppose so.

Q: What about getting rich? Can you invest the money you earn?

A: You can put it in the bank and get seven percent interest.

Q: Seven percent? Oh, boy! I get only two-and-a-half percent. What can you spend it on?

A: Admittedly, there are not many material luxuries. They have no washing machines or vacuum cleaners. The housewife's chores are accomplished as they have been for centuries — with muscle power. But theatre tickets are cheap; they can buy jewelry, or a *dacha*. Vacations don't cost much. One reason few travel abroad is that the ruble is not *valuta*. That is, they can't exchange rubles for foreign currency at any old bank as we can with dollars. Rubles have value only in the Soviet Union.

Q: In their old age ... what do they live on if they can't buy stocks?

A: That's no problem. Everyone gets a pension when he or she is incapacitated or retires. They don't have to hoard wealth either for economic security or social position. Their rent is adjusted to their income — never more than three or five percent. All education is free, even books and pencils, and total health care, too.

Q: How does it work?

A: Because the profits from any enterprise go, not to the bank accounts of private individuals, but into the general kitty, from where they're distributed according to need — to start new factories, replace machinery, for research, schools, hospitals, and things like that.

Q: Are there no indigents anywhere in the Soviet Union?

A: I wouldn't say that, but I've not seen any.

Q: Supposing your husband earns enough to support you both well, would you still have to work even if you didn't want to?

A: No. Many women are full-time homemakers. And they, too, get a pension at a certain age. In my own case, I receive royalties on some small pieces of sculpture that are being mass-produced and sold all over the country. Theoretically, I could live on that income and work independently as a freelance.

Q: If you should die, what would happen to your royalties? Can you will them to someone?

A: No. They'll stop when I die. Any cash or movable possessions — yes, I can leave to anyone.

Q: I've heard there's private enterprise on a limited scale. Does that not suggest that Capitalism will come back?

A: The private enterprise you're referring to is limited to those who are self-employed — such as tailors, artists, hairdressers, and farmers who sell their surplus produce on the open market. There are doctors who have private practice on their own time. It's not Capitalism until you make a profit from the work of your employees.

Q: You're describing a society where everyone is secure. Doesn't that stifle ambition and initiative?

At this point, Ellis jumped up and shouted, "I wonder if any of you know what insecurity does to the less fortunate multitude. Just go to some of the big cities in our country and see. If what they suggest were true, how do you account for all the ambitious young men who *inherited* fortunes and went on to increase them in spite of their financial protection? Our president is a good example, and the Rockefellers, and look at all the families right here in Honolulu who live ambitious lives on what their grandparents earned!"

The host broke in. "All right, Ellis ... a good point. I think we can have refreshments now."

Everyone else must have thought so, as well, because we all began discoursing among ourselves in an attempt, perhaps, to dispel the growing tension. Ellis strode up to me. The expression on his face showed mocking humor.

"Some people take themselves too seriously," he said. "They're scared as hell the Commies are coming to filch their property — just as they took it from the Hawaiians."

A young couple joined us. One of them said, "We all know, wealth is relative and subjective. But are there many affluent Russians?"

"Moneywise," I answered, "not many. But I've learned to count wealth as cultural ... as investment in the sort of things that don't depend on the stock market."

"You mean such as getting an education and developing one's talents," the young man commented. "I couldn't agree more."

Ellis left without saying good-bye to anyone. There were no more questions about the Soviet Union that evening.

As I drove home, I couldn't help thinking that I shouldn't expect a large audience at my lecture.

Chapter Nineteen

I had never before stood in front of a group larger than my senior English class at Punahau School. In the classroom back then were only twenty-five or so people, all friends I had grown up with, and my assignment was nothing more dire than reciting a bit of Shakespeare from memory. Still, I used to blush, and couldn't stop my voice from trembling.

Five years later, on that November evening in 1934, it was a thousand times worse. I faced a mass of unknown faces. Not only was every seat in the auditorium filled, but people stood around the walls, while more tried to squeeze in through the doorways.

How many of them were friends? How many hostile? More alarming, how many would laugh at me? What if I lost my voice or forgot what I was going to say?

I looked down at my notes on the lectern. My mouth went dry. I was no public speaker. Even after a big sip of water, my mouth remained parched. Why had I agreed to do this?

Suddenly there was silence, and Katy McLean was on the stage introducing me. I didn't hear what she said — I only saw, surprisingly, smiles in my direction. Katy left me alone, hands applauded, and suddenly, I was at ease. Those people hadn't come to analyze me, but to hear about Russia. I was merely an instrument, invited to convey certain information to that undulating ocean of heads and shoulders.

My notes reminded me to stick to cultural matters: literature, theatre, architecture, painting, and sculpture, in Russian history and today.

My first sentence explained that cultural reconstruction was as much a part of building Socialism as industrial renovating. The fundamental task was to teach the underprivileged eight percent to read and write. Every country needed educated, skilled and trained workers in all fields. The publication of magazines, newspapers, and books had doubled in a few years. There were technical tracts along with classical and contemporary literature. As the scholarly terrain was cultivated, new novelists, poets and playwrights sprouted in all corners of the

Union, with no shortage of stories to tell.

I was about to relate an anecdote, when a commotion began at the back of the hall. A heckler called out offensive remarks with the obvious intention of causing a disturbance. Two academy employees escorted the man out and, when the rest of us had settled down, I felt a new empathy between the audience and me.

In detail, I described how every theatre constituted a school, each distinguished by its own method of interpretation, acting technique, and presentation. Every actor identified with one style during his career. Three producer-directors — Vakhtangov, Meyerhold, and Stanislavsky — influenced drama far beyond Soviet borders.

I told about the factories which made period furniture and decorations, glassware and porcelain, and fabrics — sometimes satin and brocades, for the stage, even while basic necessities were rationed to the public. The rest of the world scarcely realized how much of the traditional remained wholly unchanged in the theatre —- especially the ballet — that distinctly Russian art form. Their favorite diversions — opera and ballet — were as much enjoyed by a proletarian audience as by the court society that used to sit in the czar's box.

I closed by stating that nations should be judged by the quality of their cultural contributions to civilization rather than by their economic or political systems. More than anything else, it was the arts that raised people from darkness to enlightenment and survived revolutions. The enthusiastic applause surprised me and seemed to signal that they agreed.

During question time afterwards, most of the queries were intelligent and unprejudiced.

Inevitably, however, emotions effervesced.

Not impolitely, a man asked, "Why don't you tell us about the starving people and the kulaks sent to oblivion in Siberia?"

Before I could reply, an elderly man jumped to his feet. "Your questions, Sir, are out of order. The young lady is talking about the arts. But I can tell you, you have been misinformed ....!" The two of them, aided by others, carried on rather noisily for awhile, till Katy appeared at my side, thanked everyone for attending, and pronounced the lecture over.

Whether or not the audience liked what I said about a Marxist country, it was obvious from their expressions and remarks that the evening had been an entertaining distraction.

It was my turn to do the night shift. The floor nurse had just given my mother a sedative, so I found her sleeping peacefully.

Doctor Larson came by, stopping in the doorway. Fatigue showed in the lines of his face. Without elaborating, he mentioned only that Mama was not responding to the drugs they had given her.

"I'm going to recommend changing her medication," he told me. "She's suffering too much. I'll see you in a day or so. Goodnight, my dear."

I moved the wicker armchair close to the bed and sat down. Was she really asleep? If I talked to her, would some of what I said reach her consciousness? On other occasions it had. I clasped one of her hands and stroked it. There was no sign that she felt my nearness.

"Mama," I said softly, "the day after tomorrow is an anniversary. It's December 7th — remember? Exactly twenty years since we arrived in Honolulu."

No motion acknowledged that she heard me. I continued, nevertheless. "I was only four at the time, but I'll never forget that morning. All the passengers crowded on deck as the ship rounded Diamond Head. The sun had just come up out of the ocean and the air was warm. I was — we all were — enchanted. Everything on the island was green, from the top of the cloud-crested mountain, all the way down the valleys to the shore.

"We had come to another world from Norway. Till then, golden beaches and palm trees were only fantasy pictures on the post cards Pop sent. It was a dream world turned real.

"And when the pier came in sight, remember how excited we were? A brass band played, and a lusty soprano voice bellowed a welcome song. We soon found Papa in the crown down below, and there were flowers everywhere — exotic flowers strung into leis that Papa nearly smothered us with.

"And to think, Mama ... all of that ... thanks to a freak ruse of destiny. We were supposed to live in Norway! Pop was going to join us there after working a year in Honolulu. In June 1914, his year was up. He made a pile of money and bought his ticket westward, through the Orient to Oslo. But before he could leave, he found himself in the hospital with a burst appendix and was still there when all hell erupted in July. Europe at war was no place for a family. Papa telegraphed for us to leave at once, and in August, we were on the *S.S. Kristianiafjord* heading for New York, dodging German mines."

I still saw no sign that Mama heard. Her breathing was almost imperceptible. I went on.

"For the most part, those twenty years were beautiful. Stan was born, and Dick, and our adorable Joan. And we built the house at Kahana — *your* house, Mama. Remember?"

The next day was Astrid's turn on the night shift. The following morning at six o'clock, I hardly recognized her voice when she phoned me from the hospital. I was prepared for what she told me. Mama had died just before dawn.

Chapter Twenty

When April came, I was finally getting ready to leave. It had taken a long time to save up the money for my fare to Vladivostok. Most of it came from the sculpture lessons I gave at the Arts Academy and from several lectures to various groups. Then, at the academy's annual jury show, the three-foot torso I made won the grand prize and one hundred dollars! I had money left over!

On many social occasions, Riley Allen seemed to go out of his way to talk to me. Mr. Allen had been editor of the *Honolulu Star-Bulletin* for umpteen years. Before that, he worked with the Red Cross in Russia after the Great War. Consequently, his interest in the Soviet Union was understandable. What surprised me, however, was his asking me to write a series of articles for the paper. I agreed, of course. The going rate was only ten cents a column inch. Not much, but it would keep me in writing practice, and oblige me to open my eyes to what was around me.

The newspaper supplied me with a stack of writing paper, envelopes and a press card. My brother, George, furnished the typewriter. His old, beat-up portable Underwood still worked well except for one key that got stuck occasionally. I'd always wanted to be a writer. Here was my chance.

At a party one evening, I was telling Alex and Bea Korol how useful the portable would be, as typewriters were mighty scarce in the Soviet Union. Alex was born of Russian parents in the city of

Stan Larsen - 1934;
Private collection.

"Hawaiian Boy";
Private collection.

Alma-Ata, in an obscure, mountainous corner of what became Kazakhstan, tucked between China and Kirghizia. As a student, he came to the U.S., where he met Beatrice. He became a U.S. citizen, and eventually head of one of the Island's growing businesses — the Tuna Packers.

"Speaking of typewriters," he said, handing me a fresh highball, "I have a young sister still living in Alma-Ata with my mother — an infant when I left seventeen years ago, just before the revolution."

He clinked my glass, and after a few sips, continued, "I wonder if you would consider doing my sister a favor."

"Of course ... whatever is possible."

"Well ... would you take my typewriter with you and somehow try to get it to her? It has Russian keys."

"Certainly."

"You see," he went on, "she could teach herself to type and probably get an interesting job. In all of Kazakhstan, there are no more than a handful of typewriters."

We talked about it over another drink. Alex insisted that if I should have any difficulty getting it through customs, for whatever reason, I should simply abandon it. "I'm aware," he said, "that items of any value are written in your passport, and you have to take them out when you leave, or be fined."

I assured him I knew that, and promised to do my very best.

In May, François wrote that he was getting six weeks' vacation and would meet me in Tokyo on June 15. We would spend a whole month in Japan, where he had friends.

My feet itched to be on the move again. Sadly though, our family was breaking up. Joan would go to California to spend several months with Mama's sister on the ranch in St. Helena. Dick would make his home with George and Jessie. Stan was off to West Point and a military career. And Pop — well, he was living somewhere. The bank was about to foreclose on our home on Paki Avenue. So far, the house at Kahana was safe, but no one knew how long we would be able to afford to pay the taxes on it.

The Depression was more than five years old with no end yet visible. Financially, I would be better off in Moscow, and life was certainly more diversified in spite of the lack of material luxuries. As though to remind me of that, I got word that Anna Louise Strong, one of the founders of the *Moscow Daily News,* would be in town for one day, on her way back to Russia from California.

Her father was a minister in Seattle and her brother head of that city's YMCA. At twenty-three, she had earned a Ph.D. and had taken off for China and Russia as a correspondent for the Hearst papers. Over the years she wrote several books describing the birth pains of the Soviet Union and the stirrings of independence in China under Sun Yat Sen.

On the same ship with her was Comrade Troyanovsky, the Soviet ambassador to the United States. A friend and I took them both for a ride to show off some of our local sights.

The ambassador, a handsome, elderly man, told us of a lecture he had given in Washington, D.C., to the Daughters of the American Revolution, a patriotic organization of socialites. Members have to be not only descendants of those who fought for our liberation from England but "personally acceptable," which means, I suppose, they must not lean to the Left.

Troyanovsky suppressed a laugh as he told us, "I thanked them for inviting me to speak to them about my motherland, and reminded them that they and I had a great deal in common — we were all revolutionaries ...."

He paused to indulge in a hearty chuckle. "You would have thought I told them something new. There was an obvious uneasiness among them and gasps of shock. Can you imagine those dignified leaders of Washington society being labeled revolutionaries?"

Back in 1931, I looked on my native land from above and saw all was perfect. It could do no wrong. My father prospered.

In 1935, however, I perceived it from below, from the point of view of the dispossessed and disadvantaged — the majority. My father was broke and in debt, with no work in sight.

In four years, I had learned many things. There was a lot more to life than social position and material possessions. Peoples of other cultures, whom I used to consider foreign, cherished their flags as I did mine. I had worked, played and feasted with them, and learned their languages. They were no longer alien. I would never again be blindly patriotic — I would be an *internationalist* who would remove all frontiers that separate nations, while respecting their customs and dialects.

Idealist? Yes, but being a visionary was not yet illegal.

Tokyo
June 20, 1935

Dear Everybody,

When I was in Tokyo last year, it was only for a couple of days, and I didn't have the chance to see much. This time is different. We know people, and we'll be here for four weeks.

Our hotel is Japanese-style — we sleep on the floor on thin mattresses that maids roll up every morning and put in a closet.

We've traveled by train to Nara to see temples and pagodas, and to Kyoto, a cultural center. The landscape is diminutive — small mountains, small trees and houses.

When the train stops at stations, one can buy refreshments from little carts on wheels. We each bought a tray with a pottery teapot and cup with dainty goodies to eat. The pots and cups were handmade, and ours to keep! They're treasures, and cost pennies!

Our old friend, Sakakura, from our Paris days, is working here as an architect and has introduced us to a professor of art and to a painter, who is married to an opera singer.

And François knows a Czech architect, Antonin Raymond, and his French wife, who is a sculptor. They came here after the earthquake to work with Frank Lloyd Wright, stayed on, and have done well. We spent a few days at their vacation house at a sea resort. In town they have a modern villa.

I'm glad I didn't listen to those people in Honolulu who tried to convince me to stay on. They argued that I could bring a new dimension to the arts there because of my having worked and studied in Europe and Russia.

That may be true, but too many think I'm politically dangerous, and <u>they</u> are the ones who control the arts, who decide whose pieces are bought by the museum, who wins prizes, and who gets to work with architects.

Sure, I did win an important prize for a torso, but I think that was a "carrot." Later, I had the distinct feeling they thought I didn't say enough negative things about the Soviet Union. It's not funny being shadowed by the F.B.I.

The Russians have treated me well, even though I'm not a Communist. By going back, I'll learn more of the world, which I would not do in Honolulu. The 18th century Anglo-Irish writer, Oliver Goldsmith, has been a model of mine ever since I read his "Citizen of the World." Just because I happen to be a native of one country does not oblige me to deny my curiosity of the rest of our earth and of how others think.

The U.S. is as afraid of and as opposed to Communism as the Soviet Union is of Capitalism. I can understand why the paranoids might be suspicious and apprehensive of Agnessa. Without knowing it, they flatter me.

Then, of course, there's François. He hasn't the least interest in living in the States. Our standard of living doesn't attract him, while the quality of life, he says, is superior in Europe and Russia. He's not a materialist, you see.

Don't forget I'll be waiting for news of all of you — especially of Joan — how she's adjusting. I'll write to her soon.

With love to everyone,
Agnessa

Chapter Twenty-One

Honolulu Star-Bulletin	**July 31, 1935**

Vladivostok — Here I am at the Far-Eastern gateway to Russia, founded in 1860. The city and hills of "The Golden Horn" stretch in a magnificent circle around one of the finest harbors in the world. Its name in Russian means *vladi,* "most important point or center" and *vostok,* "East." In other words, "the most important center of the East." Its growth has been rapid. The Trans-Siberian Railroad has its terminus here.

During the Russian Civil War, 1917-1920, it was occupied repeatedly by various armies, including American, and held by one or another until 1922, when the first companies of the victorious Red Army entered the city. They have been here ever since. Today the harbor, although still poorly equipped, presents a busy scene. Ships from every port of the world dock here to exchange goods.

When our ship came up to the wharf a lot of curious people gathered to see what the latest tourists from Japan and America looked like. I guess we weren't so remarkable after all because they soon lost interest and went off. But I kept on looking at them.

The men wear the typical Russian cool-weather costume of high leather boots, some muddy and some shined, Russian blouses buttoned at the side or front of the neck, eliminating the need for neckties, and shirttails out with a narrow belt around the waist. Most of the blouses are embroidered at the wrist and neckband with a fine cross-stitch. For the head the usual gear is a cap.

The women wear plain blouses and skirts, print dresses, jackets, often of navy blue serge, and usually short socks and simple shoes. A few wear lipstick. Few are beautiful from the standard American point of view, but so conspicuously healthy and hale it's a pleasure to look at them.

Here are no stereotyped mannequins out of a fashion magazine or Hollywood. One suspects that behind every face are problems of more importance than whether the coat should have one button or two.

I've never been through customs in New York but I'm sure it's more complicated here. Every cubic inch of every one of my ten bags was carefully gone over. It happened that I had a bit more than my allowance and had to pay duty on one pair of shoes, two purses, and two boxes of face powder. Printed matter was also carefully examined.

The sudden change from casual, orderly Japan to a country where everyone is working very hard with few material comforts put me in a serious frame of mind. The average tourist may consider the city an insult to nature. The streets and sidewalks are in bad condition and most of the buildings in need of repair. Among the bearded old *moujiks,* the tradition of drinking vodka till drunk still remains.

It's not surprising the city lacks modern equipment and necessary conveniences. Consider the tremendous distances from more developed European parts of the Union, and the difficulties of transportation across these vast areas. The population, including Koreans, Chinese, and primitive nomadic tribes from the far north, as well as transient sailors and miners, has tripled in the past ten years. All of them are entitled to work.

The future economic development of this region depends on its closeness to the ocean and the wealth within its soil. The seas abound with salmon, cod, sturgeon, mackerel and other fish.

On the island of Sakhalin and the Kamchatka Peninsula, northeast of Vladivostok, there are already tremendous fishing canneries. The standing timber is of great value, not only because of its size and abundance, but also because of the variety of valuable woods. There are wonderful potentialities in the development of the fur trade.

Little has been done so far to investigate the mineral wealth in these parts, but some 150 different locations have already been marked out where the existence of deposits is certainly indicated. Gold is found almost everywhere, and iron ores, as well as rarer metals, and coal and oil. There are, however, no salt deposits — essential to the development of commercial fishing on a large scale.

In a few years full use will be made of the industrial and agricultural potential provided by the natural wealth of the region, and the projected urban reconstruction will be completed. Vladivostok will then be the splendid city it deserves to be.

I have been looking over my list of gifts for friends in Moscow to see that no one has been forgotten. For the women I have mostly compacts, lipsticks, purses and pretty underwear, and for the men, cigarettes, pocket knives, mechanical pencils and neckties.

One woman asked if I would please bring her some American chocolate. She tasted some as a girl and has never forgotten it. A young man wants a special line for mackerel fishing in the Black Sea.

A neighbor of mine plays the violin in the Moscow Beethoven Quartet. As I was leaving my apartment for the train station, his wife ran out to say good-bye and handed me a folded piece of paper. On the train I read the message written in English, "When you return, please bring some shirt studs for my husband's tuxedo."

I have all these things and a few more. I only hope Soviet light industry hasn't improved so much in the past year that my trifles won't be appreciated.

———

In the article I wrote for the *Star-Bulletin,* I couldn't possibly tell the whole story of going through Soviet customs. The baggage examination was so thorough, François and I were exhausted and hungry when the officials finally returned our passports and let us go with our numerous suitcases.

After a tasty supper of fish and potatoes, we went directly back to our hotel. I set about struggling with the opening sentences of my first article while François thumbed through our passports to read over the list of things the customs officials had recorded. We would be required to produce these items — such as our camera, watches, pieces of jewelry — when we next left the Soviet Union.

Suddenly François shouted, "They didn't write in your two type-writers!"

"Oh, dear me! What'll we do?"

We looked at each other in silence. Then I saw François' eyes twinkle, and the germ of a scheme simultaneously turned up the corners of our mouths.

"Are you thinking what I'm thinking?" he asked.

"Could be," I whispered.

"Well, we'll try it anyway. First thing tomorrow I'll go back to the customs officials and see what I can do."

We discussed possible alternatives but came to no decision. The next morning, François went out with both passports while I stayed at the hotel typing on my portable Underwood and worrying about syntax and proper punctuation.

Around ten o'clock, he opened the door with a flourish. Triumph was conspicuous in his stride as well as on his face. With mock arrogance, he tossed the passports onto the table where I sat. I squealed.

"You *did* it! Tell me what happened!"

"It was so easy I'm beginning to think I have chosen the wrong career. I obviously have a latent talent for smuggling. I found the two officials who saw us yesterday. I showed them your passport and said, 'Look here, Comrades, I'm sorry to disturb you, but you remember examining my wife's and my luggage yesterday, don't you?'

"They said they did, and I said, 'You forgot to list her typewriter here in her passport.'

"They both inspected what they had written in, nodded, apologized, and asked me to describe the machine. I said it was a portable Underwood. See? There you are. They completely forgot about the other one. So — officially, you don't have it. And now you can send it to Alex's sister with impunity."

Chapter Twenty-Two

Trans-Siberian RR, en route to Moscow — Flagpole sitting is excellent training for the railroad trip from Vladivostok to Moscow. The first four days are the most difficult. The next four are easier as the travelers begin to get accustomed to not moving about very much. On the last day, the passengers become restless.

Comparatively few go the whole distance from Vladivostok to Moscow, but then some travel all the way to the Black Sea — almost fourteen days at one sitting.

There aren't yet enough passenger trains to fill the need, so it isn't as easy to get accommodations as in other countries. My husband and I had to wait five days to get tickets. Now we're settled comfortably in a first-class compartment.

There are fewer cars than on the American Transcontinental. After the locomotive, post, and baggage cars comes the first-class or International Car that goes through to Europe, then the restaurant and five more cars: "soft" and "hard." At night each wooden, or hard, bunk gets a mattress, sheets and a blanket.

So we were off at 6:00 p.m. and for one day traveled north to Khabarovsk, our first big stop, and then went west. Khabarovsk played an important part in the "sovietization" of the Far East. In 1917, a Soviet convention was held there. Later the city was occupied by the White Guards and other armies of intervention, and for a few years suffered looting.

On leaving the city the train crosses the great Amur River by a bridge over a half-mile long. During the struggle for the possession of the region, one of the numerous spans of this bridge was dislodged and thrown into the river. All traffic crossed the Amur by extemporized ferries. The replacement of the enormous span was one of the earliest triumphs of industrial recovery.

In a few hours we reach the area between the rivers Bira and Bidzhan, set aside for settlement by Jews with a legislative body of its own. Agriculturally rich, and with modern equipment and collective methods, it's being developed from virgin land.

For the next couple of days the scenery is much the same: mountainous and wooded, with many rivers. If it doesn't rain, it's dusty, and if it's hot at the same time, you just sit and try to recall the pastimes of the flagpole-sitting days.

Stations come every two or three hours as a relief, and everyone dashes out in spite of rain or dust. Some, with kettles, run for the shed, found at every Russian station, eternally giving forth boiling water for tea. Others rush to the improvised counter where farmers sell fresh milk, hard-boiled eggs, newly churned butter, cucumbers, roasted chicken, fruit, and other tempting things, and hurry back to the train to prepare a picnic meal. Even if they usually eat in the restaurant they seldom miss the fun of making their own tea and eating sandwiches off their knees.

At one station a little boy carried a basket, selling raspberries and cucumbers. The raspberries tempted me and I asked how much they cost.

"One ruble a cup" he said.

"But that's expensive," I told him.

"Well, then, buy the cucumbers. They're cheaper," he replied.

On the third day we came to the region where the nomad warrior Genghis Khan was born. The scenery, still wild and densely forested, is otherwise peaceful. The region joined the Soviet Union in 1922.

I had never heard of Lake Baikal until I first came to Russia two years ago, probably because I'd been too far away. It's situated about half way between Vladivostok and Moscow, and is so different from the rest of the journey it supplies a welcome break. Knowing we'd come to the lake at dawn, I went to bed with my window blinds up so I'd be awakened by the first bit of light sky. At 5:30 a.m. I could see the water about fifty feet below.

Baikal is an inland sea 250 miles from north to south. Its width varies from 10 to 35 miles. In places its depth is almost one mile. Three hundred streams pour into it from the surrounding mountains, and then issue on in the powerful torrent of the Angara River.

We followed the winding southern shore for six hours. The dark green water was so clear I could see fish swimming about. It looked cold. I put on a heavy sweater so I could keep the window open and get some Siberian summer air into the compartment. It never gets warmer than a dozen degrees above freezing.

We went through over thirty tunnels, some long and others so short and near the edge of the cliff they reminded me of the toy tunnels that came with electric trains when we were kids.

I would like to see it sometime when there's a storm. Experienced sailors consider the Baikal tempests worse than the typhoons of the open ocean. The wild winds from the mountains can disturb the surface of the lake until it seems to actually boil.

A violent tempest about thirty years ago wrecked a whole fleet of vessels and a fishing barge and cast its crew more than twenty feet up on the rocks. How many terrible legends reeking of blood and iron are gathered about this beautiful spot!

After Baikal the land suddenly becomes flat and more cultivated. The vastness of the terrain on either side of the train, the few little distinctive towns and villages, and the sharp cold wind that often blows, can be found only in Siberia. It is beautiful: black soil; green, yellow, and orange grain fields; pine and birch woods; and little brown log houses. A herd of cattle or a horse and buggy, even close to the train, seem small and out of scale with the immense landscape.

Construction of the railway spanned a dozen years: from 1892 to 1904. The difficult stretch around Lake Baikal alone took five years.

No Soviet citizen cannot afford to travel. A laborer whose wages are small gets especially reduced rates for himself and his family. These rates are not only for the train but for room and board at whatever place he has chosen to stay, as well. If he has worked particularly well, his vacation may be free.

From the train one can follow the advancement of the second track. It is completed only in certain localities and won't be finished all the way before next year.

More interesting than the rail itself is the group of people installing it: one of the projects of the Prisoners' Collective. Instead of serving their sentences within prison walls or working somewhere under guard and returning to their cells at night, the convicts here are employed at productive, organized labor. Each man works according to his trade, and if he has none, is taught one.

They live as free laborers — with a minimum of guards — receive wages, premiums for good work, and in some cases even get leave to visit their families. At the end of their sentences they return to society decent citizens. The object is not to punish, but to correct.

Chapter Twenty-Three

For a few days after boarding the train, we stayed pretty much in our self-contained compartment to rest from the activity of the recent weeks. It was a relief not to have to dress up and go outdoors to see the sights. With no exertion more strenuous than raising our eyelids, we enjoyed the panorama as it glided past the train window.

We soon had enough of that, however, and rejoined the company of our fellow travelers. Among the most interesting of the passengers were two men who boarded the train at Chelyabinsk, at the eastern foothills of the Ural Mountains. Their table adjoined ours in the dining car. At first we bandied small talk, then over beer, progressed to discussing more serious matters.

They were Vanya and Gregor, both delegates from their respective factories to the Moscow Soviet — or council — on their way to spend several days in the capital. Vanya guessed at once that I was American but thought François was Russian because of his Slavic accent and fluent vocabulary.

Gregor said he had read all of Jack London's books in translation and considered his short story, *To Build a Fire*, a masterpiece. He added that he had a great respect for Walt Whitman, as well, because he spoke for the common man. Raising his glass, he said, "Let's drink to that common man. May he never have to suffer another war."

We all drank, then fell silent. No one seemed to want to say anything. I felt intuitively that, like myself, the others were all thinking about the revolution, which had affected the lives of every person in Russia, and touched many far beyond its frontiers, including me.

Barely thirteen years had passed since the end of the fighting, and memories of it remained grievous in the consciousness of many. That ugly scar on the side of Vanya's head was probably his least painful memento of the conflagration. I wanted to ask a lot of questions but couldn't think of how to begin tactfully.

Watching me, Gregor said, "Comrade Vanya did battle with your compatriots in the Far East."

Vanya poured himself another glass of beer and toyed with the empty bottle, apparently trying to frame his thoughts into words. I knew that U.S. forces had occupied Siberia in 1918 and 1919, as far inland as Lake Baikal, and that we left after two years because we thought it was valueless land. I had never before spoken with a former foe of my country.

Vanya stroked his scar absently and looked at me with a wry smile. "Yes," he said, "for two years we were enemies trying to kill each other. The Americans were of the 339th Infantry Division. Their cause was hopeless. Though well armed, they couldn't win. They invaded our sovereign land but didn't know why.

"We, on the other hand, inadequately armed, sometimes with nothing more then pitchforks, were defending our motherland and a new life that would free us from oppressors. Revolutions are like that, you know. All through history — everywhere — in France and your own country almost two centuries ago, when people finally get fed up and, as Lenin said, 'have nothing to lose but their chains,' by God, they can fight. And we'll do it again if necessary.

"They thought they had us surrounded. More American troops invaded Murmansk and Archangelsk, up there north of Leningrad on the Barents Sea. They fared no better. Just a year ago we sent to America the bodies of the last fallen Yankees."

He nudged his friend. "Gregor, here, was fighting off the foreigners and our own czarist troops down near the Caspian Sea."

We looked expectantly at Gregor, who shrugged his shoulders and smiled sheepishly.

"Comrade Waiter!" he called out. "If you please ... we're out of beer and have to drink another toast to peace." To us he said, "I was just a young goat then — about seventeen — a tenant farmer, like my father. The landlord lived in Paris, so we never saw him or any of his family, only his agent. Farming was usually profitable, but for the landlord, not for us.

"It was, however, oil that generated the real wealth in the region. There was plenty of it under, around and beyond the Caspian Sea. The czar had foreign companies work the wells, so when we overthrew the czar, France, Britain and the U.S. tried to take the power from us. They would not be satisfied with compensation for their lost treaties, but wanted the properties themselves."

The waiter brought a new supply of beer. With our glasses refilled, Gregor said solemnly, "I never have a drink without this toast: '*May no nation ever endure another war!*' The devastation was incredible. Revolution, counter-revolution, espionage, sabotage, blockades, corruptions, famine ... and I saw only a small part. All of Russia was ablaze. Four endless years with no intermission.

"When the czar's army broke up, the troops deserted or joined us. The workers in the oil fields, mostly Russian, were on our side. Germans and Turks controlled the Caucasus Mountains.

"The British invaded through Persia, and Cossack bandits got support from them. Armenians, egged on by the British, massacred thousands of Turks in the city of Baku. The Turks took revenge, swept in from the north, and killed 30,000 Armenians.

"Power changed hands from week to week. Chaos continued long after the Germans capitulated in Europe in 1918. The British and Italians controlled Baku for almost two years. Russians had to get a British visa to enter their own city. Everyone wanted our oil. The year 1919 was the roughest of all. Foreigners financed counter-revolutionaries and captured a lot of oil fields.

"I joined the Red Army. Slowly we gathered strength. From ill-fed, ill-clad and disjointed bands, we gradually organized ourselves under one command. Those Russians who worked the oil fields for the foreigners knew we were closing in, and revolted. Our Red troops pushed in and declared the fields national property in April 1920."

Before going on, Gregor looked away, out of the window, trying to mask his emotions. "It is said a tiger fights best when cornered. We fought like tigers! Writers and poets have enough material to keep busy for generations.

"And finally, there was peace. The blockades were broken, the foreigners routed, and Russia — exhausted. What followed was the worst famine of modern times. The livestock was gone. We could not till the soil without implements, or plant without seeds. Even weeds would not grow because there was no rain. We've had famines since, but not like that one. Desolation you cannot imagine! Thousands of orphans wandered the streets living by their wits ... and dying for want of shelter and food.

"The old oil wells were ravaged. Water filled the ones not steadily worked. We bailed them out and dug new ones. Little by little, with out bare hands, we managed to produce some oil and sell it abroad. Our transportation system was reborn — functioning poorly, but functioning. The famine was overcome but left horrible scars."

François commented that they had done wonders in so few years.

"Well," Gregor continued, "we believe the greatest strength of a nation is in education and health care for every citizen. We got busy establishing schools and hospitals, paid for from the profits of our oil. We started day-care centers so parents could work, and organized homes for orphans.

"I went to night classes because I'd had to quit studying when I was twelve and could barely read and write. I'm a qualified engineer now, and a part-time teacher."

We talked and toasted till well after midnight. Other passengers and one of the waiters joined us. Conversation was relaxed, about vacations spent at Black Sea resorts, or boating down the Volga and other rivers, and camping in wild regions. We spoke of our plans for a walking trip through the Caucasus Mountains the following summer and got a lot of suggestions and advice.

"Tiflis is fascinating, and the shops have more goods than Moscow's."

"You really ought to go climb Mount Elbrus."

"— And go into the Valley of Svanetia. It was discovered only during the Great War by the flying machine. The inhabitants didn't know about the wheel."

"When you've done all that, you'll need a rest on the gorgeous beaches of the Black Sea."

"Be sure to take along good walking shoes."

"You won't see what I saw," Gregor said. "Today, there are grain elevators, snug villages and towns, and railroads that run pretty much on time. It's far from perfect, however. But don't think our material shortcomings are due entirely to the Communist revolution. Historically, we have never been famous for technological skill. That could, of course, change in the future, but at present, Russians are, first of all, poets — great poets, I believe.

"Technology should be left to those who are best at it — the Germans and Americans, and let us and the French and Italians indulge in the arts. That way, we'd all get along."

326

Gregor leaned his arms on the table, looked around the gathered comrades, then addressed me. "Can you imagine how rapidly you in the States, with all your efficiency, know-how and money, could build a perfectly running Communist society? It's going to take us decades, generations maybe, even with help from good, expert foreigners like you."

"I'll drink to that," said the waiter. So we drank, and the waiter went on, "We got tractors from you and combines and credits that changed, almost overnight, our farming methods from the primitive hand-plow and scythe. Maybe we all don't know how to keep the tractors running, but we're learning."

"It's my turn," I said, "to toast to peace and international cooperation."

Several voices said, "*Molodiets!* Good for you!" making me feel warm and proud of being an American. Not all of us wanted to see their social experiment fail before a chance to prove itself.

Chapter Twenty-Four

Honolulu Star-Bulletin	August 28, 1935

Life in Moscow

During the year I was away from Moscow, I read and heard accounts of the plan for the development and improvement of the city. It meant not only many new paved streets and additional buses, but also the reflection of these factors in the daily life of the population.

I left Moscow when the modernizing machine had not yet removed the traces of hard times. I remember walking through streets in the rain, muddy up to the knees in spite of galoshes; streetcars (the main means of transport) bulging with tired and cross people at 5 p.m.; the many hours I spent in slow moving queues to buy my groceries because of insufficient stores and supplies.

So here I am in the Moscow of 1935, when the fundamental tasks of the plan of reconstruction have been fulfilled and the second step (plan of extension) is on its way.

It is necessary to consider the fact that for the municipality of Moscow, the problem of private property does not exist. On this basis one can understand how it was possible to blaze through a disorderly arrangement of structures from the last centuries and create a broad, straight route corresponding to contemporary needs, to be called "The Way of the Palace of the Soviets" forming the main artery of traffic. From this avenue the Gothic and Renaissance of the Kremlin, and the rare elegance of the university built during the empire are given a new perspective.

The whole system of radiating and circular streets, as well as the quays of the Moscow River, have either been or will be widened, straightened and paved. On practically every block I have discovered modern buildings where last year there were dilapidated houses. They can raze a building now at a speed comparable to that of ants.

Together with the planning of new roads and parks goes the problem of reorganizing transportation. The first task was to thin out the crowds on the streets, so the "most beautiful subway in the world," a six-mile line, was installed in the record time of two years.

The synchronization of rhythms above the ground and under is so characteristic it is difficult to imagine the subway line itself without the various improvements in the houses and squares along the route of the line. Likewise, one can't disassociate the second line, which will be ready for use in two years, from the Central Stadium of the Soviet Union. This is a sports compound being built at the line's terminus, and including a stadium for 200,000 spectators, and a dozen smaller, special arenas.

Traffic above ground has been improved by the addition of 400 new taxis, more street cars and buses, and a new trolley line. It's now possible to board a streetcar and not be jabbed in the ribs by elbows or cursed at for accidentally stepping on someone's toes.

To me the most remarkable improvements, and a direct result of so many changes, is found in the people themselves. Leisure hours are becoming more agreeable every week. Hundreds of new shops of all kinds have opened. This alone is of great significance. It means production under collective methods has proved successful.

Prices for some things are still high but going down. By winter the prices of meat, bread and dairy products will be reduced 20 percent.

Delivery service — unused for years — and the convenience of being able to order by telephone are in practice again.

Besides stores, hundreds of new restaurants have replaced old, insufficient ones, and not only has the food improved in quality but so have service and decorations. One may have jazz and dance with his meal, or eat to soft music under the open sky, or grab a sandwich and a mug of beer in a hurry at a counter.

In summer there is a general exodus to the country where people settle themselves in cottages in the woods by a river until the chilly autumn sends them back to town. Last weekend I visited friends who have rented a couple of rooms and a kitchen about 30 minutes from town by electric train. We ate out under the trees, played basketball, and swam in the river. Nobody objects if one swims nude.

In the city is the enormous Park of Culture and Rest on the bank of the Moscow River — really what the name claims it to be. One may hear a symphony concert or a lecture, learn to fence, ride a Ferris wheel, high jump, play chess or anything else.

This is vacation season when most theaters and orchestras go on tour, performing in large and small towns all over the union, and at collective farms in the rural districts. In September, Moscow's 200 theaters will reopen. I don't know how many movie houses and concerts will play to packed houses every night.

———

Moscow
August 30, 1935

Dear Family,

Part of me wasn't sure how I would respond to Russian life after my absence. I needn't have felt concerned. Enough has changed to make each day an adventure. Food rationing is gone, making our meals more varied. Clothing shops offer a rather pleasing choice of summer-wear.

The city itself is undergoing alterations. New streets have cut through blocks of old structures, and modern buildings are going up everywhere except near the very heart, in and around Red Square. Suburbs spread into the outskirts to take care of new apartment buildings and factories. Back in 1933, the city was an overgrown village — intimate and charming. I suppose this is progress.

Housing is still scarce. François and I don't yet have our own place. We have to rent from a family who has a room to spare.

My old colleagues and friends welcomed us with parties. Some of the foreigners have left, however. Others keep coming, looking for work. I'm looking, too. But there's no rush. The articles for the "Star-Bulletin" take more time than I expected. I'm not a good writer and have to revise a lot. No lack of subject matter.

I'm awfully glad to be back!

> With love,
> Sisi

Chapter Twenty-Five

Honolulu Star-Bulletin	September 15, 1935

Housing in Russia

Although Moscow is modernizing itself by great strides in every respect, its housing situation is far from satisfactory. The city is dense — that is obvious. There are seldom vacant seats on streetcars, buses or metro; in some cases five people live in a small room, sharing the kitchen and bathroom with fifty other people. I'm having a difficult time finding even the simplest room to rent.

Before the revolution Moscow was a city of merchants and artisans mainly, with few factories of any size. Wealthy families lived in huge mansions with pillared porticos and classic details, set among branching trees and gardens. In these houses, with retinues of servants, lived the characters of Tolstoy's novels and Chekhov's plays. Only 40 percent of the buildings were over two stories high. The city was often short of water and had no sewer system.

In 1917, when the disinherited 90 percent took power, the old social order inevitably came to an end. New laws relieved owners of their property.

The most important problem facing the newborn Union of Soviets was to reestablish industry and agriculture, which fell to 20 and 60 percent of their former value, respectively. Without an industrial basis, it is difficult to realize municipal construction. Only in 1928 were industry and agriculture firmly enough established to permit the reconstruction on a large scale.

Imagine the capital during those first years following the war. Fighting and intervention left their marks. Although not much had been destroyed by guns, the fact that no repairs had be been made was reason enough for the situation the capital found itself in. More than one winter was endured in houses with paneless windows and heatless stoves. The need for building and repairing was urgent, but materials were scarce.

Former mansions of the rich, and churches were transformed into hospitals, schools and offices, or divided into apartments for workers. Barracks of wood and brick were hastily erected.

Soon new factories made machinery to produce building materials. Workmen were trained. Architects, engineers and technicians came from abroad to show them foreign methods of construction.

Out of pre-war Moscow grew a city suited to the needs of the new civilization. The contrast between the modern architecture and the old is as dramatic as that between the two social orders. Structures of the feudal days are no longer useful, except as records of history, or for their beauty as museum pieces. Only a few examples remain. Victims of the plan of reconstruction and expansion, they had to give way to modern apartment houses, offices, clubs, and so on.

In all new apartment buildings, the object is to supply every resident with the maximum of comfort — elevators, central heating, good ventilation and drainage systems. Of great importance is the profile of the streets, controlled so that the height of the houses never prevents the apartments and the streets from getting sufficient light.

It's important to mention that the population has grown from 7,000 in 1920, to 2,800,000 in 1931. During that time, 5,000 houses were built to lodge one-half million people. Even though hundreds more have been completed since then, it's still not enough.

Who gets first choice for these new living quarters? Those who have worked well and productively, whether they be laborers, scientists or government officials, and those whose homes were in the buildings razed to make room for new ones.

Every employed person has the right to at least nine square meters of living space for himself and each of his dependents; professionals, such as engineers, doctors or actors, have the right to at least twenty square meters per person.

Rent is regulated by the size of the apartment and the salary of the person to whom the rooms are given.

Chapter Twenty-Six

Honolulu Star-Bulletin   **October 1, 1935**

Russian Artists

Moscow — Last evening I went to see some young friends who had worked with me last year as sculpture students, and who, a few months ago, had moved into their new rooms and studios. I was given the directions: Take street car No. 3 and get off at the bread factory No. 13; the house number is 83 — I couldn't miss it because the building used to be a church.

It was 8 p.m. and dark when the conductor informed me I should get off. In the street I was doubtful as to the direction to go for house No. 83, so went up to a militia man for advice.

In my best Russian I said, "I'm looking for a building that was once a church."

"Oh, that," he said. "used to be a cemetery. I'll escort you."

We walked the half block together then stopped at the gate of a high, whitewashed brick wall. With another broad sweep of the arm, he said, "Here is the sculptors' studio. Good-bye."

Among the trees in the garden I saw the ancient church, painted red. The doors were heavily padded so in winter the cold couldn't get through the spaces between them and the frame. Entering, I saw across the vestibule, in what used to be the nave, a gigantic girl athlete in green clay caught in action throwing a discus. She held her place majestically in the center of the big whitewashed space.

I found my friends talking around a bas-relief hanging on one of the walls — a composition of masks and musical instruments for a new theater. Another sculptor was casting the completed figure of a man, more than twice life size, in four different sections. Plaster legs, arms, body, and head lay in various parts of the room.

The gigantic girl athlete was a commission for the grounds of a sanatorium near the Black Sea. There were other figures and groups of figures in clay draped in wet sacks for the night. On one wall hung a telephone. I noticed that the smaller of the two bins full of wet clay had a design of flowers and crosses painted on it.

"Oh, that used to be a baptismal font," explained one of the young men when I asked about it.

An artists' cooperative owns the church, and each member living or working there pays an average rental of two rubles a month. That's nothing considering that for his bas-relief the sculptor was getting 1,000 rubles, aside from the cost of the materials.

No trouble at all finding subjects. The continuing struggle for a better life culturally, biologically, materially inspire contemporary Soviet artists. Sculptors, painters, writers, actors, and musicians are all caught by the same fever. They have so much to say and want to say it all without waiting. No park, square or new building is complete without the touch of an artist.

But the results are not always objects of beauty. It is obvious the artists have tackled problems unsuited to their technically inexperienced hands. However, it is enough at present that the government is the leading patron of the arts.

Chapter Twenty-Seven

Honolulu Star-Bulletin	**October 15, 1935**

Food Prices

Moscow — On September 26, Soviet newspapers created a sensation. They announced the Party and government's decision to drastically reduce again the prices of food for the whole U.S.S.R., effective October 1 of this year.

The town buzzed. Housewives saw a glorious future of better menus, and men talked about how it would help the family pocketbook.

Newspapers reported that the decision had inspired meetings in factories and plants hailing the news, regarding it as evidence of the strength of the Soviet Union and the care of the Party and the government for the welfare of its workers.

All the stores prepared for a rush of buyers as the new prices went into effect. Gastronom No. 1, the largest grocery store in Moscow, increased its staff of employees from 260 to 300. Its supplies increased in quantity and assortment. The average daily turnover went up by about 25 percent the first week. New offices have opened where orders may be placed for home delivery.

Forty new special meat and sausage shops, and 359 new meat, fish and vegetable stores began operating on October 1.

Unfortunately, I had to shop on the first day of October. I needed only a little butter, sugar and some meat, but it took me over an hour to get them. Each item was at a different counter and the queues at each counter so long that, even though they moved quickly, it took up much time.

People scolded each other for trying to be waited on out of turn; salesmen scolded shoppers when their minds weren't made up as to what they wanted; shoppers scolded salesmen when they thought they didn't work fast enough.

The store filled not only with buyers. Some came in just to see if the newspapers told the truth. Finding they did, there was more buzzing and exclaiming. A skeptical old man, obviously literate, but who evidently didn't believe in signs, asked a salesgirl how much the butter cost. That made everyone laugh. When I left the store I felt as tired as after a full day's work.

In 1929, farms were reorganized under the collective system. The change was accomplished in a relatively short time. It meant that for a few years only those who worked, and their dependents, could buy in certain stores, and only a limited supply. Those whose work was physically or mentally difficult received the highest rations. Children, housewives, and students got special rations.

Those years were not easy. If one wanted more, he had to buy either in the "open" stores, also state-controlled but where prices were exceedingly high, or at the market where farmers could set their own prices. This situation inevitably caused speculation.

Chapter Twenty-Eight

Honolulu Star-Bulletin   October 30, 1935

October Revolution

Moscow is preparing to celebrate next week for the 18th time the biggest day in the Soviet calendar: the anniversary of the October Revolution.

When the Bolsheviks took power, the old Russian calendar showed the date October 25, 1917, but according to the calendars of the rest of the world, the day was November 7, 1917. Although the Soviets adopted the system of dating used by other countries, the event is still referred to as the October Revolution.

The greatest demonstration is always in Moscow, the capital, but every city and village has its own festivities for the anniversary.

From the Ukrainian city, Kharkov, comes news that all collective farm cottages are being repaired as part of a cultural drive in honor of the great day.

In Novosibirsk artists and architects are preparing to decorate the streets and buildings. Workers of the city's enterprises are competing with one another for first place in the demonstration parade. The award will be given to the one with the highest production results.

In Moscow the whole town is being dressed up for the occasion by outstanding architects and artists, as well as amateur organizations. The achievements of the U.S.S.R. in industry, trade and culture will be put before the approving and proud eyes of the public.

Two years ago I knew a group of artists working on masks and banners that a railroad organization was to carry in the demonstration that November. They worked for a week steadily before "October Day" shaping wire, pasting paper, cutting cardboard, and painting. The theme was "to rid the railroads of bureaucracy." The big masks and cardboard cutouts depicted two trains colliding due to engineers who had their minds off their jobs.

This year one of their slogans says, "Railroad workers! Let us fulfill and overfulfill with honor the autumn and winter plan of transportation! Let us insure the industrial centers supplies of coal, metal, cotton, bread, vegetables!"

On four of the green-roofed towers of the redbrick wall surrounding the Kremlin Palace, there remained, until a few weeks ago, the gold-plated two-headed eagles, the emblem of Czarist Russia. Beautiful though they were, they had been there eighteen years too long. In their stead are four giant stars with the Soviet emblem, the hammer and sickle, in the center of each, inlaid with precious stones of tremendous size from mines of the Union. Some of the gems weigh as much as one pound.

This year I'm doing my part to prepare for the demonstration by making, with a group of sculptors, a head of Lenin about eight feet high, to be carried in the parade. It is first made in clay, then cast in plaster. From the plaster cast will be made a form of *papier mâché*, painted, and placed on a pile of giant-sized books on wheels. The top of the float will be about twenty-seven feet from the ground.

There seems no end of money, materials and energy ready to make this day the greatest for the whole country and for each individual.

Apartments are being cleaned and painted, parties planned by children and adults, wardrobes looked over. Dressmakers, tailors, hair dressers and others are working overtime.

Chapter Twenty-Nine

Honolulu Star-Bulletin　　　　　**November 10, 1935**

Anniversary of the Revolution

Moscow — Early in the morning a few days before the anniversary of the "Great Proletarian Revolution" a friend of mine came to my apartment with the news that a rush order had come for several more floats for the parade, and asked if I wanted to earn 1,000 rubles by helping him make one. I was ready in a jiffy and went off to an improvised workshop at the terminus of the subway line where already several other artists were giving instructions to carpenters, and bending wire into the forms of heads and bodies.

On the second day our labor began to show results, and we worked late into the night. On the third day the trucks came, and we put the floats into place.

Ours showed the gray and black two-headed eagle (emblem of old Russia) lying dead on its back. Between its two necks was the crowned skull of Czar Nicholas the Very Last, with a great red hammer descending to crush it. As the truck drove off at 5:00 we applied the last dab of paint and then hurried to the center of town.

For three hours there was a flood of dancing, singing, cheering, laughing youngsters through the central streets. Banners they held told us, "We, as our Soviet Fatherland, are now of age." From the ten districts of Moscow they flowed to the square in front of the opera house and then passed up Gorki Street, which was brilliantly illuminated by floodlights, torches and flares.

In float after float, they satirized czarism, the church, fascism, and imperialism, and portrayed their own opportunities under socialism, expressing complete confidence in the future.

The next morning, the day of the big demonstration, I left home early. Not having a ticket for a seat on Red Square, I went with friends to the restaurant on the seventh floor of a central hotel, from where we could see the Square very well.

At 10:00 cannon fired sixty shots from the Kremlin. Stalin and other members of the Party and government had just ascended the tribune on the mausoleum of Lenin amid a thunder of applause.

Until noon the defenders of the borders of the U.S.S.R. passed in splendid formation on foot, on horseback, in tanks, tractors, armored cars, trucks with machine guns, artillery, searchlights and detectors. Men of the Red Fleet in black coats and white gloves, Red Partisans who, eighteen years ago, helped win the war.

Chapter Thirty

Honolulu Star-Bulletin   **December 1, 1935**

New Era for Soviet Labor

In mid-November 3,000 heroes of labor met in the large hall of the Kremlin Palace to discuss this new Stakhanov movement that, in two months, has swept the entire country like a hurricane.

The movement takes its name from the 29-year-old Donbas miner, Alexei Stakhanov, who on August 30 cut in one six-hour shift, 102 tons of coal with his pneumatic hammer instead of the normal seven tons. It seemed impossible, and few people believed him.

At the conference he said it was necessary to follow up this work, to show all the doubters that 102 tons and more were possible without much exertion, that it was necessary only to organize labor properly. And so, on September 3, the Party organizer of his section went down into the mine. Although in one shift he produced 115 tons, he was not believed at first. They sent a second man down, and a third one who set a new record of 125 tons. A few days later, Stakhanov broke all records by mining 227 tons in one shift.

It became clear to all that work in the section could be reorganized in such a way as to achieve 100 percent utilization of the pneumatic drill to increase several times the productivity of the workers.

Under the Stakhanov method, output and wages increased in the whole shaft and in a few days, the young miner was famous. His achievements were the subject of conversations, arguments and meetings all over the Union.

In September at the Gorki auto plant, foundryman Busygin forged 1,050 crankshafts with his hammer instead of the norm of 675.

Back in the Donbas a couple of days later, the engine driver, Krivonos, sped his locomotive up to 53 kilometers per hour instead of the usual 30.

The movement spread and caught on like wildfire. The weavers,

Dusya and Maria Vinogradov at Vychuga, began to operate 144 looms instead of 24. In far northern Archangel, the frame worker Musinski, at the city's largest saw mill, reached 221 cu.m. per frame shift instead of 95.

What about quality? Stalin asked for proof that it was maintained. Busygin replied that formerly out of 500 crankshafts, 20 were scrapped, but now out of 1,100, only two are discarded.

The conference agreed that the Stakhanov movement succeeded because of new efficient techniques in the hands of skilled and qualified workers — men and women happy and eager to show their trust in the socialist system.

Chapter Thirty-One

Honolulu Star-Bulletin   December 15, 1935

Ivanovna

Moscow — The weather's getting cold again, so cold there's frost on the inside walls and window panes of the streetcars. One has to blow on the glass and make a peek-hole in order to tell what the stations are.

It's all right if the ride is short, but if one has to go a long way and sit motionless for a half-hour or so, he has to wiggle his toes to keep his feet from becoming too uncomfortable. Thank goodness for the subway. Besides being fast, it's so warm and comfortable it's almost cozy.

In a month or so even the Russians will admit it's cold. It's a good thing the houses are warm. All the windows have double panes, and just before the cold starts, the sills between them are padded with cotton, and the cracks between the glass and their frames are sealed with strips of paper. A tiny section, called a *fortochka*, is hinged so it may be opened to ventilate the room. The steam radiator heats so well we leave it on most of the time.

The woman in whose apartment we rent a room, and her maid, Ivanovna, never agree about the *fortochka*. Ivanovna likes it open and Ekaterina Georgovna likes it shut.

Ivanovna looks as though she could be half Gypsy. Her hair is black, shiny and straight, and combed from a central part to a sturdy knot in back. Her round, brown face is set with a pug nose and Tartar eyes, like black shoe buttons.

She comes from a place two days east of Moscow by slow train, where there is now a flourishing collective farm. She and her husband used to own a good part of the land that makes up the collective. He, poor man, fell in the war, she told me.

About a month ago she had to go back to renew her visa for Moscow. Because of the congestion in the capital, everyone must have a permit to live here. She said she'd return in a week, but two weeks passed and we were still washing our own dishes and buying our own groceries, and beginning to think she wasn't going to get her visa.

A couple of days later she returned glowingly happy, but gave us no details of the visit with her friends. After some days, however, when she and I were alone in the kitchen, she suddenly said, "Comrade Agnessa, forgive me, but I must tell someone ...." With hands clasped tightly together, she looked at me.

"What is it, Ivanovna? Tell me."

"The truth is ... I didn't go to visit friends. I don't want Ekaterina Georgovna to know .... I went to spend two days with my husband in prison. He didn't die in the war, or even fight. He was, as you know, a *kulak* (landlord), and three years ago was sentenced to five years for spreading propaganda against collectivization."

Then she grinned all over again. "But he's a good man and they've already taken off one year from his sentence."

Ivanovna

341

Moscow
January 10, 1936

Dearest All of You,

I'm not going to write any more articles for the "Star-Bull." Haven't time. Have been conceiving a mural for the bar of the Architect's Club. The design is of musical notes in the shape of dancers prancing across a staff. I've done only the drawings. Specialized muralists will execute it.

Now I'm making thirty-six snowflakes, more or less a foot in diameter each, and each one different. They'll be cast in white plastic and stuck to a bright blue ceiling of one of the rooms of the Pioneer House. Pioneers are like Boy or Girl Scouts. They wear red ties on white shirts, go camping in the summer, and generally are expected to do good. At the Pioneer House, the kids come in when they have free time to pursue all sorts of hobbies: chess, scientific research, music, and lots of other things, especially cultural or intellectual.

I'm doing the original snowflakes in plasticene so they won't dry before being cast. I had a big wad of the stuff in my bag the other day when I called on Carol, who has a three-month-old baby. The child was crying when I arrived, and wouldn't stop. Carol said, "She's not hungry, wet or tired, so I let her cry."

Well, I took out my plasticene and, in a half hour, modeled her bawling head, life-size. It came out well.

Our social life is active. We've made several new friends — a Hungarian sculptor named Beni, his wife, Liza, and a woman chemist, Pilko, who is also Hungarian, but has been living in Vienna.

At a New Year's party, we met the mother and sister of Vasily Kandinsky. He's a famous abstract painter whom Madame Scheyer represents in America. He lives in Paris, but didn't move there until 1933, so I missed knowing him. His mother is the granddaughter of a Mongolian princess.

People keep coming here from Europe, the U.S. and Canada, looking for work — doctors, musicians, engineers, artists. It's harder now to get a job than when we first came here. The Great Depression seems to be hanging on, making the unemployed populations restless.

CHAPTER THIRTY-ONE

"Crying Baby's Head"; terracotta. Private collection.

March 12, 1936

Darling Family,

The excitement in our lives these days is the trip we're planning for this summer — to the Caucasus Mountains in the Soviet Republic of Georgia (Gruzia in Russian). There'll be six of us — five about our age and our leader, about forty, who knows the territory well. I'm the only woman.

We've been meeting every couple of weeks to plan what to take in the way of food, clothing and equipment. Our main objective is to climb Mount Elbrus, the highest peak in Europe, 18,500 feet. It won't be difficult or dangerous — no steep cliffs or ropes, only a glacier or two with a few crevasses. And we'll have a professional guide on the spot to teach us how to breathe.

François and I will fly down and spend a few days with friends before meeting up with the other four.

343

Otherwise, we're enjoying our concerts, operas and ballets, and plays. Oh, the plays! Meyerhold and Stanislavsky — both producers and directors extraordinary. The former, who is sixty-two, is original, innovative, avant-garde, and opposed to stylized naturalism. The latter, seventy-three, has taken the psychological approach to interpreting. I'm no authority on drama and can only say I find their work refreshing and inspiring. So do directors in the West, I hear.

There's an art exhibit on in Moscow at some club. I'm among the exhibitors — I'm showing the head I did of Carol's crying baby.

I may not have time to write before we leave for the south. I'll keep a diary on the trip and send it to you.

Till then, love to all,
Agnessa

P.S. Remember the Russian typewriter I smuggled in for Alex's sister in Alma-Ata? Well, with no trouble at all, I packed and mailed it to her. She has written to say she has received it and is delighted. Typewriters are not yet manufactured in the Soviet Union, and are worth their weight in gold, especially one like hers with a Russian keyboard.

❖*Part Four*❖

Chapter One

At five o'clock on the morning of July 25, 1936, François and I boarded a small passenger plane heading south to a town called Mineralnye-Vody (about the distance from Portland, Oregon to L.A.).

After months of planning, we were finally on our way to the Caucasus Mountains to climb one of the twin peaks of Elbrus, over 18,000 feet high. All through the past winter and spring, the six of us — Misha, Yurka, Timofei, Aptekar, François and I — studied and organized the details.

We limited our baggage to what we could stuff into our knapsacks, so our hands would be free at all times. In our packs had to be hiking boots; clothing for heat, snow, wind and rain; cooking and eating utensils; and first aid-kits to serve for several weeks.

The plane carried only six passengers, each of whom was allowed five kilos (eleven pounds) of luggage. Faced with a stiff surcharge for excess, we didn't want to go over, so, before leaving home, we dressed in all the woolen clothing we could load on ourselves.

The plane would make two stops — first at Kharkov, then Rostov-on-Don — en route to Mineralnye-Vody. Once there, François and I would get a train to Giorgievsk, and then find our way to an isolated farm at a mere dot on the map called Stanitsa Neslobnia. There we'd spend a couple of days with Bogdanov, a colleague from Moscow, before joining our four climbing comrades at Nalchik, the point of departure for our Caucasus adventure.

The takeoff from Moscow was on time and smooth. I, who had never flown before, didn't know what to expect. In a way it was not unlike being on a miniature streetcar, with the pilot sitting up front as a motor man, shouting occasional comments to his riders. The main difference was the heat and noise. Even after peeling off our woolen things, we were warm.

Though the roar of the motor discouraged socializing with the other passengers, we found enough distractions to pass the time pleasantly. When I tired of looking down at the endless steppe, stretches of woodlands, towns and hamlets, I took out my *New Yorker* magazine and read not only every story, article and poem, but each word of all the ads.

Then we landed at Kharkov's expanding airport, where the plane refueled. François and I enjoyed the best breakfast we'd had in ages. It was ten o'clock and this was our first meal since the previous evening. Nothing could have tasted better than those Ukranian cucumbers and giant tomatoes on dark, whole-grain bread. It wasn't only hunger that made them so good.

We took off again. The farther south we flew, the richer the earth became, and the larger the plots under cultivation. Often we could discern people working in the fields, and tractor-combines threshing grain. I gave up trying to tell what kind of produce was growing. At one point, we saw a collective farm airport with four planes parked on the runway.

We landed at Rostov-on-Don right on schedule. The first person off was the pilot. He jumped to the ground, opened the door to the passenger cabin, removed his helmet, bowed with a flourish and said, "Well, comrade passengers, I am proud to say you may check your watches. It is exactly one o'clock!"

From Rostov, the pilot took us up to the clouds where it was so cold we put on all our woolen sweaters again. Far below one enormous steppe divided into geometrical patches of browns, greens and yellows, cut now and then by a river. We saw no mountains.

And so we reached Mineralnye-Vody — "Mineral Waters" — one of scores of spas on the northern edge of the Caucasus Mountains. Though we were close to our destination, several hours still separated us from Bogdanov's farm. A short ride on a toy-like train brought us to Giorgievsk at ten o'clock in the evening. Only one leg remained. We asked the attendant about a train to Stanitsa Neslobnia.

"There's one every night at eight-thirty. It left long ago," he told us.

Perhaps we could find a horse and buggy. Outside the station were two of them. The first driver said he'd take us for forty rubles. We offered him twenty and settled for thirty.

The night air was warm, and the sky filled with stars. The horse trotted along in the dark unguided, apparently acquainted with all the flaws in the road.

The driver knew the Bogdanov farm well. "The family's been here for generations," he told us. "The young fellow, your friend Leonid, comes every summer to visit. He's an architect now, designs buildings,

I understand. Say ... is it true there are some in America over fifty stories?"

"Even higher," I said. "I've seen them in New York."

"Well, Comrades, I'm sorry, but that just can't be. Why, even in Moscow, they don't build them nearly that high."

"Have you been to Moscow?" François asked.

"Not yet. Some of my friends have, though. You know what? They have queues at all the shops up there. Down here, we're not very important, but our stores are full of things, and we don't have to stand in line to buy them."

"How long have you lived in these parts?" I asked.

"I was born here, but my folks came from Iran. I've never seen the old country. I'd like to some day but don't want to risk not being able to come back here."

"This is beautiful country," I said. "The name — Stanitsa Neslobnia — what does it mean?"

The driver chuckled. "Don't know where it comes from. Have often wondered. There must be a story behind it. 'Neslobnia' means something like 'not getting angry,' or 'not to anger.'"

Fields stretched out flat on either side of us. How clean and sweet the air was. We saw no houses or animals or people. The only noises were the regular clopping of the horse's hooves and the cracking sounds the wooden wheels made as they rolled over the dirt road. Could anything in such peace anger a soul?

Suddenly the driver snapped his whip in the air and pointed ahead to the right. "See the lights? We'll soon be at the farm, Comrades."

It was midnight. The Bogdanovs were still up. Although we had never met Mama and Papa, they welcomed us as long-lost children, and sat us down at the kitchen table with sausage, bread, butter and jam, all homemade, and a samovar for tea.

François and I slept comfortably on the floor in one of the rooms. Having been awake and alert for twenty-two hours, our bodies didn't need an inner spring mattress to relax and recover energy. Besides, we had to get used to bedding down in the wilderness.

At seven o'clock in the morning, our friend, Leonid, took us down to the well under the fruit trees, where we washed in ice-cold water. By then, however, the sun was already shining hot on us, and on the pears and apples, almost breaking the branches with their weight.

The three of us spent most of the morning out of doors, cavorting, sunbathing, talking, and laughing. After a cursory survey of the farm, Leonid took us to the top of a hillock close by, from where he pointed to the north.

"See down there where all those trees are? That's our village of Neslobnia."

"I don't see any village," François said, making a sham telescope with his hands up to one eye.

Leonid laughed. "Darn it. I'm sure it was there yesterday. Pretty small, you know — only a few shops hidden under the oaks and birches. We buy our important stuff in Giorgievsk, where the school is, and the clinic, and barbershop."

Between our hill and the village ran a river — narrow, yellow and rapid; and way off to the north, past the boundless grain fields, the edge of the world was flat. To the east, close to the river, stood a grain elevator and a mill, and farther on, southward, jagged blue mountains broke the skyline. Beyond them, two rounded, snow-white peaks glistened against the sapphire infinity.

"Look! There's Elbrus!" François shouted.

"How beautifully matched the peaks are," I said.

Bogdanov nodded. "Down here we say they're like the breasts of a buxom young woman."

"Not bad," François commented. "How far is Elbrus from here?"

"About a hundred and twenty kilometers — eighty miles — in a straight line. You'll be there in ten days or so, won't you?"

"That's our plan, more or less," said François.

"And where will you go from there?"

"You've heard of Svanetia, haven't you?"

"Sure. That's a valley south of Elbrus that was discovered only during the World War. The people didn't know about the wheel, I've heard. You're going *there?*"

"Yes. If we don't run into any snags. There are no roads in yet, I hear. We'll have a donkey and get in by walking over the mountains. The only other way is by plane. In fact, we'll fly out, and finish our vacation on one of those gorgeous beaches of the Black Sea."

"You'll need a rest after all that. Wish I could go with you. Hot, isn't it, up here? What d'you say we go down to the river where there's some shade, and have a swim before lunch?"

The glacial water flowed so swiftly we had to cling to the branches overhanging the bank in order to stay afloat. The current swung and twisted our bare bodies this way and that, to the accompaniment of our squeals and the gushing water.

Around the kitchen table once more, the conversation moved easily from our morning's adventures, to alpinism, to farming, to local history. That is where Papa Bogdanov took over. Unintentionally, I pitched him straight into his pet topic by asking if Cossacks were indigenous to those parts and if their name had any particular meaning.

With a broad grin he pushed aside his plate and rested his folded arms firmly on the table. "I can go on all afternoon," he said, and cleared his throat. "The name is Turkish for "adventure" or "free-man." In Russian we say *Kazak*, as in the Republic of Kazakstan. Back in the 15th century, Neslobnia was only one of many Cossack villages that formed groups of horsemen and settled in military communities in the Don and Dnieper regions — fiercely independent fighters, and self-governing. They spread all over — into Poland and even Siberia. The czars, of course, felt threatened and eventually managed to dominate the Cossacks, making each man serve twenty years in the czar's army in exchange for private land and the privilege of being upper class."

Papa Bogdanov shifted his position and went on. "But their freedoms eroded and, a couple of centuries ago, one of their chiefs, a fellow called Stenka Razin, led them to rebel ...."

Mama Bogdanov interrupted in a successful effort to divert her husband's monologue. "In our folklore," she said, "Stenka Razin is still a hero and, oh my, what a romantic figure! When the youngsters play games and pretend they're fighting the czars, every boy wants to be Stenka Razin."

She left her chair and moved across the room. "I'm going to start the samovar for tea."

Two days later, when the time came for leave-taking, our hosts assured us we'd be welcome back at any time. Mama kissed my cheeks and said, "The sooner the better."

Prophetic words. I would return in less than three weeks ... alone.

Chapter Two

Leonid drove us to the railroad station in the family horse cart. Our train was in, but would leave later than scheduled because the locomotive needed repairs. How much later, no one could tell us, so we said good-bye to our friend, found two benches in an empty car, and lay down for a long nap.

A couple of hours later, the locomotive connected itself to our train with a jolt that shook us awake. We were on our way to Giorgievsk. Once there, we caught another train to a junction called Prohladnaia, where we took the direct line to Nalchik, for the rendezvous with our climbing companions.

At one of the stops on the last stretch, a surprise awaited us. We had left the train to buy something to eat when François said, "Look! That fellow over there on the platform, the heavy-set one eating an apple. He looks an awful lot like .... I'll be darned — it *is!*"

It was, indeed, Aptekar, the senior member of our group. He and the other three were on our train, only two cars away from ours. Aptekar, the logical one to lead us, had spent many years in the region during and after the revolution, and spoke the local language.

Late in the morning of July 28, we at last reached Nalchik and immediately dispersed in four directions. Aptekar had to arrange passage for us on the truck to Baksan, a ride of four hours. From there, our travel by foot would begin. Timofei headed for the barber. Misha and Yurka decided to look up a friend, and François and I wanted hats for the sun, and maybe a *boorka*.

Made of sheep's wool and fashioned to protect against rain, cold and heat, a *boorka* resembles — but is much more than — a cape. Over the centuries, it became a symbol of heroic manliness. From its pointed shoulders to its wide bottom edge, nearly touching the ground, the effect was elegant. Some were white, but more often brown or black, and as old as Cossack history.

I could imagine a dark and dashing rider (Stenka Razin, perhaps?) galloping across the steppe on his purebred steed, his fur cap askew on his head, and his *boorka,* held at the throat by a silver buckle, waving behind him in the wind. I could sit behind him, under the *boorka,* hidden so well no one would suspect I was there.

So François and I looked around the Nalchik marketplace for a *boorka,* which we could also use as a double sleeping bag. By turning it upside down, our four feet would fit in the shoulder part, while the bottom edge would amply cover our upper bodies.

In a broad open field we found a crowd of two hundred or so vendors and buyers in orderly confusion. Some of the merchants sat cross-legged in rows with their wares before them on the ground or on boxes. Others, with livestock in tow, strolled about. Things such as rusty door hinges, broken mirrors, a table with a broken leg, were common. But we saw new articles, as well. Among the hats were shabby straws, an English bowler, caps, and astrakhans of Cossack style. We wanted ours of local tradition: white felt, with a snug-fitting crown and little felt tassels on the peak, and a wide, flat brim with fringed edge. We each bought one for fifteen rubles.

The first *boorka* we saw was a black beauty slung casually over one shoulder of a vendor who walked about, tall and straight, in his jet leather boots. By some uncanny intuition he knew we wanted what he had. Our eyes met, and he stopped. With a deliberate flourish, he demonstrated how the *boorka* should be worn.

What legerdemain was that? Did Stenka Razin still live? He had come swashbuckling before us, almost exactly as I fancied him.

François, who didn't notice anything unusual, asked what the *boorka* would cost.

"Three hundred rubles," the man replied.

"We'll give you a hundred and fifty," François told him.

Stenka's eyes narrowed. One side of his face smiled. Then he frowned, turned, and walked away shaking his head.

"Well, that's that," said François. "Stay if you want to, Agnessa. I'm going to help Aptekar buy supplies."

I lingered and had another look around the market. While examining an old Afghan shawl, I turned and saw Stenka smiling at me.

"Well, do you want the *boorka?* What'll you give me?"

"A hundred and seventy-five," I answered.

"Nothing doing. No less than two hundred and eighty."

"It's not worth it." My attempt to sound knowledgeable failed.

The gallant Stenka Razin bowed, and went away. I almost gave in but returned to the truck base instead.

Aptekar assured me there would be other *boorkas* at the Baksan market the next day when we shopped for a donkey. Perhaps, but it wouldn't be the same.

For much of the way to Baksan, the rough dirt road twisted between a swiftly flowing river, white with foam, and high granite cliffs. At seven o'clock in the evening, the driver deposited us and our baggage on the bank of the river, where it rushed through a plain near the village of Baksan. With our equipment spread out on the ground, we just stood and looked at each other, wondering where to start.

Feigning dogmatism, Aptekar announced, "First of all, we'll uncork a bottle of Georgian wine and drink to what is most important: our health and harmony. Only then will we set up the tent and cook our first meal."

The dinner was good, the tent roomy, and the river warbled lullabies all night long. An auspicious beginning.

Chapter Three

Right after breakfast the next morning, Aptekar, Timofei and François went in search of a pack animal and a *boorka*. The rest of us stayed at the camp to tidy up.

While Misha and Yurka were down at the riverside doing the dishes and laundry, three local girls came by, carrying baskets. They smiled timidly and dallied.

"Good morning," I said, and my intuition prodded me to add, "have you something to sell?"

"Oh yes," all three replied in chorus as they gathered around me.

They had brought potatoes and eggs and milk. I bought their entire stock at once. I asked if they'd bring some fresh green vegetables. Indeed, they would.

"We have *airan*, too."

"What is *airan*?" I had never heard the word.

"It's made of cow's or goat's milk ... fermented. Everyone drinks it here."

The oldest one said a few words in the Balkar language to the younger girls, who ran swiftly away. "My sisters are going to bring you some."

To make conversation, I commented on her good knowledge of Russian.

"We start learning it in the fourth grade," she explained.

"And in your school you're taught in your native language?" I asked.

"Yes. Before the revolution, Balkar was not a written one. Now it's been put into the Latin alphabet."

"So," I said, "all your history and music and literature will be preserved."

The girl nodded. "Oh, yes. We're very proud. Our culture goes back to ancient times."

I told her I, also, learned Russian recently, and that English was my native tongue.

"Oh! You're from England! I know where that is. English is spoken in Australia, too, and Canada, isn't it?"

"Yes, and in the United States."

We were interrupted by Misha and Yurka coming back from the river with the laundry and dishes. "It was too easy!" Yurka shouted. "We just held the pieces in the water one at a time. The current was so strong it irrigated and rinsed every darn thing as clean as new. Look!"

"What's this?" Misha asked, having discovered the potatoes and eggs. Looks like the local farmers have found some new customers. What a feast we'll have today!"

"And that's not all," I said.

Coming down the road were the two younger girls bringing vegetables and a supply of fermented milk.

In mid-afternoon, the three animal hunters returned without a donkey. François, however, had found a *boorka*, a brown one, finer than Razin's, and so supple it took up relatively little space when packed. Even with Aptekar to haggle, he paid three hundred rubles.

"Oh well," I said, "it's as good as my fur coat, and that cost four hundred. And it's only half of what I got paid for my little bust of Marx."

The last adventure of the day started when two young men — tanned, well-built fellows — approached the camp. After the usual greetings, we learned they had come down the previous day from Mount Elbrus and were staying at the tourist camp in Baksan.

"And how's the climbing?" Aptekar asked.

"Fine," said the younger one. "That is, if you don't mind the monotony of just going. You keep putting one foot in front of the other, and go and go, and when you've gone some more, you go some more, and then you turn around and come back." He laughed, with the palms of his hands raised in a gesture that said, "That's all there is."

"Hold on there," his friend said. "It's not bad at all. I might come back next year with my wife. But you aren't going to carry all that gear, are you, Comrades?"

"No, only our backpacks," Aptekar told him. "We're going to buy a donkey. Didn't have any luck this morning. Maybe tomorrow."

"Hey, we know one on sale for only three hundred and seventy-five rubles. We'll take you there now if you like."

Misha and Yurka went with the young men, and returned well after dark leading the seventh member of our team. All that remained was to give the gentle beast of burden a name. We drew lots to see who should have that honor, and I won.

Misha tapped me on the shoulder. "Tell me, Agnessa, how do you say *ostòl* in English?"

I told him it was donkey.

"Yes. Now I remember. So what are you going to call him?"

"Well," I said, "he reminds me of a gentleman — kind, intelligent, and shrewd in an asinine sort of way. I'm thinking of an actor named Adolph Menjou."

They all knew who he was, and agreed, but Misha was scratching his head and smiling the way people do when up to something.

"Out with it, Misha!" said Yurka.

"I was thinking ... we should call him ... Hotey." He looked around at our vacuous expressions. "You don't get it, do you? Donkey Hotey! Don Quixote ... windmills, and all that ... you know."

On the morning of July 30, we packed our rucksacks, loaded our tent and other equipment firmly on Adolph's back and started for Tegenekli, our next camp site.

The road followed the river between fields and high mountains. Once we paused at a farmhouse for a refreshing drink of *airan,* and a little farther on came to a post office where we mailed cards. My rucksack seemed awfully heavy, though there wasn't much in it. Maybe that was only because I was unused to carrying any weight for more than a couple of hours at a time.

We reached Tegenekli well before dark. Adjoining the campground was an Intourist Hotel and restaurant crowded with vacationers. At a level spot as far from them as possible, we let Adolph loose to browse. Aptekar and Misha put up the tent, and François and Yurka scouted for firewood, while Timofei and I went off with a pail to see what we could buy from the farm on the other side of the river.

Instead of a bridge spanning the torrent, we had to cross on two slim logs tied together. Twirling the pail in one hand, Timofei literally skipped along the trunks. I stayed behind squealing in alarm. He landed safely, turned to face me, bowed low with cap in hand and said, "*Merci beaucoup*, Madame Agnessa!" Then he skipped back to escort me across, laughing the whole time.

"Where on Earth did you learn to do that?" I asked when I could speak normally.

"Oh, I'm a professional acrobat."

"No you're not. You're an architect in the same office as François."

"Correct. But before that ...."

All the way to the farmhouse and back to camp, I listened to an astounding story of a ten-year-old boy orphaned by the upheavals of the revolution. He survived years of cold and hunger with scores of other children who roamed the streets, living by their wits, till agencies generated by the new government gave shelter and education to the poor and homeless. Timofei's natural agility led him first to tight ropes and tumbling, then a chance conversation opened the door to architecture.

"And now you and Clavdia have a little boy and a comfortable apartment."

"And, don't forget, I'm realizing another of my daydreams: climbing Mount Elbrus!"

Tegenekli was where the road ended and the trail began. Delivery trucks could go no farther. All supplies destined for higher bases had to be carried up from there on the backs of men or donkeys. One more camp, Terskol, lay between Tegenekli and Krugozor, where we would rest and prepare for the ascent to the summit across the glacier.

In cold, drizzly, foggy weather the trail took us in and out of woods fragrant with moss and dank undergrowth. The valley became narrower and the river smaller, the higher we tramped.

When we reached Terskol, it was barely two o'clock. We might have camped there, but a noisy group of seventy teenage alpinists discouraged us. We'd have pushed on at once, but Yurka discovered a barbershop and decided he wanted his head shaved. The rest of us had a lunch of tinned salmon and chocolate bars while waiting.

The rain turned to fog, and the route became a rocky trail up a steep hill and on through some woods. Out in the open again, we found ourselves in a large field but could not locate the trail. It was seven o'clock but seemed much later.

"We have two choices, Comrades." Aptekar's voice was devoid of enthusiasm. "We can pitch our tent here in this quagmire, or ask at that house at the edge of the clearing where the trail is. Shall we vote?"

Misha groaned. "Please, Chief, don't say such funny things. Laughing would hurt my poor muscles."

The little white house with cows grazing around it looked like an illustration for a fairy tale. Three generations of Balkars came out on the veranda and welcomed us with cups of *airan*. Had we, indeed, moved into a fable? Aptekar explained our predicament. "We're on our way up but have lost the trail."

A boy of twelve or so stepped forward. "Now the trail is wet and slippery, and difficult to see in this twilight fog. Even in dry weather, it's one-and-a-half hours up to Krugozor. Besides, with all that baggage, you'll need a couple more donkeys, it's so steep."

After a prolonged silence, Aptekar asked, "Could you, then, rent us a room for the night?"

The boy translated to his elders who discussed the matter. At length he smiled. "Yes. You may sleep in my room — for one ruble apiece — if you buy milk and butter from us in the morning."

The room, a palace compared to the alternative, was plain and not spacious — about nine feet by twelve. A large, built-in clay oven, for heat in winter, took up one corner. Next to the boy's bed, under the window, stood a table, leaving barely enough room for us. No pictures hung on the walls, and no rug covered the wood floor.

After a supper of milk thick with cream, and rye bread and butter, we lined up our six places close together on the floor and turned in early. The boy got in between his blankets without removing a bit of clothing — not even his leather slippers or fur cap.

Chapter Four

I awoke with a start. Something cold and moist had skimmed across my face. In the dim light of early dawn I saw a frog hopping away toward the half-open door. Everyone else in the room was apparently still asleep. It must have been around half past four. From the veranda came noises of human activity.

A few moments later, a woman came into the room. Silently, she went to the boy's bed and sat on the edge with her back toward me. Ever so faintly I heard her speaking to the child. Only love could have put such tenderness in a voice. Since it was not Russian being spoken, I did not understand, but I imagined what she said:

"Darling, it's your mother. It's time to get up. There are chores waiting for you."

The boy moaned. "Go away, Mama. Let me sleep a little more, please."

"Not today, my dear." She leaned down and kissed him. "That's a good boy. Your father's going down to Baksan, and you have to guide the Russians up to Krugozor. If you don't, Grandpa will have to. Come on, show him you're a little man."

The woman stood up, and the boy reluctantly emerged from his warm blankets to the chill of the morning. Hand in hand they left quietly.

Soon afterwards, François stirred, and whispered, "I'm going to get dressed and go out. I think the weather's improved."

The rest of our squad made sounds of wakening. François hollered for us all to come out and look at the scenery.

Misha grunted, said, "It can wait," and turned over. Everyone else hurried out of doors to find the rain-washed air a blend of aromas: newly cut hay, damp earth, and manure. The sun, still hidden by mountains, grew warmer every minute in a creation totally different from the nether world we had entered the evening before.

In back of the house, a brown mountain wall went straight up to the blue sky. On the left rose another wall, verdant with vegetation. Beyond the wet green field and woods we had come through, was a ridge buttressing Krugozor, and behind that soared a distant range topped by snow-capped peaks, pink in the early light of day.

A cow or two mooed. On the veranda a girl scolded her little sister. I went over to see what they were doing. Secured to the railing, an important-looking contrivance had been set up. It had an arm with a handle, which the older girl was turning. On the floor were two pails.

I watched for awhile, then asked, "What are you doing? I've never seen such a gadget."

The older one looked at me with surprise and a touch of disdain. "Don't they have these in Moscow?"

"Not that I know of. What does it do?"

"It's a milk separator. We bought it only recently. You see this bowl here on top? We pour plain cow's milk into it, then turn the handle. Skimmed milk runs into this pail, and the cream goes into the other. What do you think of *that?*"

"It's wonderful! What makes it work?"

"It's the machinery inside," the little one told me, and then added with emphasis, "It's *not* magic!"

Around eight o'clock, the first rays of sun crept over the eastern wall of the valley and flooded our little world with warmth. A half an hour later we had loaded three donkeys with all our possessions, said our farewells, and started on the climb up to Krugozor. The Balkar boy managed his two animals while we took turns guiding Adolph. An occasional pause allowed us to take pictures, or admire the valley behind us and the majestic peaks above. Not even a tiny cloud crossed the heavens, and only a weak breeze fanned the air. As we left the tree line there was no longer any shade to protect us from the increasing heat.

The few groups of climbers we passed on their way down gave enthusiastic accounts of their expeditions, and cheered us on. About half way up, a new range, stretching beyond infinity, came into view on the left. Snow glistened on its sharp peaks, and glaciers filled the valleys. Between the new range and us was a vast gorge, the floor of which was covered with a massive green ice pack.

So far, we hadn't had a glimpse of Elbrus, but when we caught sight of a red flag fluttering atop a pole, we knew Krugozor wasn't far. Timofei cheered, whooped and bounded ahead with Yurka and François at his heels. Before reaching the level area of Krugozor, they stopped abruptly and gesticulated energetically for us to hurry and to look to the right. By then I was so tired I thought every step would be my last. Right behind me were the three donkeys keeping a steady pace with Misha and the boy. Trailing us by a hundred yards was Aptekar.

One foot in front of the other, I plodded on and up, keeping both eyes on the far right till, at last, the tip of one lovely, rounded peak of Elbrus showed. A few more paces and the second appeared.

I kept thinking, "How white the snow! How blue the sky!" and forgot how tired I was.

Chapter Five

Camp Krugozor occupied two levels. On the lower stood a row of sixteen large tents, each with ten bunks, and twenty smaller tents for sleeping bags. Close by was an outdoor kitchen and a house where the camp director and personnel lived.

On the upper level we found another Intourist Hotel and a glassed-in restaurant with a greenhouse attached. Who would have expected such comforts so high in the sky? Those facilities were in business only during the summer months, but the Academy of Science station, next door, functioned all year.

At noon, we let the donkeys loose to graze, then headed to the restaurant for our own meal. I couldn't recall ever enjoying a dinner as I did that day. Maybe it was the white linen tablecloths and napkins, the elegant waiters, or maybe the view — breathtaking in every direction. I wasn't the only enchanted one. At the table next to ours sat three men and a woman, all in the uniform of the Red Army, who had just come down from the summit.

"We had a wonderful time," the young woman told us. "Great sport, and so easy. I'm ready to go up again."

I commented that the two peaks looked deceptively close, as though with no effort one could run up and down in an afternoon.

The officers laughed, and one of them said, "Don't take Nina's describing it as easy too literally. But I had the same impression. Until we were nearly at the top, the peaks seemed always the same distance away. When are you planning to start?"

Agnessa and comrades at Krugozor; Elbrus in background - 1936

"At the first light of morning," Aptekar said, "about four-thirty."

"Good," another officer said. "It's a six-hour climb to the halfway house. After ten-thirty, the sun gets terribly hot. You'll be grateful for a little inactivity. Your guide will make you rest well before the final stretch to the summit — in fact, that night and all the following day. At about ten o'clock at night, you'll start tramping. That part takes eight hours, so you'll reach the top at six in the morning."

The young woman couldn't wait to declare her enthusiasm. "I've *never* seen anything so wonderful! The stars were so close and brilliant, and the snow so luminous! Just like a fairy tale. And then — coming back down here to Krugozor — the whole way took less than four hours. On the glacier we removed our crampons and slid down part of the way."

Promptly at four-thirty the following morning, the six of us and another party departed Krugozor, single file behind our guide. Immediately behind him was the only other woman in our group. I fell in line after her. A few of us had bamboo poles tipped with spikes, or alpenstocks, and all carried crampons to fasten to the soles of our boots when we reached the glacier.

Boots! Mine were special, made to measure for me in Prague in 1933. Ever since, I had cared for them with respect and love and saddle soap. The sturdy and supple hand-sewn hide fit perfectly over my woolen socks. For skiing, they served me well. The real test of their worth, however, was tramping through the Caucasus Mountains. So far, they had passed with high marks. From what I observed, there were no boots in all of the Soviet Union like mine.

"All right, Comrades!" The guide shouted so all of us would hear. "Our pace must be slow. And you must breathe in rhythm with your stride. That way you won't tire. The weather's in our favor — no clouds, no wind. We'll stop occasionally to count noses and admire the view. Is everyone ready? All right — let's get going."

Someone commented that we were lucky to have only seventeen in our group. The party of seventy we met at Terskol had gone up a couple of days earlier. The man behind me said, "Two weeks ago a company of a hundred doctors went up. Before long they'll have to install traffic signals along the way."

At first the leisurely pace seemed foolish, but after a hundred meters of steep climbing over a ridge of rough rock, I was glad to slow down. Looking far below we saw the valley we left the day before. Up ahead loomed the glacier we had to cross. Before undertaking it, we rested and strapped on our crampons.

By then the sun had already warmed the early morning, so we removed our outer garments. François and Timofei stripped off even their shirts and were edging away from the rest of us. They were up to something. François blew me a kiss and waved. "We're taking off!" he called.

Timofei strode over the ice, stopped and shouted, "See you later — up at the halfway house!"

The guide started to call after them, then changed his mind and shook his head. "Crazy guys. They've no idea how dangerous it can be — not knowing the route."

At a slower pace, we clambered on and up over the ice. Zigzagging, the guide steered us clear of all crevasses, the sight of which evoked horrifying possibilities. We all knew stories of unwary climbers falling in and being brought out severely injured or dead, or lost forever. Everyone was glad to leave the ice. The next lap was another steep trail up bare lava rocks. Before taking it on, the guide granted us a twenty-minute rest.

"You might want to eat your chocolate bars now," he advised. "And if you're thirsty, the glacier water is drinkable. Take your time. We have to wait for our trailing comrade, anyway."

Trailing us, indeed, was Aptekar, by well over fifty meters. When, heaving and puffing, he rejoined us, we cheered and applauded, and urged him to share our chocolate. Only then I noticed Yurka was missing.

"I let him go after those two lunatics," the guide said. "Maybe he'll talk some sense to them. Now I've got to make sure Aptekar is in good shape. Can't be too careful. Mountain sickness can be serious, and at this elevation, not uncommon."

There was no sign of François and Timofei or of Yurka. I said nothing for fear of betraying my anxiety.

We hadn't gone far over the rocky terrain when we met a party of teenage boys and girls on their way down. The kids went right past us with cheerful hellos, but their guide stopped to chat briefly with ours, as friends do.

Before continuing, our guide lifted his binoculars to his eyes and scanned the broad span of snow up ahead of us. Without a word, he handed the lens to me and pointed leftward. When I adjusted the focus, my heart pounded. There they were — three animated dark specks, moving over the bright snow. Above them, the two white peaks of Elbrus were serene and stable against the blue sky.

Thank goodness. All was right so far.

Chapter Six

We were on the last leg — a stretch of snow — part level, part steep. The guide repeated, "Keep a slow ... steady pace. Strike a rhythm ... with every step ... and every breath. Never ... miss a step. If you don't go forward ... mark time." He droned on, echoing himself. The tempo of his words matched the measure of his stride.

Aptekar dropped behind once more, and Misha left the group to be with him. We paced onward, occasionally skirting a stony patch — higher, always higher.

At last, the halfway house came into view. Impulsively, everyone cheered. There it perched — the brown cabin on a mass of red and black rocks. All around it were tents — a score or more in the snow, several on the bare boulders and four on the roof of the cabin. A few more strides and we could identify individuals. Some dozens of teenagers romped about, and there was François sunbathing, and Timofei. They both waved. I wanted to cry for joy. Someone was skiing down the hill, heading straight for our group. Yurka had come to meet us. With a wave and a shout he glided past, then came to a graceful halt next to Aptekar and Misha. It was eleven o'clock.

By noon I, too, basked under the hot sun. My boots and rucksack were stowed with François' in one of the tents. I had eaten an adequate lunch, refreshed myself with a long drink of lemonade and, while massaging my limbs with oil, listened to the lunatics' account of their uphill trek.

"We've been here two and a half hours," François bragged.

"You know what you did was dangerous, don't you?" I asked.

"Sure," Timofei said, "but it was worth the risk."

"I was worried. At least you didn't get trapped in a crevasse."

"Don't think there was no possibility of it," said Timofei. "When we left you, we had no idea where the trail was, so we took the shortest route — straight up — where most of the crevasses were. We went around some of them, but that took too long, so we decided the best would be to cross them, which we did by jumping."

"But some are wide, gaping abysses!"

They both laughed, and Timofei said, "Oh, those! Well, we had our bamboos, you know, so we simply pole-vaulted across."

While I gaped, incredulous, the two of them chuckled. "I did slide into a small one," Timofei added. "François handed me an end of his bamboo and pulled me up. It was great sport. Then Yurka came up and added to the fun."

"What about the summit?" I asked. "Are you going with us?"

The glances the two men exchanged gave me the answer.

We passed the afternoon in fruitful idleness. The director of the halfway house showed us an architect's sketch of a hotel planned to take the place of the cabin and tents. The three-story building — oval shaped, with no corners, to resist the stormy winds — would house a couple of hundred guests at a time.

Mount Elbrus was first scaled in 1868, we learned, by a British explorer named Freshfield. He wrote several volumes on climbing in the Italian Alps and the Himalayas, as well as the Caucasus, with eloquent descriptions of the natural beauty. When we could find no record of the first woman on Elbrus, François said he'd bet I was the first American woman. "If I am," I said, "include it on my epitaph, and make me famous."

The view from our tent was like the setting for a play. My position in the "amphitheater" looked onto a broad snowbank, the top of which curved, similar to the back of a stage. Beyond, stretching from far left to far right, paraded rugged peaks, black and white against a sapphire sky. The action varied constantly. Cirrus clouds clung to the cliffs and then moved on. And cumuli, blown by winds, sailed high over the mountain range, casting ever-changing shadows, like protagonists treading the boards, enacting a drama. The spectacle ended only when the curtain of darkness fell.

After sunset, the temperature plunged to below freezing. The six of us dressed warmly and gathered in front of our adjoining tents to plan the agenda for the next two days. Aptekar decided not to attempt the final trek. Misha and I would go with the guide and the group we came up with from Krugozor. The other three, after conferring with our guide, were still determined to go it alone, even though a regulation forbade unaccredited alpinists to ascend without a guide. There were, however, only two guides at the halfway house, both attached to groups: ours and the seventy kids who planned to leave that night. So the three nonconformists had either to break the rule, or wait and go with us.

"We've made a pact with our guide," Timofei said. "In exchange for his indulgence, we've agreed to do the lower of the two peaks, to follow the marked route and, if any one of us feels the least bit ill, he must not go on and not be left alone. No one will go up by himself. In other words, either the three of us or none will make the climb."

At ten o'clock that evening, François, Timofei and Yurka, their pockets filled with snacks and a flask of vodka, left for the summit under a full moon.

Misha, Aptekar and I, in our respective tents and wrapped well and warmly, went to sleep. Around midnight the youngsters made their noisy departure. I couldn't go to sleep again. I was cold and could find nothing else to put over me. My stomach began to hurt. I sat up, looked out over the moonlit panorama, found our bottle of vodka and took a swig. Still, I lay awake. The next time I aimed the flashlight at my watch it was half past two.

A few minutes later I heard a man outside say, "What happened?" The voice that replied, "Nothing serious," was François'.

Our three wayward ones stood there in front of the tent.

"We didn't make it," Yurka said. "I got mountain sickness."

All had gone well until only a few meters from the summit. Then Yurka suggested they rest and have some zwieback and salami. They started again at a slower pace. After fifty meters, Yurka vomited, so they rested once more. Relieved, Yurka thought he could finish the climb. He didn't want to be the cause of their turning back. But after a mere ten paces, the poor fellow collapsed.

Chapter Seven

When daylight came, I awoke with nausea and more pain. The thought of breakfast repulsed me. Our guide, then the director recommended I return to Krugozor where a medical doctor was on duty.

"It may be mountain sickness," the guide said, "but it could be more serious. It's best not to gamble."

So we got ready — Aptekar, Timofei, François and I. The other two decided to go to the summit with the guided group. Yurka had to prove he could do it, all 18,500 feet.

It wasn't till noon that I felt able to travel. François carried both our rucksacks, but no one could do my walking for me. Though the midday sun was scorching, we didn't consider waiting till the next morning.

The deep footprints we made in the snow coming up marked our downward trail. The going would be easy — or so we thought. Under the cold, white blanket, the snow was silently melting in ever-growing rivulets.

Timofei, first in line, shouted a warning when his boots met the slush, but too late to help us. Although we were sometimes able to cross on dry, rocky patches, most of our descent to the ice pack was dank, at best. Progress was slowed further by my need to rest.

On the glacier a superficial thaw eliminated the slipperiness. The going was so much easier my mind once more turned to the misery in my stomach. How much more could I take? I was not religious and had prayed only as a child who mumbled, "Now I lay me down to sleep ...." before going to bed. What harm would there be in trying again?

"Oh, God, I want only to stop walking. The others can leave me here and go on to Svanetia. Please let me lie down and die!"

For awhile nothing changed. I continued putting one weighty foot in front of the other, mindlessly lifting each only enough to graze the frozen crust. Finally the ice ended and somehow we crossed the last stretch of snow and rocks. There ... was that the hotel or a mirage? Would I make it? With delirious relief I was vaguely aware of being placed between clouds of downy linen fragrant with cleanness.

God had answered my prayer. I was in Heaven.

Two days later I felt better and left the comfortable hotel room. Yurka and Misha had conquered the crown. All together again, we discussed our plans over a late breakfast. The camp doctor wanted me to be examined by a specialist and had ordered me to a hospital. The nearest one was in Nalchik — a world away!

"No," the doctor said, "it's not all that far. You'll have to walk down to Tegenekli, where the road begins, but from there you can get a lift with the delivery truck that calls every day at the hotel. Here is a voucher signed by me with instructions to help you on your way."

The discussion at breakfast was whether or not François should leave the group and accompany me to Nalchik. I wouldn't hear of it.

"It's bad enough that *I* have to bow out," I said. "Why should François miss the expedition to Svanetia? There'll never be another chance to go. I'll be in good hands."

It wasn't easy to convince my husband that I could manage alone. Eventually we agreed he would escort me as far as Tegenekli, and we'd meet again on the Black Sea Coast, at Batumi, on or near August 18. That was a couple of weeks away.

Even though the weather had cooled and François carried my rucksack, climbing down the cliff was arduous. The worst of my pains were gone but so was most of my vigor. We rested often, especially when passing people on their way up who invariably wanted to talk about the summit.

Down in the valley we didn't stop at the little Balkar house where we'd spent the night, but went on into the woods. Half way through we met Leya, a young woman employed at Krugozor, returning to the base.

"You're a lot sprier than when I saw you two days ago," she said to me. "Where are you off to now?"

"The doctor has ordered me to the hospital in Nalchik."

"Oh, I've been there," she said. "Had my appendix out last year. Head physician's a woman. You going there, too?" she asked François.

"No, only as far as Tegenekli."

"Well, Comrade Agnessa, I wish you good health. Say ... you did remember to take your passport, didn't you? It may come in handy."

Horrified, we found we didn't have the document. At first, François said it didn't matter. "The others are coming down later with Adolph, you know. They'll have everything with them."

By the time we left the woods at Terskol, however, there were other considerations. We met a man with a horse cart about to leave for Tegenekli.

"If you hitch a ride with him," François said, "that will save you a long walk. Meanwhile, I can go back up, meet the others wherever they are, get the passport and bring it to you. It's not yet three o'clock. I should see you again before dark."

It sounded reasonable, but Murphy's Law mandated that if anything could go wrong, it would.

The man with the horse cart brought me safely to the Intourist Hotel at Tegenekli where I booked a room. The delivery truck had not yet arrived, and probably wouldn't until the next day. I spent the afternoon in the garden enjoying the cool ambrosial air, having tea, and watching some of the guests amuse themselves — slices of life, unrehearsed.

Playing volleyball, apparently for the first time, a dozen children frolicked about the court. On the veranda an elderly man, with his daughter and grandson, discussed the literature of Tolstoy. Standing by the bannister were two stout, middle-aged women who, I learned from the waiter, intended to lose weight. After a daily breakfast of a glass of milk and a tomato, they took a walk till five o'clock in the afternoon, then had a light supper.

At eight-thirty I, too, ate a light supper. Darkness fell. The delivery truck had not arrived and neither had François. An hour later I gave up waiting and went to my room. Shortly afterwards a knock at the door made me run to open it. Not François but Yurka stood there with my passport in his hand.

"Don't worry," he said, puffing. "Your husband is all right. It's Adolph. François expected to meet us half way up the cliff but we were still at Krugozor, looking for the damned donkey. Still hadn't found him when I left. François wanted to come right back down but we wouldn't let him — he was too exhausted."

"You're pretty well drained yourself, Yurka, and walking for an hour in the dark. Come on, let's go and get you some food."

Yurka took a tent for the night at the tourist camp near the hotel. We said good-bye in case I should leave before he got up the next morning. When I didn't see him at breakfast, I assumed he'd returned to Krugozor.

Finally, at noon, the hotel manager told me the delivery truck arrived and would leave with me aboard at six in the evening. Good news! Even better was the sight of François and Yurka coming into the dining room as I finished lunch.

"I thought you were all on your way to Svanetia!"

"No such luck," said François. "They're still up there looking for Donkey Hotey."

At six o'clock, they tucked me into the cab of the truck next to the driver. I was dressed for warm weather, with light shoes on my feet. Since my boots couldn't fit into the rucksack, I hung them on top of the sack, with the laces tied together.

As we rode away, François called out, "See you at Batumi on the 18th."

I was on my own. The spate of bad luck had not run its course.

Chapter Eight

The driver was good company. Not only did he say little, but he did his best to avoid the potholes and bumps in the unpaved road. Before long we reached Baksan — where our expedition began, where we bought our *boorka* and Adolph. It had taken us a couple of days to walk from there to Tegenekli but hardly any time to drive the distance back. Had they found the donkey yet? They must have.

At dusk we stopped at a roadside counter for a bite to eat and a drink of *citro*. After the driver checked the tires and filled the radiator, we continued along the narrow road cut into the sheer cliff. Far below us roared the river. The moon had not yet risen. In the darkness we could see nothing but what was illuminated by the headlights dancing on the dusty road in front of us. The truck bumped on. I felt too awful to think of fear.

Down on the level plain the driver stopped beside a creek to refill the radiator with glacier water. We met only one vehicle in six hours. Shortly after midnight we came to the hospital, a large, new building on the edge of Nalchik. The driver, holding me firmly by the elbow, escorted me to the reception desk and waited till I was admitted.

In exchange for my rucksack and the clothes I wore, a nurse gave me a regulation shift and bathrobe and helped me take a shower.

"I'm sorry to tell you," she said, "every bed is occupied. We'll have one for you tomorrow, but tonight there are only the benches in the corridor. You will have proper bedding, of course."

It didn't matter to me where I laid my weary body. I slept well.

Dr. Merkoff examined me early the following morning. I had expected an older and — so far from a metropolis — rather dowdy woman. Instead, the doctor appeared no more than forty, was well-coiffured and wore makeup.

"Well, the probe tells me what I suspected. I'll have to give you a curettage. It won't be pleasant, my dear. I'm very sorry, but we're short of anesthetics and must reserve them for critical surgery. You're strong and brave, I'm sure."

Her brief statement gave me no option. With a nurse at each side bracing me, I endured the inevitable. It felt like my innards were being scraped with a serrated ladle, then washed with iodine. Fire and brimstone! Hell!

But I survived, and two hours later was talking to a nurse in a room shared with three other patients. "... But I didn't even know I was pregnant," I said. "Sometimes I skip a month when I'm physically very active ...." I asked her when I would be able to leave.

"We'll keep you here two or three days at least to be sure there are no complications. Now that you're in a real bed — just let yourself be lazy. I'm going to bring your breakfast."

When the nurse left, the pretty woman in the next bed spoke to me. "Hello, my name is Tatiana. Did you have a miscarriage, too?"

I was glad she wanted to talk. "Yes," I answered.

Tatiana and her husband, I found out, lived in Moscow and were spending their vacation in Nalchik where her parents lived. Her mother was Russian and her father Ossetian. The Ossetians, Tatiana explained, were once-powerful nomads who wandered the steppes till they were disbanded by the Huns in the 4th century A.D.

"There are countless tribes in the Caucasus region," she said. "Still some isolated valleys with pockets of people living much as they did centuries ago. Like in Svanetia, where your friends are going."

"I'm supposed to meet them at Batumi on the 18th, but I don't even know how to get there from here."

"Oh, it's easy. From Nalchik you go to a place called Prohladnaia, then take a train to Ordzhonikidze, where you'll get on a bus and ride over the mountains to Tiflis. From Tiflis there's a train straight to Batumi. You should be there well before the 18th."

Prohladnaia. Hmm .... That was close to Stanitsa Neslobnia and the Bogdanov farm. I had the time. Why didn't I go there to recuperate a bit among friends and do some laundry? That afternoon I sent off a letter to the Bogdanovs.

Tatiana promoted lively conversation in English after discovering it was my language. She eagerly practiced what she had learned at school with questions about life in America. I missed her when Dr. Merkoff pronounced her well enough to leave.

Her bed lay empty only long enough for the sheets to be changed. The next occupant, a woman of about twenty, was a strange patient. Two nurses had to help her into bed though she apparently was not physically disabled. Curious, I stared at her, but she paid no attention to me, even when I spoke. At lunchtime a nurse held a bowl of food and fed her with a spoon. Between bites the woman mumbled a few unintelligible words.

Noisy confusion interrupted my afternoon nap. The new patient was sitting up in bed, crying, with her upper sheet twisted about her. When the nurses had restored order and calm, I asked one of them what was wrong with the woman.

"The poor thing has never slept in a bed before. She comes from a backwoods tribe, doesn't speak any language we know. She's bewildered and homesick. Her husband brought her in a horse cart; took two days over the mountains."

Early the next morning I received a hand-delivered note from Tatiana, written in English.

Dear Agnessa,

My husband is sent by me to help you. There is a train that leaves at 10:55 in the morning.

I think you can get it if you want. My husband is for your service, to carry your baggage to the station. Good health to you.

Tatiana

I replied at once.

Dear Tatiana,

Thank you for your kindness. I am well, but Doctor Merkoff wants me to stay an extra day because I have so far to travel.

I shall leave tomorrow on the 10:55 train. My best regards to you and your husband.

Agnessa

Several other patients were discharged with me. At the hospital entrance families and friends waited to take them home. From out of the crowd a handsome blond man came up to me.

"Comrade Agnessa? I am Pavel, Tatiana's husband."

We shook hands, and he took my rucksack. We walked along the boulevard toward the bus stop, chatting like old friends. Tatiana was fine, she sent best wishes .... Yes, they were enjoying their vacation. Their house was near a river .... Wasn't it a beautiful day ....

It *was* beautiful — glorious to be outside and feeling well. Green trees shaded the streets and the gardens around little white houses in the old city and even some large buildings in the new part. Beyond, the steppe stretched out flat in all directions, bordered on one side by the towering Caucasus giants merging their white tips with the sky.

The bus took us to the railroad station where I bought some fruit, a newspaper and a ticket to Prohladnaia. Pavel figured I'd get to Stanitsa Neslobnia shortly after five o'clock in the evening. As the train pulled out, we said good-bye, with promises to meet again in Moscow.

So far, I was doing okay on my own. How about the others? Had they found Adolph? It was August 11. I had another week.

Chapter Nine

The Bogdanovs made me welcome. I spent three days recuperating in clover at the farm, enjoying meals around the kitchen table, eating pears and apples in the orchard, swimming in the river, and taking leisurely walks. Too soon the time came to travel again.

Early on the morning of August 14, Leonid Bogdanov accompanied me to the railroad station, on the provincial train to Georgievsk, then on the local. The local train was late, however, so I missed my southbound connection by twenty minutes. There wouldn't be another in that direction till eleven o'clock. Leonid insisted on waiting with me. He suggested we get my ticket and wait in the restaurant with a glass of tea.

Oh, if only it had been so simple. Kismet, Fate, Destiny and Murphy's Law — they all must have had a hand in the plotting of my odyssey. Who was I to foil their schemes?

At the closed ticket window was a queue of a dozen people. Leonid asked the woman in front of us if she knew when the tickets would go on sale.

"I should say I do *not!*" she burst out. "I've had this place in line for two days trying to get a ticket for Baku. How many trains have come and gone? I haven't counted them. Sometimes the ticket window doesn't even open. If it does, it may sell one, two, maybe five tickets and slam shut." The woman stopped to take a deep breath and went on, "Too many people want to go south. It's August! Everybody's on vacation. When the trains leave the big cities they're already full up. We haven't a chance in this God-forsaken dump unless someone gets off. And who would get off here?"

Having said all that, she seemed to feel better, but we felt worse. I didn't want to spend two days there.

The woman agreed to save our place in line while we went into the garden behind the station. People were everywhere, sitting on bundles and suitcases along the path; whole families camped on patches of grass. Mothers nursed their babies. Between the platform and the garden, farm women sold bread, milk, fruit and vegetables. One old man was devouring an entire watermelon by himself.

Leonid and I watched the scene in silence. Words were unnecessary. We returned to the queue. A notice on the bulletin board said the eleven o'clock would be ninety minutes late, and the next train, the two o'clock, would be one hour late. Curses!

Leonid wouldn't hear of going back home till I was on my way. We went to the restaurant and drank beer. We took a walk. We read newspapers. We exhausted topics of conversation. At twelve-thirty we got back in line. The dozen people ahead of us had become twenty-four. Behind us stood another twenty. The platform bell rang announcing the arrival of my southbound train. It puffed noisily into the station, but the ticket window remained closed, even when people banged on it. The bell rang again and a conductor called out, "All aboard that's going aboard!" What irony.

The train pulled away. We went to the restaurant, ordered dinner and ate slowly. At a quarter to three, the ticket window opened, sold four places, and closed again. The train came and left.

"It's getting serious, Leonid," I said. "What would you think of my going up north to Mineralni-Vodi? That's a large city and a junction. Lots of people will get off there to change to other lines, and I might have a chance. What do you think?"

He thought it brilliant. The northbound train at three-fifteen had no place for me. At six o'clock, however, there would be another, and if I bought a "soft" ticket (first class), I'd be on it for sure.

The final three hours were the most difficult to endure. I was tired and didn't want to say so. The pitiless sun seared everything in its path and even wilted what was under cover. I didn't want to eat or talk, or read or take a walk. If I napped, I wouldn't want to wake up.

Somehow or other the hands of the clock moved to the hour of six. The northbound train came in and left with me in a compartment to myself. My travail had ended ... I thought.

At Mineralni-Vodi, without even having to stand in a queue, I bought a ticket to Ordzhonikidze, "hard," by way of Beslan, where I would change trains at three o'clock in the morning. We left punctually at nine-thirty — southward at last.

When I boarded, the car I chose was not crowded. The wooden benches, at a right angle to the walls, stood in two tiers, one above the other. Over them were the baggage racks, some of which were occupied by people, not belongings. One was still empty. I clambered up and stretched out my exhausted body. Under my head I adjusted the rucksack for a pillow, with the boots safely to one side.

Just as the train started rolling, I fell asleep in spite of the noise and confusion around me. The narrow corridor was filled with luggage of every shape and size and people of all ages who laughed and scolded, and shouted to be heard above the pandemonium.

The last I heard was the sound of an accordion and men singing a folk song in harmony, as only Russians can. I could sleep till three in the morning. What luxury! Five whole hours ....

The next I knew, someone was shaking my shoulder and saying, "Wake up! The conductor is here ... ticket control."

In my shirt pocket I found my ticket. The sky outside showed a hint of dawn. The conductor, carrying a lantern, made his way among the passengers till he came to me. While I rested on one elbow, he studied my ticket, then raised the lantern to my face. "What's the matter with you, Comrade?" His voice was hoarse with disbelief. "Why didn't you get off at Beslan? We stopped there over two hours ago!"

In the abrupt silence I heard my heart thump as it fell to the floor. "But why didn't anyone say so, when we were there?" Several passengers assured me the name of every station was called out in a loud voice, and how were they to know I wanted to get off there?

"Quiet, please!" commanded the conductor. "Comrade, you come with me. Get off at the next stop. There'll soon be a train back. I'll probably get fined for this."

I didn't care whether he got fined or not; I was worse off than he.

All of the passengers were awake by then and united in renewed chaos. With my rucksack and dangling boots slung over my shoulder I followed the conductor to the exit at the end of the car, where I had a long wait. There was a humorous side to the fiasco — my own darn fault for sleeping so soundly. It wasn't hard to laugh at myself along with the other travelers. As we came to a standstill, someone behind me called out, "Hey, Comrade, the returning train is already on the other track! Hurry and get your ticket!"

I rushed from the car and across the open-air platform to the station house. No queue. I bought my ticket and hurried back. The train I had left was still there, blocking my way to the one I wanted on the other side of it. I stood frozen, waiting. *No!* The one I wanted was moving ... gaining speed .... I missed it. And as I stared, the one I'd come on pulled out. I was alone. No other soul was in sight. The village was miles away, barely visible down in the valley. Tears filled my eyes as I removed the rucksack from my shoulder so I could console myself in comfort.

Damnation! *MY BOOTS!* They were gone!

True. I looked around the platform and in the station house. My beautiful boots were gone. Some hooligan had cut the laces during the confusion just before I hurried off the train. "Damn him!" The words squeezed through my clenched teeth. There was no one to hear them.

"*Damn him!*" I shouted into the wind as tears ran down my face. "*Damn him!*" The curse reverberated far into the valley. I gave in to an uncontrollable yearning to cry without restraint. I didn't have to be strong and brave. Dawn turned to daylight and I still sobbed.

Finally, with emotions spent, I went to the restroom in the station and bathed my face. Seven o'clock. The world, even that microcosm on the steppe, was awake and back at work. The young waiter in the canteen cheerfully wished me a good morning when I ordered breakfast. Others came in and exchanged greetings with me.

With exquisite relief I knew I had exorcised the pent-up pain my heart had stored too long.

Sure, I was angry someone had filched my boots, that I had overslept and then couldn't get on the returning train. But those events were just a catalyst for my outpouring. Not till then did I taste the bitterness of losing my baby. I had always boasted I'd never want a child to interfere with my career, to tie me down. I pretended indifference to the miscarriage. And then ... I was suddenly alone on an isolated platform where I faced myself and discovered a vulnerable woman.

Oh, if only François had been there to share our loss. *He didn't even know!* I had wept for him, too. And there was my mother ....
Not since she died a year and a half before, was I able to express my grief, to show how much I loved her ... not once ... not till that early morning alone.

I finished my breakfast at eight o'clock. Four hours still remained till train time. Good. I could bring my journal up to date.

Chapter Ten

I was still writing in my diary at eleven o'clock when a young woman came in and sat at my table. "Hello, are you going to Ordzhonikidze?"

I nodded.

"So am I ... to visit relatives. My husband can't come. He has to work. He's a teacher on a collective farm."

"Oh?"

"We have to change trains at Beslan, you know."

"Yes," I said. "I know."

"I live in the valley ... walked all the way up here." She called the waiter, ordered breakfast, and went on, "He earns three hundred rubles a month."

"Who? The waiter?"

"No. My husband. We get our house free and all the produce we need."

"Oh?"

"How many children have you?"

"None," I said.

"Neither have I. Once I thought of going back to school to study something, but haven't got around to it yet. I have a brother and a sister — she's fat — and lots of nephews and nieces .... They want to go to university ...."

The woman talked on and on without saying anything that mattered to me, not minding that I contributed only monosyllables. The world we inhabited was one entity. Clear on the other side of it, in Honolulu, there were tedious housewives exactly like her. In a way, that was comforting. It demonstrated that, after all, there was only one race, the human race, with prismatic variations.

I couldn't escape her till after we had changed at Beslan and were on the train to Ordzhonikidze. I found a place in a compartment occupied by two elderly couples and a young boy.

The women were having a lighthearted discourse on the correct pronunciation of Ordzhonikidze. Apparently, one of the couples was native to the Caucasus, while the other came from Moscow. The local woman was laughing and saying to the Muscovite, "Our city was named for one of our famous sons who's now in the Politburo. You'd better learn to say it right, Comrade Irena. When you die and go to Heaven, Lenin is going to ask you about him, and if you can't pronounce Ordzhonikidze, he won't let you in." She shook her finger playfully while we all had a good laugh.

Who said religion was dead in the Soviet Union? Transformed, perhaps, but not defunct.

The afternoon was still full of life when we reached our destination. My first priority was to find a bus to take me over the mountain to Tiflis. Motor vehicle was the only means of transportation between Ordzhonikidze and the capital of Georgia. The date was August 15. If I left the following morning, I'd have two days and nights in Tiflis, not much to time to spend in a city fifteen centuries old.

At the ticket window in the bus office the clerk told me, "Come back tomorrow morning at five o'clock, Comrade, and take a place in line. The office opens at six, and if you're in luck I can book you for the Seventeenth."

Not good enough. I knew there was no other bus line, but I'd *have* to find a way to leave sooner than that. Around the corner was the Intourist Hotel. At the reception desk I showed my passport and asked for a room.

"That may difficult," the clerk said in flawless English. "A party of twenty Americans is due any moment now, and we're full. Maybe tomorrow .... They're going to Tiflis in the morning."

A cue! Run with it! Briefly, I related my ill-fated saga.

The man listened sympathetically, and then said, "If you'll wait over there in the lobby, I'll see what I can do."

Wait? I was an expert. In that setting it would be a pleasure, especially since a copy of the *Moscow Daily News* lay on one of the tables.

I hadn't seen a newspaper in English for weeks. It was four days old, but new to me. The main story told of the three Soviet heroes just returned from their historic one-stop flight over the Arctic and back to Moscow and the great possibilities ahead for transportation.

Soon the twenty Americans trailed in — young or youngish men and women — students and teachers, I figured. As they dispersed to the bar or upstairs, a Russian woman and the desk clerk came over to me.

"Meet Comrade Aliza," he said, "Interpreter for the Americans."

She and I shook hands and she said, "If you don't mind, you're welcome to share my room."

I certainly did not mind. One hurdle cleared, one to go.

The quiet room on the top floor, three flights up, had a fully equipped bathroom. Aliza explained she and her Americans arrived by train from Rostov-on-Don and had not slept much in the past twenty-four hours. While she napped, I showered, changed into a fresh skirt and blouse, and went down to dinner in the hotel garden, where the desk clerk caught up with me.

"I know a student," he said, "who has an old Ford, and shuttles people back and forth to Tiflis in the summertime. I've been in touch with him. He's going to stop by here early in the morning. Maybe he'll give you a lift."

Was I over the last obstacle so easily? Why not be optimistic? Meanwhile, how should I spend an evening in town after emerging from the backwoods so recently?

On the boulevard, the strolling men and women were better dressed than in the Russian capital. The shop windows, unlike those in Moscow, displayed consumer goods with no lines of would-be shoppers in front of them. Just looking was entertainment. I paused at a movie theatre to examine the publicity photos. How would an ordinary Georgian film compare with one of ours? To find out, I bought a ticket. Along with a growing crowd, I waited in the foyer for the next showing, entertained by a three-piece orchestra playing tangos and fox trots.

The movie was with sound, but in the Georgian language. Russian subtitles, however, allowed me to follow the story. The cast includes a handsome, but poor young Georgian, a marriage broker, an ugly, rich prospective bride, a collective farmer, and his lovely young daughter. The broker is also a horse thief, who unsuccessfully tries to corrupt the young man. Inevitably, the hero exposes the broker and wins the farmer's daughter, who is more of a treasure than any dowry.

Chapter Eleven

Aliza was wide awake when I returned to the hotel after the movie. "I've good news," she said. "We were talking about you this evening, and there might be space for you to ride with us to Tiflis. We've two buses, you see. Maybe we can squeeze you into one of them."

After an early breakfast the next morning, I waited expectantly in front of the hotel. My desk clerk friend was back on duty and talking to the drivers of the two buses. By twos and threes, the twenty Americans appeared and took seats. Aliza and two of the students, Betty and Catherine, were the last to board. There was no room for me in either of the coaches.

I looked at the clerk. Why was he grinning?

"Don't you worry, Comrade," he said to me as we waved to the Americans, "You won't be stranded."

Only a few minutes later an old touring car, a model T Ford painted shiny black, came to a stop at the curb. The driver, whose name was Georgi, said yes, there was room for me and asked me to suggest a price. I knew the fare on the state bus service was thirty-five rubles, so I offered him fifty.

"That's kind of little," he said, "but I guess it will do. If you're ready, you can sit up front with me, and we'll be off."

In the back seat were a man with his small son, and a woman. She wore a knitted white silk shawl wrapped around her head and shoulders. The sun was already hot and glaring. It was after nine o'clock.

At first, conversation was limited to small talk between Georgi and me. The other passengers spoke no Russian, he said, only their native languages. The man and child were Armenian, and the woman Georgian, and none was inclined to verbosity.

On the outskirts of the city, we passed one of the Intourist buses stopped beside the road. It looked like engine troubled. Georgi slowed down, but the bus driver waved him on.

In an effort to learn a little about the man I'd be sitting next to for six hours, I said, "I suppose you know something about cars."

He chuckled. "Something? When I bought this car it was a pile of junk. I'm an engineer, you see. Used to fly planes ... until I cracked up few years ago."

"You did? What happened?"

"There were four of us. I was piloting. The landing gear jammed. I came down as carefully as I could, but when the plane touched the airstrip, it overturned. I only broke a leg, but two of my comrades were killed. There was a trial and I was exonerated. My leg never healed properly, so I got a pension of 450 rubles a month for life."

"And now what do you do besides this ... uh ... this ....?"

"This hackney driving? My wife and I are students at Tiflis University. In two years we'll both graduate hydroelectrical engineers. Chose that because the country needs a lot of them."

While Georgi talked on, the model T hummed smoothly up the well-paved highway, past thick woods of evergreens and bare, rocky crags. He and his wife had two small children, Georgi told me. His mother took care of them during the week. In summer they moved to the country where he joined them on weekends.

The sun blazed. The Georgian woman had almost completely covered herself with her shawl. The little boy had fallen asleep with his head on his father's lap. Georgi put on his big, dark goggles.

"Nice looking glasses," I commented. "Are they foreign?"

He pulled them down on his nose and peered at me mockingly over the rims. "No, *Madame*. I bought them in Tiflis. You can buy *anything* in Tiflis ... not like in Moscow where, I hear, they have nothing."

We passed the remains of an ancient fortress high above us on a ridge. Georgi said it could be a couple of thousand years old. A detour led us downhill over a bumpy, dusty road to the Terek River, where we crossed on a provisional wooden bridge. The new concrete span was under construction downriver a hundred yards. Then we went up again over several lateral ranges and canyons, culminating in the famous Daryal Gorge, a huge gash in the earth, showing several ages of geological strata. From there, we skirted the base of Mount Kazbek and made our first rest stop at Kazbek Station, a collection of a few houses and a store.

Farther on, we came to several miles of cliffs, with sides rusty red from the mineral water that trickled down. At one point a little shed had been constructed over a spring so anyone could help himself to a drink. Some small boys crowded about the car offering us glasses of the water, but we wanted to get some ourselves from the source. I couldn't drink much, it was so cold, but better than any I'd ever had out of a bottle.

Off again, we soon reached the Gudaur Pass (nearly 8,000 feet in elevation), where we overtook the other Intourist bus, descended the zig-zagging Zemo-Mletski Declivity into the soft green Keishur Valley of the Aragva River, and arrived in the Republic of Georgia. Away up high, near the tops of the almost-perpendicular mountain slopes, were cultivated fields.

"Why," I asked, "would people go to live in such inaccessible places when there seems to be a lot of spare ground closer to Earth?"

Georgi shook his head. "I often wonder the same thing. Probably because their ancestors moved there centuries ago to be safe from invaders."

During a stop when all five of us had lunch at a roadside inn, I asked when they would build a railroad between Ordzhonikidze and Tiflis.

"Never, I hope," Georgi said with fervor. "From a train you can't smell the flowers or drink at a spring or eat chicken roasted over a wood fire and vegetables fresh from the garden."

Back on the road he recited the names of more ancient towns as though declaiming a canton — Mletny, Passanaur, Ananur — and told me about the Aragvian guards who protected the old feudal aerie. Somewhere along those parts we parked several minutes to admire the view from the Dushetian Heights.

Shortly before arriving in Tiflis, Georgi said, "We're now at Mtskhet, the cradle of our culture, and our capital until the fifth century. After that, it had a colorful history."

"In what way?"

"Well, from then till 1801, it was captured or sacked by the Persians, the Byzantines, the Arabs, the Mongols, Tamerlane, and finally the Russians."

In Tiflis, Georgi drove first to the railway station to drop off the other three passengers and then said he'd take me to the Intourist Hotel. We drove through the new part of the city, up the main boulevard with its modern white buildings, streetcars, buses and a profusion of traffic — pedestrian and vehicular.

At last I had arrived, and with time to spare. All of the next day I could poke around the old streets. With no exaggeration, I told Georgi how driving with him had enriched the trip.

"I should thank *you*," he replied. "It would have been mighty dull if I'd had only those lumps in the back seat to talk to for six hours. Say, Comrade Agnessa, let me take you to dinner tonight, will you? About eight o'clock?"

How could I refuse? We shook hands.

In my grimy clothes and dusty face I sauntered up to the desk at the Intourist Hotel, passport in hand, and asked for a room.

"Sorry, *Madame*, we are fully booked. A party of twenty Americans is arriving shortly from Ordzhonikidze."

Chapter Twelve

The desk clerk repeated, "We're fully booked for the present, *Madame*. Try the Palace Hotel. It's two blocks away on the left."

I found the Palace Hotel. It, too, was fully booked. "Try the Kavkaz." I did. The clerk at the Kavkaz couldn't help me and suggested I try the Intourist Hotel.

So back I went, looking and feeling like the tramp I was. The clerk smiled sympathetically as I said in English, "There are no vacant rooms in Tiflis. I'm tired and dirty, and also a foreigner. Will I have to go to the militia to find a place to sleep?"

"Madame, I am sorry. I will do my very best to help you. In an hour I'll find something. Meanwhile, you're welcome to use our washroom. It's back there, on the right."

I looked at my awful reflection in the mirror. The application of soap, a hair brush, a towel, and a clean shirt, however, improved it immensely. The desk clerk seemed to think so, too, when I approached him an hour later.

He smiled. "My compliments, *Madame*. I'm happy to tell you one of our guests is checking out at midnight. You may have his room. Till then, you may leave your backpack here with me."

To wait for Georgi, I sat in the lobby watching samples of the world's population come and go. There were Westerners, Semitics and Asians, some in European apparel and others in their native dress — a pageant of heterogeneity. I recognized a few of the American students who nodded amicably in my direction.

The sculptor in me examined, scrutinized their walk, their equipoise, and the cut of their facial features. No one else had the classic, well-chiseled bone structure of the Georgians. Their elderly did not wrinkle and sag as my Nordic race did. They were the original Caucasians. *We* call ourselves Caucasians. Oh, well, but that was genealogically speaking. I couldn't help wondering how they managed to preserve their physical appeal.

Punctually at eight o'clock, Georgi appeared, wearing creased trousers and a belted white tunic with an embroidered Russian collar. With eyes that surveyed aesthetically, I gave him high marks.

"We're walking tonight, Comrade Agnessa," was his informal greeting. He took my elbow and ushered me out onto the sidewalk. "We're going to the top of Mount David on the funicular. It's only a couple of blocks away."

The ascent offered a spectacular panorama as the city spread itself out below, flicking on its lights in the blue dusk. Lively folk music, blaring from a loudspeaker, met our ears long before we reached the summit. Crowds in a recreational mood filled the streets, the park, and all the eating places. We found a quiet table with a view far beyond the town.

Georgi did most of the talking. For awhile we discussed the news that the name of the city was being changed to Tbilisi. Georgi had just heard it on the radio.

"It's the ancient name," he said. "I applaud not losing the past. Like Svanetia ... suddenly reappearing from the stone age. I'll never forget flying in there ... it was five years ago ...." He was on his favorite topic. "As I neared the valley, I realized my maps were incorrect and unreliable. In one place I had to maneuver between two cliffs that were so close together, I thought the wings would scrape the sides, especially since the air currents made it impossible to keep a straight course. I landed safely, nevertheless, in one of the towns, and the entire populace — hundreds of astounded people turned out to see the 'bird wagon' as they called it. For a week the event was news in the local press.

"Another time, several comrades and I made a goodwill flight to Turkey and, quite by accident, got mixed up in a street brawl that nearly caused a diplomatic catastrophe." He laughed nostalgically, was silent for a few moments, then abruptly changed the subject.

"Tell me, how do you foreigners like our food?"

"I, personally, find it very good — tasty and varied. But some Westerners, my compatriots included, are used to plainer dishes."

"Is it true," he asked, looking at me sideways, "that you eat the legs of frogs?"

"Yes."

"And cheeses that are green with mold and have worms?"

"Yes. That's roquefort and gorgonzola — delicacies."

"Hmm .... Well, don't talk to me about your plain food. We'd spit on a frog, and when cheese gets moldy, we throw it away."

Shortly before midnight, we returned to the hotel. My room had been vacated but wouldn't be cleaned for half an hour.

"I'll wait with you," Georgi said. "Let's have a beer in the bar."

Conversation hadn't lagged all evening. Georgi asked scores of questions about life in the U.S.A. — about what he considered the most important issues: education, jobs, and medical care.

"I wouldn't change countries," he said, "but I concede yours is in a depression and it's not fair to compare. Under our system, however, we don't have depressions."

I let him have the last word. Before saying good-bye, I tried to pay for my share of the beer. Georgi protested. "You forget, dear comrade, you are a guest in my country. It has been my privilege to be your host."

The whole of the next day, August 17, was mine to do with as I pleased. There were no trains to catch, or buses. I had a private room, was fed and washed. Tiflis ... no ...Tbilisi was at my disposal for a day.

And where was François, and the others? Did they ever find that donkey? Would they be at Batumi on the 18th? I'd know before long.

Out on the street the sun shone hot and bright. Women wore colorful print dresses. A newsboy hurried up the sidewalk calling out the names of his papers. I'd never seen that before in the Soviet Union. A fountain in a square shot its water spout high into the air. Men tipped their hats to women. At the railroad station, I bought a third-class ticket to Batumi for the next morning, then headed for the old section down by the river. Some men on the sidewalk sold articles from glass-topped boxes. I bought a bag of peanuts and went on in the direction of the market.

As well as to see the sights, my purpose in going to that part of town was to find an old Georgian belt, like the one Georgi wore around his tunic. It had been his grandfather's. The soft, black leather was an inch wide, with a buckle of carved silver. From the buckle, the silver-tipped band passed through two loops of silver on the left side and hung down about twelve inches. Ornamental silver studs on one side held silver-tipped strips of leather about three inches long.

On a side street several tiny shops appeared to deal in leather goods — new and repaired. Saddles, bridles, and boots hung from the walls and ceilings. Glass cases displayed a variety of knives and daggers in sheaths, and diverse odds and ends.

In one of the shop windows I saw a few belts, so I went in and asked the corpulent proprietor to show them to me.

"If you please, *Madame*," he said, bringing them onto the counter with gallant gestures. "You look like a foreigner — from Moscow?"

"Yes. These belts are new, aren't they? Have you any others?"

"Sorry. They're all I have."

"But what about the one you're wearing?"

"This?" He hooked his thumbs onto it. "But this is old, *Madame*."

"Would you sell it to me?"

"Of course." He took it off his ample waist and held it for me to examine. What a beauty! On the right side, suspended by two strips of leather, hung a slender silver box, used perhaps, for snuff or hashish in the old days. The buckle and studs were also of silver."

"I'll give you two hundred rubles for it," I said.

"I'll sell it for three hundred, *Madame*. A bargain."

He was right, but who ever paid the first asking price? I held to my offer. He came down little by little, and only when I started to leave did he say I could have it for my bid. We shook hands, and I said I'd come for it in the afternoon. He put it back around his tunic, and I continued my circuit of the old town.

The road ascended. At a point where I could see across the river, I had to stop. From the rushing yellow water, the precipice on the opposite bank rose several hundred feet straight up to buildings constructed at its very edge. It looked as though they were an extension of the cliff. Into the sheer rock wall steps had been dug. I could see people walking up and down them. To the left, at the bend in the river, an ancient church with a golden, cone-shaped roof on its tower, seemed to have sprouted from the earth.

I turned onto a side street where the houses were smaller, older and closer together. An alley brought me to a courtyard where, on all sides, quilts and rugs hung from balcony railings. Corn and cabbage grew in a small garden patch. At a wooden tub in a corner, a woman washed clothes while two little girls skipped rope nearby. A baby's gentle wail came from one of the windows, so as Browning, the poet, might have repeated, all was right with the world. I went back downhill to find the market.

Sounds of confusion and loud voices guided me. A low, green fence delineated the market's domain — two rows of stalls under a tenuous roof, a feast for all my senses.

Vendors stood at their counters or squatted behind their scales, and hawkers strolled about, all shouting in a dozen languages and dialects, exhorting the public to buy their wares. Exotic aromas of incense and spices titillated my nostrils. My eyes picked up a conglomeration of colors and shapes in the fruits, the vegetables and the assorted attire of the customers.

A pile of watermelons drew me to the stall of an old man. He looked fierce in his fur hat with strands of kinky sheep's wool sticking out all around and hanging down over his eyes. From his polite manner, however, which included picking out a good melon for me, I could tell he was as gracious as the rest of his countrymen.

The timid boy from whom I bought some plums made a cornucopia from newspaper for carrying the fruit. I added a flat loaf of bread to my purchases and returned to the hotel to eat and have a nap.

Chapter Thirteen

It was almost three o'clock and time to pick up my purchase. I counted out two hundred rubles, put them in an envelope and set off. Out on the street, I met one of the older women from the American group going in my direction.

"Hello," I said. "May I fall in step with you?"

She smiled, surprised. "Oh, you *do* speak English, don't you?"

"Of course. I'm American."

"Are you? In Ordzhonikidze we weren't sure. How nice. What are you doing here?"

I told her about my belt and invited her to come along with me. "The haggling has already been done," I said, "but you may like to see the place, anyway."

"How do you know the man will keep his word?"

"Because ... because we shook hands. It's a simple matter of honor."

She was dazzled by the streets of the old city, by the shop, and the charm of the stout proprietor, and found the belt so beautiful I was almost convinced I had bought a rare object.

Back at the hotel, we sat in the bar for a long drink of mineral water. Several of the group of Americans came in and joined us. The belt was an attraction, and how I had bought it off the man's waist proved a good story. Over supper I was still talking to two students, Betty and Catherine, whom I had met briefly in Ordzhonikidze, asking and answering questions, exploring one another's social and political views.

"We're going into our junior year at Vassar," Betty told me. "And guess what?" Her eyes twinkled, mischievously. "We're members of the Young Communist League."

"At Vassar?" I asked, incredulous. "I thought ...."

"You thought we were a conformist school for the *Junior* League," said Catherine. "Lots of people do. But our founder and benefactor was Samuel Morse."

"You mean the inventor of the Morse Code?"

"That's who. And he was no stuffy conformist, in spite of his clergyman father. He studied painting in Europe, and came back to find Americans didn't appreciate new ideas in the arts and politics. So now it's a tradition at Vassar: investigating new thought."

The evening gave us a complete change. At a theatre in a green park with fountains, people out strolling, and tables under the trees, Armenian folk dances transported us generations into history. Drums and stringed instruments accompanied the numbers, all performed in traditional costumes.

To most people, August 18 was much like any other summer's day. To me, it was the end of my travail. For the past two weeks, I'd had enough travailing. I'd earned a rest on a sunny Black Sea beach.

The train rolled through wooded, mountainous country, past small bucolic hamlets. I was alone in my compartment. The American group was on the same train but up in first class. It would be nice to talk to them, or to anyone. My thoughts went back to François. Would he be at Batumi? Of course. If not on the 18th, then the 19th, or .... Was he wondering where I was? Was he all right? The conductor came to the doorway of the compartment. He reminded me of a genial Dutch uncle of mine.

"Good morning, Comrade. May I see your ticket?"

I showed it to him and, because I could think of nothing else, said, "This is very beautiful country."

"You traveling alone, young lady?"

"Yes."

"I'll bet you're American, aren't you?"

I nodded.

"I've a good idea, Comrade. Two coaches up ahead there's a crowd of your country fellows, about twenty of them. Nice young people like you. Listen. You take that sack of yours and go on up and sit with them. Will you do that for me?"

The next few hours sped by. Betty, Catherine and several others, aware of the tryst I had with my husband, were as eager and apprehensive as I. Being with them comforted me. I was relatively relaxed until the train approached Batumi.

With a gauche but gallant attempt at humor, one of the boys said, "Don't worry. If he stands you up, you come along with us."

Betty stood at the window beside me as we pulled into the station. My eyes darted everywhere, inspecting the crowd on the platform.

"He's not here," I whispered. "I don't see him."

The train slowed and came to a stop. Even after I got off and looked about at the new arrivals hugging their friends and relatives, I couldn't see François. I put my rucksack down and turned to Betty.

"Oh, well, there'll be another train in a few hours. He may be on that. I'll wait here. I don't know where to go."

From the far end of the platform, above the din, a familiar voice hollered, "Agnessaaa!"

I turned and saw François running with arms open, ready to embrace me.

Agnessa at Batumi, Black Sea - 1936;
Photo by François.

Chapter Fourteen

Moscow,
December 15, 1936

Dearest Family,

Oh, for the warmth of those days at the Black Sea — winter is here! Thanks for all your Christmas mail and cards. The one from Joan is my favorite.

I can't believe how quickly this year passed. Since autumn, François and I have kept steadily busy with work, and local events.

Currently, we're planning another trip abroad. I'm leaving for Norway in a few days, and in January, François will go to Paris, where I'll meet him. We'll be back here in early February.

Tante Esther wrote me that Grandpa Larsen is very ill in the hospital. Esther told him I was coming to see him but didn't mention I was in Moscow — it would confuse him. Well, he told the nurse that one of his granddaughters was arriving from Honolulu to visit him. When Esther went to the hospital that evening, the nurse said, "Your father is much worse. I'm afraid his mind is slipping. He thinks he has a granddaughter coming from Honolulu."

You may wonder where we get funds to travel through Europe. We earn a lot of rubles but can't exchange them at a bank for any foreign currency. Rubles aren't "valuta," as the Russians call solid money. That's the main reason Soviet citizens don't travel abroad. We can, however, because we know foreign correspondents who are paid in valuta, and instead of going to a bank, they sell the dollars, or whatever, to us whenever we need some.

In Oslo I'll meet the Larsen aunts and uncles, and dozens of cousins. Some of them speak English, but I want to learn Norwegian. I'm looking forward to a traditional Christmas, too.

In Paris we'll haunt our old haunts at Montparnasse. Not many of our friends are there now. Harry, my friend at the Chase Bank, hasn't answered my letters. I wonder why.

Mrs. Kandinsky asked if we'd mind taking a book to her son. Would we mind? It makes going to Paris that much more exciting!

Paris,
January 7, 1937

Dearest All of You,

We've both changed — Paris and I. People talk of unemployment, the war in Spain, and the Nazis. I called the Chase Bank. Sad news — Harry died suddenly in 1933, during a trip to New York.

Zadkine, my teacher, is thriving. We had a long visit, and spoke Russian. His former wife, the painter Valentine Prax, is still with him, but they haven't remarried.

We've met an outstanding etcher, Stanley Hayter, in his studio here. People come from far away to study with him. I wish I could.

And we delivered the book to Kandinsky. His charming wife, Nina, invited us to tea at their posh apartment in the suburb of Neuilly-sur-Seine. What an experience! He is handsome and regal. They both made us feel at ease — even gave us a tour of the paintings on the walls. We talked of Moscow, sculpture, architecture, Madame Scheyer ... and the worsening world situation.

In Oslo, our relatives never gave me time to rest or stop eating. We constantly paid visits to members of the family. I had difficulty remembering names and who belonged to whom.

Grandpa (Bestefar) had already died, but I went to the funeral and cried. Bestemor — staunch and self-possessed — presided dry-eyed at the wake, which was not as solemn as I expected.

During my few days in Bergen, I hugged our handsome other Bestefar and more aunts, uncles and cousins. The main event, however, was seeing a performance of "Peer Gynt" at the opera. There aren't words to describe what it meant to me — especially seeing the Button-Moulder, the eternal conformist.

I learned a few phrases of Norwegian. Understanding it is not difficult — many words are like English. I want to go back some day and stay longer.

Must say "au revoir" now. We're invited to Le Corbusier's for dinner — an informal evening at their new villa.

Will write next from Moscow,
Sis

Chapter Fifteen

Moscow
March 1937

Dearest Everybody,

Sorry I haven't written since January. It's been hectic. We've had to find a new place to live — still only one room in someone's apartment, with kitchen privileges.

I'm hoping, too, to get a studio. It takes time, although I'm entitled to one.

There's a lot of war talk and pessimism. All is not well with the world. Maybe my studio is just wishful thinking.

Our friend, Carol, has gone back to the States with her baby. Last month, our Hungarian friends, Beni, Liza, and Pilko, moved to Vienna. Bob and Jenny, our journalist friends, are planning to leave soon.

I'll do my best to keep you posted.

With love from limbo,
Agnessa

"Have you seen today's *Pravda?*" François asked me, tossing the newspaper onto the table. "It's getting worse in Spain. German planes have bombed Guernica. And there's a long article on the riots in the Sudeten area of Czechoslovakia. The Germans living there want to become part of the Fatherland."

"It looks bad, all right. Where do you think it will end?"

"I can't see how war can be avoided. Franco, Hitler and Mussolini are a powerful combination. Hitler has already occupied the Rhineland. Mussolini has a free hand in Abyssinia. They'll go on taking more and more with impunity." I could see anxiety in François' eyes.

"But we'll be safe here, won't we?" I asked.

"For awhile, I suppose. Don't forget the Soviet Union has a lot of raw materials — oil and gold, to start with — that Hitler could use. Eventually, the Axis will try to invade."

"But war will devastate everyone. We're still paying for the last one."

"Civilians always shell out disproportionately. The instigators consider them expendable pawns."

I brought supper to the table, and we ate without saying much. At length I put my thoughts into words. "What do you think the Russians will do with foreigners like us if we're invaded?"

"Send us to Siberia, I suppose, or give us guns and uniforms."

Speculation increased every day. Our residence permits would soon come up for renewal. One rumor was that we'd be offered Soviet citizenship. If we accepted, we could stay. In any case, when war came, having foreign nationals on hand might present awkward diplomatic situations.

François worked overtime and often came home irritated. "It's that subway station we're working on. They want it to be a palace — we certainly have the marble and craftsmen — but deliveries are delayed and ... You can't believe how frustrating it is. Tell me something cheerful, Agnessa."

"Well, my love, I bought a half-pound of caviar and some smoked salmon today. After that, we'll enjoy some fresh sturgeon and mashed potatoes. If I add a bottle of your favorite wine, will I get a hug?"

For several days, all went smoothly. We were not prepared for the blow that struck on May 12: My residence permit was not renewed. I had just one week to leave the Soviet Union! The fact that my husband still had a valid permit was no help to me. I could not appeal.

What should I do? Where would I go? I'd have to work fast. I did.

First, I mailed a letter to Pilko saying I was heading for Vienna. Next, I needed foreign currency. With my ancient portable typewriter, I went to the appropriate office to receive permission to sell it, then to the largest second-hand store. The manager himself put a price on it — two thousand rubles. I could have bought a first-class ticket by train to Cherbourg then taken the *Queen Mary* to New York — for one thousand rubles. Instead, Bob exchanged the whole two thousand into U.S. dollars. I was rich, and free to live almost anywhere in modest comfort for a year — all for a beat-up Underwood!

I achieved the easy tasks. The difficult one remained ....

"You're joking," François said when I told him.

"Not at all. I'm quite serious."

"But ... but why?"

"Because," I answered, "it's a matter of principle. Four years ago I said I'd marry you on one condition. And you promised."

"Yes. I remember. But that was four years ago. Have I made you unhappy?"

"Certainly not. That has nothing to do with it."

"Please, Agnessa .... Let's sit down, and you can explain it all to me. Forgive me if I don't understand."

Over an occasional drink of wine, we talked far into the night. I defined once more my reasons for wanting a divorce, repeating what matrimony had done to my mother, my older sister, and others. "I want to prove I can make it in life on my own. Why should I love you less because we're not married? We've been through this argument many times, François, and you've always agreed with me."

Whether I convinced him or merely wore him down, I don't know. In any event, the following afternoon we went to the office of divorce. The clerk directed us to a large ledger on a counter and explained that all we had to do was sign our names on the proper lines and receive a document showing our marriage was dissolved.

Ah, victory! Triumph? Then why was there a taste of vinegar?

Ah, men!

Chapter Sixteen

My first day in Vienna began at 6:30 a.m. May 20, 1937. Pilko met me at the station. Because we hadn't seen each other since February — when she was among the first of the mass of foreigners to leave the Soviet Union — we had a great deal to talk about.

Even before the taxi deposited us and my numerous suitcases at Pilko's apartment, we had begun discussing the state of our world.

"What do people here say?" I asked. "Is war inevitable?"

"Looks like it," Pilko replied. "There seem to be two camps: the Left and the Right, with few people uncommitted. Even though I'm Hungarian, I cannot go back to Budapest."

"Why on Earth not? All your family is there."

"Yes, but because my passport shows I've lived in the Soviet Union, and the government of my country is anti-Communist, I'd be arrested and probably imprisoned."

"That serious?"

Pilko nodded and went on. "Many of my pro-Russian friends who have never been to the Soviet Union have come to live here in Vienna, and those who are Jewish have applied to emigrate to Canada or Australia or the United States."

"But your man in control — what's his name — Horthy? I've heard he doesn't like Hitler."

"That's true, but it doesn't prevent him from crusading against Communists. If war comes, he'll rush to join forces with Germany. For now, we're safe here in Austria. But for how long? Since we have a common border, Hitler could march in virtually unopposed at any time, without declaring war."

"Good heavens," I mumbled. "I had no idea things were so bad."

"You see," Pilko continued, "after the Great War, the Austro-Hungarian Empire was dismembered. Parts were given to half a dozen countries: Romania, Czechoslovakia, Yugoslavia, Austria, Poland, and Italy. Horthy will never forget or forgive the humiliation and will do anything to regain the former territory.

"Well ... here we are. We'll get you settled in, and have some break-fast. Before I go off to work, I want to hear about you and François, and your future plans ... where you're going from here."

The little table in the blue and white kitchen was already set for two. Between bites of newly baked bread, cheese, and sweet rolls, I deflected her curiosity.

"François won't leave Moscow for a few months," I told her. "He has an important project to finish. After that ... who knows? An archi-tect friend in Tokyo might have work for him."

"My goodness! That's exciting. I must admit I envy you, Agnessa."

I had to tell her I probably would not be going to Japan if François did, and why. She listened patiently, then shook her head with a skep-tical smile.

"Oh, dear me, look at the clock," she said suddenly. "I have to go to work. Here are the keys to the apartment, and some Austrian money till you get yours changed. And this map of the city is for you. Spend the morning being a tourist, and we'll meet at one o'clock for lunch at Charlie's. I've circled it on the map. *auf Wiedersehen!*"

She blew me a kiss and was gone.

Feeling somewhat detached from the scene, I took in the tasteful displays in the shop windows, the elegant pedestrians strolling in the warm, sunny air of late spring, and people chatting around small tables at sidewalk cafés along the tree-lined avenues. On almost every block, women in traditional costumes sold flowers from kiosks.

I walked a little while, then found a shady bench on the Karntner Ring and let thoughts buzz in and out of my head. Preoccupied with my destiny, I was glad to be by myself. Whether or not I was right, I owed no one an explanation. What François and I did was private. He understood that my wanting a divorce did not mean I no longer loved him. He saw my point of view and my need for space to try my wings independently. I loved him all the more for it.

We had both come to a crossroad — he free to choose his way, and I mine. Should I go to Paris? I had to prove something, something John had impressed on me when I was eighteen or twenty. Marriage had truncated my mother's singing career, and my sister's, as well. Sure, they had made their choices freely. Well ... not entirely freely. Unwritten social rules stated a woman should marry. If she didn't, it might mean no man wanted her. She'd be classified as an Old Maid — a fate to avoid if possible.

What John had figuratively engraved on my heart in 1930 was still there: *I marriage disparage.* He used to say it over and over. Mama kept reminding me that *no one's* talents should be neglected. She was sure that one day, it would be socially acceptable for each woman to decide independently what her life style would be. Sometime, somewhere, a lot of people — women *and* men — would stand up for women's rights.

The Russians already had, and I had not noticed their family life deteriorating. In the Western world, we still defied the current. A bold woman occasionally rose from the mass of her cowed sisters, thumbed her nose at the double standard, and lived according to the rules of men, or would even make her own rules. Society punished some, and tolerated others as anomalies. Two centuries ago, Mary Wollstonecraft, the illegitimate mother of Mary Shelley fervently advocated educational and social equality for women. Her efforts made few ripples.

Over a hundred years later, Sarah Bernhardt, then Maria Montessori scorned convention with impunity. Each became outstanding in her field — respected in spite of having a son out of wedlock.

Organized efforts to give us leverage began with Emmeline Pankhurst, for forty years a militant champion of women's suffrage. That gave us the vote but not much else.

And what would my mutiny contribute? Not an organizer, I would lead no campaign, nor would I preach. I'd quietly go ahead and *live* what I believed. Otherwise, I'd be disloyal to future generations. I had to be consistent.

And so ... having settled that, I got up and headed for Charlie's restaurant.

Pilko was already there, at a corner table, and with her were .... *Yes!* Liza and Beni! For several minutes we all talked at once, asking and answering questions with eager rapidity in Russian, the one language we had in common.

Finally, composed in our places, I remarked, "I thought you two had gone home to Budapest."

"That would be nice," Liza said. "But, just like Pilko, the fact that we lived in Moscow makes it impossible."

"And can you work here, Beni?" I asked. "Are people buying your sculpture?"

"Pilko chuckled. "Sculpture *and* paintings. They'll always buy the work of Beni Ferenczi — or of anyone with that family name, at least in this part of the world."

Beni told me about his one-man show scheduled for July. Then our conversation drifted to our time together in Moscow, and why he and Liza went there originally.

"You escaped to the Soviet Union in 1934," I said. "How are things different today so you could come back here?"

"When Dollfuss was killed, Schuschnig became chancellor. He was a kinder man, politically less violent, and even tolerant of us former Schutzbundlers."

"If Hitler comes to Austria, will he be lenient?" I asked.

"Certainly not. But we'll keep our noses clean and hope to survive."

"And what are your plans, Agnessa?" Liza asked.

"Nothing definite. I want to go to Paris and maybe pick up where I left off four years ago. And I'd like to study etching."

Beni raised his eyebrows and slowly shook his grey head. "You aren't thinking of staying indefinitely in France, are you?"

"Well ... it had crossed my mind."

"Forget it, my dear. We're not optimistic. There are only two alternatives: Either we give in and let Germany take over one country after another so Hitler can exterminate everyone who isn't a Nazi, or we resist, which would mean war. Most of us know what war is. There's nothing heroic about it."

"Didn't you say François might get a job in Japan?" Pilko asked.

"Oh ... it's not definite." I tried to sound indifferent. "He has probably just as much chance of going back to work for Le Corbusier. We'll know in a few months."

"So you'll be here most of the summer. That's fine. I have been authorized to offer you a temporary job," Pilko said.

It sounded appealing. Her sister, Baba, was married to a pediatrician. They and their three sons lived in Hungary, on Lake Balaton, and ran a summer camp for preadolescents with special needs. I would be in charge of recreation for the older children.

Over the next several days, while getting acquainted with Vienna and some of Pilko's friends, I learned further details of the summer project on Lake Balaton. Rather than work, it would be a continuous picnic — perhaps like the month I spent in Canada in 1931 with the Embrees — though without John.

I didn't know a word of Hungarian, but Pilko laughed at my concern. "So you'll learn. You didn't know Russian when you went to Moscow. It's enough that you make yourself understood in German. Don't worry. You'll find many people speak French and even English."

"And what about getting along with the children?"

"Just be yourself," she said.

Chapter Seventeen

Keszthely, Hungary
July 15, 1937

Dear All,

I've been here two weeks, and only now, for the first time, have I half an hour to catch up on writing, and that's because it's raining.

Adjusting to this life was instantaneous, of necessity. The dozen or so children are overflowing with energy. Even with three of us in charge, they keep us alert. Lilli, a young Romanian, takes care of the little girls, and Clary, another of Pilko's sisters, has the younger boys, while the older ones are in my care. Baba's three sons help out, especially at play time, which is always, when we're not eating or sleeping.

Most of the nicknames are brand new to me. There are boys called Bandi, Benda, Pishti, Matyi, Shanyi, and Dorchi. And some girl's names are Kato, Birzhie, Zhuzhka, and Vitsa.

Balaton has a splendid setting. The lake, 40 miles long, is always dotted with sails and motorboats, and an occasional ferry. Keszthely is on the far western end.

The evenings are too seductively warm to stay indoors. Most grown-ups, young and old, go out promenading on the pier or at one or another of the dancing places on the shore, or in the village.

August 2, 1937

I know about ten words of Hungarian and can sing two popular songs. Beyond the borders of the country no one speaks the language, so I won't try to master it. I have, however, learned something of the pronunciation. Their word for Hungarian is "Magyar" and is pronounced "Madyar." Keszthely is "Kest-hai."

August 20, 1937

Last Friday morning, fifteen of us started out on a five-mile walk to a little resort called Hèviz. Under a cloudless sky and hot sun, the dusty dirt road ran almost straight between ripe grain and potato fields.

We passed only a few cottages and some farmers on bicycles. The women carried large baskets on their heads. Their shirts, full skirts, aprons and kerchiefs were all made of the same blue homespun.

We rested in a shady grove to devour our lunch of sandwiches, pears, and watermelon, before proceeding to where two dirt roads crossed near a handful of houses and autos. A signpost announced we had arrived at Hèviz. Close by, a wooden bridge took us over a stream of muddy, green-black, foul smelling water, in which a score of grown-ups bathed up to their necks. That introduced us to the main bath farther on, of thermal waters, celebrated for curing rheumatism. The odor was sulphur.

The bath headquarters looked like something recently evolved from a primeval age. Picture a swamp bordered by lovely big trees, with a wooden structure, housing the dressing rooms, built on piles and painted a faded mustard yellow.

In the 95° water, people of all ages and both genders quietly bathed. The elderly had their own section with boards to hold on to.

I soon forgot the smell, as we all splashed around for an hour. If I grow old without suffering from rheumatism, I'll know why ....

The latest news from François is that he's going to Japan, and will stop in Vienna to see me first. That means I'll be leaving here soon. I want to visit a day or two in Budapest on my way.

With love to everyone,
Sis

Chapter Eighteen

I doubt that Budapest can look more beautiful than at early evening in late August. That's when the bus brought me there from Keszthely. We approached from Buda, the hillside, through a broad tunnel. When we emerged at the other end — behold — there was the Danube, flowing excitedly under four bridges. Beyond the waltz-provoking rush of the grey-brown water lay Pest, the city's better half, with pink and yellow tints on green clouds for a background above the modern buildings.

The bus let me off at Mussolini Plaza, a small green park with benches, and neat little shops facing it on all sides. A porter took my suitcases, and we walked up Vaci Street a couple of blocks to where Pilko's mother lived.

Only the maid was at home. A sweet, tiny woman, she welcomed me, and explained in German that Frau Doktor (Pilko's mother) wouldn't be back till late that evening.

Mrs. Doktor shared the large apartment with her four sisters, all widows or spinsters, now away on vacation. Without waiting to unpack, I went out to see the town. The streets looked much like those of other Central European cities, but the shop windows were done with better taste, especially for women's clothes and shoes. Should I buy a pair right away? The Danube beckoned, so I walked along the quay with hundreds of Budapestians out to see whom their friends were walking with and how they were dressed. All too often I noticed men giving the Nazi salute.

Along the embankment, a string of cafés with bright lights enticed me to find a seat. On the cliff side of the river, floodlights illuminated the ancient fortress and castle, while twinkling stars in the twilight sky studded the scene with magic.

I ordered a cup of coffee and an English newspaper. I enjoyed the coffee, but the paper — the *London Daily Mail* — was full of gossip, half-truths and distortions about Spain and the Soviet Union. What a shock to return to this part of Earth after the peace and relative quiet of Keszthely. For almost two months, I hadn't thought about wars, then, suddenly, I learned that in Austria an amnesty had been declared for illegal Nazis. The Japanese were invading all of China, and Shanghai was burning. Picasso had painted a mural to commemorate the rape of Guernica. The Wall Street stock market was still declining. Amelia Earhart hadn't yet been found. One more man had killed his sweetheart because he loved her, and Helen Wills wanted a divorce. Not much good news. In Russia the purges continued.

History went on, dragging disasters in its wake. I wondered if it would get much worse before it got better. Where did I fit into that kaleidoscope of events? Was there a place for me in any country where I was not a citizen? Who would buy the work of an unknown sculptor? How would I survive if war came?

To myself I whispered, "Don't think that far ahead ... it won't happen tomorrow. There's time ...."

When I reach the consummate age of sixty, I hope I'll be as spry, mentally and physically, and as progressive as Pilko's mother. She and I got up early and climbed the hill on the Buda side of the river, up to the old fortress. We paused occasionally on the steep, stone steps, and Mrs. Doktor pointed out landmarks far below us in the breathtaking landscape.

We had breakfast on the sunny terrace of a restaurant lodged at the base of the fortress, and talked for two hours. Mrs. Doktor seemed to enjoy recalling the past — how she and her husband used to walk up there every morning to have breakfast.

"Yes," she said, "every morning until I started having daughters — six of them, as you know, one after the other."

"And they're all lovely, intelligent women," I said.

"Yes." She sighed, and looked away, thoughtfully. "I'm proud of all of them. Young women now have advantages that didn't exist in my day. You can choose a career, and also choose to have, or not have, children. We grew up ignorant of our bodies. My husband was a physician, but I got no advice from him."

She went on to tell me that, although there was no profession in particular she had wanted to follow, she was indignant that the public underrated the value of women.

"No matter what our talents," she said, "society demanded we marry, and give in to the whims of our husbands. We still have a long way to go.

"It's not that all women want to escape from the house, but we should be permitted to question the double standard, and to have a direct say in the laws we must obey. Not many people stop to think that behind every successful man there's a devoted woman. And women who have prospered have usually done so against odds."

I started to comment that the Nazis weren't in favor of progress for women, but just then the waiter approached. Mrs. Doktor gave me a mute signal to be cautious, so I said, "This afternoon I'm going to the Modern Arts Museum, then to visit Beni's sister, Noemi."

Chapter Nineteen

Klickity-klack,
Back on track,
The rhythmic klack
Of the singing track,
Klickity-klack,
Taking me back-back-back-back-back ....

In just a few hours I'd be in Vienna again, waiting at the station for François' train. Over and over I asked myself questions I couldn't answer: What would happen from here? Was he as eager to see me as I was to see him? His letters had been noncommittal. Had he planned his future without me? How could I decide on mine, or even seriously examine my options? What options? We hadn't seen each other for over three months. I couldn't deny I'd be glad to be near him again. Even closer than near. He would stay four or five days. Not very long. The outcome would depend only partly on me ....

The late summer landscape sped past the window, making no more impression on my mind than did the three or four chattering people with whom I shared the compartment. I was on another plane, grappling with the obscurity of my impending encounter with the future.

I remembered my talks with Mrs. Doktor. She had made me even more determined to stand my ground — not only for my sake, but for our gender, and those to come.

Then I had met Noemi in her studio, and seen how successful a woman could be on her own — a rarity in a Nazi-controlled country. Paris, as Moscow, was full of career women — single and married, and all very feminine. It seemed that outside France and Russia, however, society put roadblocks in the way.

Noemi reminded me of Madame Scheyer. Both women radiated vibrancy and vitality, making me want to be free to explore new paths.

I took away with me a formula I've applied many times since: First, consider your priorities. Then know there's always a better way. Look for it.

> *The rhythmic klack*
> *Of the singing track*
> *Said, "Move on, not back!"*

Chapter Twenty

Even after some six decades, I recall our reunion with the same intensity felt at the time. What I'm able to share is the following: François' train was late, leaving me to pace nervously for an endless half hour. When, finally, the cars rolled in, I writhed at one end of the platform until I saw his face — about five cars away. We raced into each other's arms.

Déjà vu? Two years before, at the train station in Batumi, the meeting was almost identical.

And there was the summer of 1932, when I returned to Paris from Italy and went to see him at Le Corbusier's office .... The joy of seeing each other again had not diminished.

The following day, Sunday, Pilko said at breakfast that Beni and Liza had invited the three of us to dinner. What a relief! Relief, because for me it meant postponing the hour of doom. François and I had not discussed our future. I didn't know if he wanted me to go with him to the Orient.

Even before the happy greetings were over, Beni asked for news of the comrades he had left behind in Moscow — those who had chosen to stay, and the others who went back home to Western Europe and the States. For a time we talked of our mutual friends and reminisced about the good times we'd had.

Then Beni said, "The local newspapers are telling us that many good old Party members are in disgrace, and have even been 'eliminated.' Marshal Tukhachevsky and Carl Radek, among others. Is that true, or malicious invention?"

François put down his glass, leaned back in his chair, and sighed slowly. "I'm afraid it's more than gossip. Lots of well-known names are mentioned every day in *Pravda*. 'Betrayers of the Proletariat' they're called, and 'Traitors to the Party,' 'Conspirators'...."

"Do people believe it?" Liza asked.

François frowned. "What did people believe three years ago when Kirov was killed? Kirov! One of the Old Bolsheviks, buddy of Stalin. People believed what they were told — an accident. But now there are whispers that his death was made to look like an accident, that Stalin thought Kirov demonstrated too much independence in the Politburo, and considered him a rival. To cover up, Stalin shed crocodile tears, and had several towns and regions named after him. Even the new subway station I've just completed is called Kirov."

Beni's expression clouded. After a few moments he said, "That would suggest there are others. Yes. Now that I think back ... I wondered at the time .... There were comrades ...."

"You mean Sasha," said Liza, "and Georgi. Their friends said they'd gone on a trip, but didn't know where."

Beni nodded. "They were Party members. And as far as I'm concerned, none more loyal."

"They used to tell us," François said, "that there were widespread conspiracies from abroad to eliminate the Soviet leaders, and on those grounds, Stalin had to deport or execute thousands. No one knows what to believe."

"Of course," Beni said, "the growing threat of war would inevitably make them suspicious. I could name several countries that would like to destroy the Soviet system and who probably do have saboteurs working full-time to undermine it."

Liza put up both her hands. "Enough of this depressing talk! I want to hear about Agnessa and François' plans." With a broad grin, she looked expectantly from one to the other of us.

"Well," I said, "we haven't had time yet to talk about what we're going to do." I glanced at François, who showed no discomposure.

"These days," he said, "a lot of lives are uprooted. I'm going to visit my folks in Czechoslovakia, but don't intend to stay there. We couldn't beat the German army, if they invade, any more than Austria was able to some years ago. So ... I'm taking off ... for Japan. I've a job there with a Czech architect. It's about doing a building for some yogis in India, in French India, near Madras."

"How splendid!" Liza clapped her hands. "When are you leaving, Agnessa?"

Before I could reply, Pilko — sensitive, perceptive Pilko — stood up and suggested we all go for a walk. "Come on! Summer's out there beckoning, and bands and dance floors in the parks are waiting for us. This may be our last chance at frivolity before the world ends."

Whole families enjoyed the brilliant afternoon. Some young couples pushed perambulators, others courted, children cavorted, all unaware that in less than seven months, Hitler would invade and occupy their country and their thoughts.

I could write on, page after page, about how I became an apprentice to a master plaster caster and learned the trade, and I could describe the charms and beauties of Vienna and the Viennese as I saw them in the final months of their freedom. Instead, I shall bring this part of my story to a close.

Regarding my life, there remained only one significant matter to be resolved — the future relationship between François and me. I'm glad to record that the first ten years of my adult life had a happy ending.

The five of us came to a crowded park where a band played popular songs. We found a table under the trees, ordered ice cream, and joked about things of no consequence.

"I hear a fox trot," Beni said and, taking Liza by the elbow, led her off to the dance floor. Pilko recognized some friends at a nearby table and went over to talk to them.

François looked at me with a quizzical smile, then drew me to him and kissed me on the lips. "Now," he said, "let's stop wondering what the other is thinking. You are right to want your independence. Another war is on the horizon — far worse than the last one. And when it ends, many things will have changed forever, especially the role of women. So you must decide, Agnessa. I won't impose any conditions." He paused and waited for me to speak.

"What do *you* want, François?"

"I want to spend the rest of my life with you."

"Married?"

"Married or not — it doesn't matter. The important thing is that love, not a legal document, will keep us together. And I love you."

My eyes filled with tears — tears of happiness, that I didn't try to hide.

He went on, "That's why I came to Vienna — to ask you to share all the years ahead. Are you going back to Paris, or coming to Japan with me?" His voice was gentle, and his eyes probed mine.

Timidly, I said, "I'd like ... to do both ... stay a couple of months in Paris and then join you. I've been wanting to study etching with Hayter."

I don't think I've ever loved him as much as at that moment. "I know you have," he said. "And if I were in your shoes, I'd do the same."

The fox trot ended, and the band began playing a Strauss waltz.

"Hear that?" François said as he clasped my hand and stood up. "This is for us."

On the way to the dance floor, he put an arm around my waist and whispered, "This reminds me of a certain August evening in Paris, when a waltz played magic and brought us together. Do you remember?"

Did I? I have never forgotten.

Epilogue

To recount all my adventures and misadventures since 1937 would fill a thousand pages. That's for another time. For now, let me briefly relate my story in the years that followed.

From Vienna, François went to Tokyo, while I spent three months in Paris studying etching. We reunited in India — in Pondicherry, a French colony at that time, on the Coromandel Coast facing the Bay of Bengal, about thirteen degrees north of the Equator. All I knew of the subcontinent was the British Raj. Before leaving Paris I read Forster's *A Passage to India* and bought dressy clothes, high-heeled shoes, and party hats. I wore none of them.

François was there to construct a large four-story guest house for an ashram. *Ashram?* A retreat for adherents of a distinct philosophical belief. Scores of new words soon enhanced my vocabulary: *yoga, karma, guru, jiva, prana, purusha, prakriti.* They, and more, remain a part of my glossary.

Intrigued, I asked ingenuous questions and received intelligent answers. I was an atheist. So what? Yoga didn't conflict with any religion or non-religion. Many Westerners think it is only a form of physical exercise. The word "yoga" means the art of conscious self-finding, a spiritual discipline and realization, attainable by means of several paths: Hatha, Karma, Raja, Bhakti, Jnana, Purna ... all valid.

Sri Surobindo, the guru, or spiritual teacher, of the Pondicherry ashram, had his own course: Purnayoga. In 1910, after openly working eight years for independence, he had to flee British India and take refuge in the French colony. Many became his disciples and joined the ashram, among them two elderly women from the West. One was the widow of French historian Gabriel Monod and daughter of Alexandr Hertzen, Russian revolutionary thinker who lived in Paris, and the other, President Woodrow Wilson's daughter, Margaret.

The simple life agreed with François and me. Materially, all the essentials were supplied. For us that included a five-room house overlooking the Bay of Bengal, and four servants. With no domestic duties, I spent a good part of each day in the little studio set up for me,